CREATION AND THE HISTORY OF SCIENCE

THE HISTORY OF CHRISTIAN THEOLOGY

Edited by Paul Avis

The History of Christian Theology aims to provide an extended introduction to religous thought in the Christian tradition from an historical perspective. It presents the unfolding of Christian thought in its various departments: doctrine, ethics, philosophical theology, and study and interpretation of the Bible, interaction with the sciences and with other religions. The various volumes of the *History* will eventually constitute a set of fundamental resource books of wide usefulness in religious education and in ministry. The approach aims to combine clarity of presentation and ease of reference with academic integrity and theological depth.

Volume 1: *The Science of Theology*

Gillian R. Evans
Alister E. McGrath
Allan D. Galloway

Volume 2: The Study and Use of the Bible

John Rogerson
Christopher Rowland
Barnabas Lindars

Volume 3: Creation and the History of Science

Christopher B. Kaiser

Creation
and the
History of Science

Christopher B. Kaiser

Marshall Pickering, London

William B. Eerdmans Publishing Co., Grand Rapids

First published 1991 in Great Britain by Marshall Pickering
and in the USA by Wm. B. Eerdmans Publishing Co.,
255 Jefferson Ave. SE, Grand Rapids, Mich. 49503

Marshall Pickering is an imprint of HarperCollinsReligious, part of
HarperCollinsPublishers, 77-85 Fulham Palace Road, London W6 8JB.

Printed in the United States of America

text set in 10/11.5 Plantin
by Input Typesetting Ltd, London

Marshall Pickering ISBN 0-551-02035-0

Library of Congress Cataloging-in-Publication Data
Kaiser, Christopher B.
　　Creation and the history of science / Christopher B. Kaiser.
　　　　p.　　　　cm.　　　　— (The History of Christian theology; v. 3)
　　ISBN 0-8028-0197-8
　　　1. Creation — History of doctrines.　2. Creationism — History of
　　doctrines.　3. Religion and science — History.　I. Title.　II. Series.
　　BT695.K35　　1991
　　231.7′65′09 — dc20　　　　　　　　　　　　　　　　　　91-123
　　　　　　　　　　　　　　　　　　　　　　　　　　　　　CIP

CONTENTS

CREATION
AND THE HISTORY OF SCIENCE

Can Christians think out their faith in the laboratory and observatory as well as in the church and seminary? From the beginning, Christians have been divided in their attitude to secular knowledge and how far it should influence their theological convictions. A major sphere of this interaction between theology and the sciences has concerned creation and cosmology. Theology has drawn on the philosophical cosmologies of the ancient world and the scientific discoveries of modern times. In its turn, natural science has been profoundly influenced by theological presuppositions.

This third volume of *The History of Christian Theology* relates the theology of creation to the history of science from the early Christian Fathers, through the recovery of Aristotle in medieval thought and the beginnings of modern scientific method in the Renaissance and the Enlightenment, to the post-Newtonian mechanics of the nineteenth century, concluding with an assessment of the theological implications of the views of Einstein and Bohr, the founders of twentieth-century physics. The study ends by pointing to the challenge of a new age in which scientists no longer operate on creationist presuppositions.

Christopher B. Kaiser, who is qualified in both natural science and theology, has achieved a masterly survey of a vast field and his synopsis of a complex development is a model of clarity and condensation. This work is assured of its place in every theological library as a resource for all concerned with the interaction of Christian theology and natural science.

Paul Avis

1

THE EARLY CHURCH AND GRECO-ROMAN SCIENCE
(through the twelfth century AD)

1. BACKGROUND: FROM INTERTESTAMENTAL JUDAISM TO BASIL OF CAE-
SAREA

The emergence of the early Christian church must be understood in continuity with earlier developments in intertestamental Judaism. The military conquests of Alexander the Great (late fourth century BC) led to the formation of an international Hellenistic culture which drew on the traditions of various Near Eastern populations: Egyptian, Phoenician, Babylonian, and Persian as well as Greek. The forceful inclusion of the Hebrews in this ecumenical world brought about the first real contact between the faith of the Jews and the philosophy of the Greeks. It also brought about a new appreciation for the indigenous cultures of the Near East, particularly the Egyptian and Bablyonian. The Jewish dialogue with this international Hellenistic culture probably began in the early third century BC, but the first records we have of it date from the late third and early second centuries. Already in them, some characteristic features are readily apparent of what was to become an ongoing contest between progressives and conservatives within the community of faith.

Early Jewish Responses to Greek Science
On the one hand, there were those who adopted a receptive attitude toward the dominant Greek culture and made an attempt to promote it amongst Jewish youth in Jerusalem. On the other, there was a conservative reaction against the process of Hellenization based on the quite legitimate fear that it would undermine the distinctive values of the Jewish law (1 Macc. 1:11–15; 2 Macc. 4:4–17). Consequently, the claims of Greek science and technology were perceived as part of a broad cultural challenge affecting all aspects of life,

1

much as Western European science and technology are perceived in many parts of the 'Third-World' today.

In the context of this intense cultural interaction, we find the first instances of what we might call Jewish apologetics in the second century BC. The intent here was partly to gain respect for the Jewish faith in the eyes of non-Jews and partly to reassure those Jews who were properly impressed with the accomplishments of Greek culture that their own tradition was equally good or better. It was argued by Artapanus, for example, that the Egyptians learned their science and technology from Moses. Eupolemus claimed that astronomy (or astrology – the two were not distinct) had been invented by Enoch and that it was Abraham who later taught it to the Phoenicians and Egyptians, from whom the Greeks were in turn supposed to have learned it. Even Pythagoras and Plato borrowed philosophical ideas from Moses according to Aristobulus. All of these sources date from the late third to mid-second century BC.

What we find in these early sources is not only a courageous affirmation of the value of Greek science (or natural philosophy) and technology, but an underlying belief in the essential unity of all knowledge. The Jewish patriarchs who had such insight into the laws of God and, in apocalyptic literature, into the composition of the spirit world were believed also to have complete understanding of the laws of nature.

Side by side with the above, there was a more negative assessment of foreign wisdom. First (Coptic) Enoch vi-xi associated pharmacology, metallurgy and Babylonian astronomy (astrology) with the fall of the angels and their illicit intercourse with humans. And the apocryphal Book of Baruch flatly denied that there is any wisdom in foreign cultures and criticized the younger generation for departing from the Mosaic law (Baruch 3:9–4:4). The concern in both these cases was with the adverse effects of unbridled social, cultural and technological change brought about by the emergence of new local elites patronized by foreign powers.

A more discriminating attitude was taken by Jesus ben Sirach who discouraged philosophical (or theosophical) speculation (Ecclus. 3:21–24) while sanctioning the use of Greek medicine (38:1–15, esp. the Hebrew text). As one recent study has put it, ben Sirach was 'entirely open to Hellenic thought *as long as it could be Judaized*.' The attitude here was not unlike that of Third-World nations today who seek the benefits of Western science and technology while insisting on retaining their traditional values and beliefs.

Early Christian Attitudes to Greek Science (second to third century)

The first comparable interaction of Christian faith with Greco-Roman science took place in the second and third centuries when Christians suffered persecution much as the Jews had earlier. As in Jewish apologetics, there were those who claimed all truth to be inspired by God and hence suitable material for Christian scholarship. The first clear statement of this viewpoint was made by Justin Martyr (*c*.AD 165). Justin borrowed the Stoic idea of a seminal Word (*logos spermatikos*) implanted by God in all humans and maintained that this seed inspired the best philosophy of the Greeks as well as the prophecies of the Old Testament. Hence, 'Whatever things were rightly said among all men, are the property of us Christians.' In the same breath, however, Justin noted that the various schools of Greek philosophy contradicted each other and concluded that they knew only that part of the Logos that was distributed to them and not the fullness of the Word which was embodied in Christ. And, in another context, he recounted the opinion of his own teacher that the Greek philosophers were motivated by a desire for personal fame and only taught a select few, while the Hebrew prophets were inspired by God's Spirit and 'saw and announced the truth to all'.

Such a positive attitude towards the arts and sciences was taken also by Clement of Alexandria, Origen and Pseudo-Clement (purportedly Clement of Rome) in the third century. All three were concerned with the communication of the gospel to pagan inquirers and advocated the study of what later became known as the *quadrivium* (geometry, arithmetic, astronomy, and music) as a prerequisite for a proper understanding of Christian theology.

On the other side, Irenaeus and Tertullian (late second to early third century) were more critical of Greek philosophy primarily because they had to deal with the rise of numerous heresies within the ranks of the Church. Irenaeus made a sweeping condemnation of the natural philosophers (Thales, Anaximander, Anaximenes, Pythagoras, Empedocles, *et al.*), calling their teachings 'a heap of miserable rags' from which the Valentinian Gnostics had sewed together a cloak to cover their own deviations from orthodoxy. Natural mysteries like the rising of the Nile and the dwelling place of birds, he argued, were far beyond the reach of human knowledge, and, while much could be said concerning their causes if they were properly searched into, 'God alone who made them can declare the truth regarding them'. Christians should confine their studies to the Scriptures and the apostolic rule of faith (an early form of the Apostles' Creed). If they were foolishly to inquire into the wonders of nature they would develop conflicting schools of thought, like those of the Greeks, and undermine the God-given unity of the Church. Irenaeus's attitude towards pagan learning was clearly coloured by his experience of it in the teachings of the Gnostics.

Tertullian was even more vehement in his condemnation of the natural philosophers, calling their teachings 'uncertain speculations', 'worthless fables', and 'promiscuous conceits'. The philosophers, he complained, 'indulge a stupid curiosity on natural objects, which they ought rather (intelligently to direct) to their Creator and Governor'. Like Irenaeus, Tertullian associated the influence of Greek cosmological speculation (Platonist, Stoic and Epicurean) and dialectics ('unhappy Aristotle') with the Gnostic heresies of Valentinus and Marcion and the impending dissolution of the Church into opposing sects. So when he exclaimed, 'What indeed has Athens to do with Jerusalem?', he went on to say, 'What concord is there between the Academy and the Church? What between heretics and Christians?' His overriding concern was with the unity of the Church and with the purity of its doctrine.

No one with any appreciation for Greek philosophy could fail to be offended by Tertullian's tirade. Modern critics of Christianity have frequently cited his words as evidence of anti-intellectualism in the early Church. Once one allows for the vituperativeness of Tertullian's style, however, there is really nothing to which an informed pagan philosopher of the second or third century would take exception in the substance of his comments. As modern scholars like Edgar Zilsel and Ludwig Edelstein have pointed out, the fatal flaw of Greek science was its division into a multiplicity of schools and its lack of any means of accountability that would allow the resolution of disputes. In fact, this failure was already appreciated by the leading thinkers of the second century, Diodorus, Galen and Ptolemy, to name but a few.

The long-range welfare of natural science depended on the development of an ecumenical community of scholars dedicated to the pursuit of truth. This ideal was appreciated by leading thinkers of late antiquity, but the needed substructure was not available. As we shall see in section 1.5, the ecumenical foundation of modern science was to be provided by the monastic movement of the Middle Ages, a movement based on the very discipline that was advocated by Irenaeus and Tertullian. Such are the ironies of history!

Basil of Caesarea and the Hexaemeral Tradition
The next major phase of the interaction of Christian faith with Greek science began with the recognition of Christianity as a legal

religion in the early fourth century and its progressive assumption of the responsibilities of an established religion through the sixth century. The principal figure of the fourth century was Basil, who was ordained Bishop of Caesarea (in Cappadocia) in AD 370.

Basil established what was to become a long-standing tradition in the Church known as the *Hexaemeron* (Work of Six Days), a popular series of sermons or lectures on the work of God during the first six days of creation. Now that the churches were attracting members of the middle class who had heard popular expositions of Greek science, there was a need for an explanation and defense of the biblical account of creation that would stand up to criticism.

Basil could not dismiss the philosophers wholesale, as Irenaeus and Tertullian had done. Yet he could not accept philosophical ideas quite as uncritically as Clement of Alexandria and Origen had done either. He advocated study of the *quadrivium* but pointed out that all such endeavours were futile if the student fell into the trap of believing that the world was co-eternal with the Creator, as Aristotle had taught. 'The astronomers have measured the distances to the stars', he said, 'yet they have not realized that God is their Creator and Judge.'

Basil made free use of the Aristotelian theory of the four elements to explain the appearance of heaven and earth and the separation of the dry land from the seas. He also accounted ingeniously for the predominance of the element water through the Stoic idea that water was gradually consumed by celestial fire, leading to the eventual destruction of the world. Yet he rejected the Aristotelian idea that each element has a natural place in the cosmos (earth at the centre, water next to the earth, then air and fire) and attributed the support of the earth in space and the gathering of the waters in their proper place (Gen. 1:9) to the ordaining and sustaining work of God.

Basil's *Hexaemeron* was one of the first in a series of criticisms of Aristotle, a series that was to last for over twelve hundred years and give rise at last to modern (post-Aristotelian) science in the seventeenth century. Some of the key points of this critique were:

(1) that the behaviour of the elements must be understood in terms of law ordained by God rather than in terms of their essences;

(2) that the heavens are corruptible like the earth so that the same laws of physics should apply to both;

(3) that nature, once created and put in motion, evolves in accordance with the laws assigned to it without interruption or diminishment of energy.

The importance of these ideas in the development of science has been recognized by a number of historians, though the insight of Basil and the influence of his commentary have not always been properly credited. They are the foundation of what Richard C. Dales has termed 'the creationist tradition of Christianity', a tradition that was to last for sixteen hundred years and give birth to modern Western science and technology before it degenerated into pure naturalism in the eighteenth and nineteenth centuries.

The Roots of the Historic Creationist Tradition

The historic creationist tradition is not to be confused with modern-day 'creation science' or 'creationism'. It does share a critique of naturalism, but evolutionary science can be viewed as a truncated version of the historic creationist tradition as much as creation science can. We shall offer some thoughts on the origins of 'flood geology' in the late eighteenth and early nineteenth centuries in section 4.1. Aside from that, our treatment of the creationist tradition has nothing to do with modern creationism.

We shall be tracing the historic creationist tradition through the twelfth century in the remainder of this chapter and referring back to it in others. In order to place the development in perspective, it is appropriate at this point to say something about its sources prior to Basil. At the end of the chapter we shall note the ways in which it differed in its early stages from what it was to become in the later Middle Ages.

The fundamental idea in the creationist tradition is that the entire universe is subject to a single code of law which was established along with the universe at the beginning of time. The origin of the universe is beyond human understanding, depending as it does on the wisdom and will of God, but its subsequent operation can be understood due to the fact that human reason is in some way a reflection or image of that same lawfulness or reason that governs the world. In the hexaemeral tradition of commentary on Genesis 1, a distinction was often made between the way things happened during the 'six days' of creation (usually figuratively understood) and the way things happen after the sixth day. During the first 'six days' all depend directly on God's immediate activity. As of the seventh (sabbath) day, however, God rested and nature could operate in accordance with the laws already established.

As far as we know, the roots of this tradition go back to the early stages of Mesopotamian civilization in the fourth and third millennia BC. The Mesopotamians viewed the universe as a cosmic nation-state in which the wills of the various gods, like the wills of humans, were bound by common law. In a second-millennium revival of these ideas (the *Enuma elish*), the Babylonian god Marduk was credited with having ordained laws for the stars, which were identified with the lesser gods, just as the kings of Babylon had given laws to their subjects. The writers of the Old Testament, particularly those associated with the Israelite monarchy, developed this tradition stressing the unique sovereignty of Yahweh, the God of Israel, and the complete subservience of all nature, both in heaven and on earth, to his command.

Beginning with the sixth century BC, a parallel, though divergent, development took place among the early Greek natural philosophers. Anaximander, Pythagoras, Heraclitus, and others developed the ancient Near Eastern idea of divine laws into a more secular concept of laws of nature. The seemingly naturalistic implications of this early Greek science were modified by Plato and the Stoics (fourth and third centuries BC) who developed the notion of a universal logos related to the operation of a divine world soul.

In continuity with the Old Testament tradition, and later influenced to some degree by popular schools of Greek thought like Platonism and Stoicism, intertestamental Judaism developed the concept of Wisdom as an intelligence responsible for the orderly behaviour of the world and for the reasoning faculty in humans, as well. As a result, the processes of nature were believed to be governed by laws and hence open to human comprehension (Job 28:26; 38:33; Jer. 31:35f.; 33:25; Wisd. 7:15–28; 9:16f.; Ecclus. 1:9f.; 1 Enoch 33; 41; 79). The fully developed creationist tradition can thus be dated from about the second or first century BC, the period immediately prior to the formation of the New Testament.

We have already noted at least three distinct ideas in the creationist tradition: the comprehensibility of the world, the unity of heaven and earth, and the relative autonomy of nature. To these three ideas we shall add a fourth: the ministry of healing and restoration, which is a practical programme as much as an idea. At this point in our treatment, it will be convenient to pursue the history of these four components of the tradition separately.

2. THE CREATIONIST TRADITION: COMPREHENSIBILITY OF THE WORLD

The idea that human reason is an image of the same Logos that is implanted in all the world was a recurring theme in early Christian writings. We find it, for example, in apostolic fathers like Clement of Rome in the late first century AD. It recurred in Alexandrian writers like Origen and pseudo-Silvanus, as well as in Latin writers like Tertullian and Lactantius. In the fourth century, it was articulated by Athanasius and the two Gregories, as well as by Basil.

Agnosticism Concerning Causes Beyond Human Experience

The openness of the world to human comprehension was counterbalanced by the view, held by Irenaeus, Tertullian, and Lactantius as well as by Basil, that many things in the cosmos transcended human understanding inasmuch as they lay beyond human experience. Examples included the reasons (aside from the decree of God) for the ebb and flow of the tides; the causes of rain, thunder and lightning; differences in properties among various metals and stones (Irenaeus), the causes of celestial phenomena like the phases of the moon (Irenaeus, Lactantius), and the mode of the Earth's support in space (Basil). Note that it is not the facts themselves that are in doubt, but the reasons for them.

This agnosticism with regard to causes and the consequent restriction of natural philosophy to the knowledge of patterns in nature was quite in keeping with general trends in the science of late antiquity. In the first century BC, Posidonius and Geminus had thus distinguished astronomy, which was concerned with the modelling of phenomena, from physics which attempted to discover the underlying causes. Aristotle himself was principally a physicist, but the progress of astronomy from the second century AD through the middle ages was to depend more on the work of Ptolemy who was concerned primarily with 'saving the phenomena'. Some historians have regarded this pragmatic tendency to be harmful. Others, however, have seen it as necessary, at least, for that particular period. The agnosticism of the early Christians was not anti-scientific, therefore. In fact, it assumed that deeper understanding of nature would be possible if human technologies allowed a wider range of reliable data.

Finite or Infinite?

Frequently associated with the idea that the world was accessible to human understanding was the belief that it was encompassed by God, hence that it was finite in both size and duration. In contrast to the unbounded or infinite, which was deemed incomprehensible by many of the ancients, the physical world was believed to be literally comprehended by God and hence comprehensible in the objective sense. Aristotle and the Stoics both believed the world to be finite in spatial extent and in some sense encompassed by God. The influence of the Stoic and neo-Pythagorean idea of God containing and giving coherence to the world may be detected in the biblical period in such writers as Jesus ben Sirach ('by his word all things hold together', Ecclus. 43:26), Aristobulus (the light of wisdom 'in which all things are comprehended'), the Wisdom of Solomon ('the Spirit of the Lord . . . holds all things together', Wisd. 1:7), Philo ('God contains all things and is contained by none'), and Paul (Acts 17:28; Col. 1:17).

Some scholars have argued, however, that there was also an independent source for the idea in the early rabbinic description of God as the 'place' (Hebrew: *maqom*) of the world. As early as the late third century BC, the Egyptian historian Hecataeus described the God of the Jews as one who surrounded the world as its heaven (cf. Gen. 24:3; Neh. 1:4; Ps. 136:26, passim).

The belief that God is the place of the world and that he contains it by his word or by his power is repeated in numerous early Christian writings: The Preaching of Peter (*Kerygma Petrou*), The Shepherd of Hermas, Theophilus, and Irenaeus being among the earliest (all second century). Many early Christian writers also argued against the idea of the eternity of the world which was held in one form or another by virtually all of the Greek philosophers. The arguments varied, but in the main they were based on the belief that God was the sole origin of all things so that the world, including the matter of which it is formed, must be limited in duration as well as in spatial extent.

An emphasis on the sovereignty of God could also lead to an emphasis on the inexhaustibility of the world from the perspective of fallible, finite minds (e.g., Job 38:16–38; Eccl. 3:21ff.; 8:16f.; 11:5; Jer. 31:37; 4 Ezra 5:38; Wisd. 9:16; Ecclus. 1:2ff.). The inexhaustibility of the divine order did not contradict its comprehensibility, however. The two ideas frequently appeared side by side in Scripture and were tied together by the belief that God's wisdom was available to humans who sought it (Job 28:12–28; Jer. 31:31–37; Wisd. 9:13–18; Ecclus. 1:1–10, 19; 17:1–12; 24:19–34).

A similar juxtaposition of teachings was offered by Origen of Alexandria in the first half of the third century. On the one hand, the eternity and omnipotence of God suggested to Origen that there must always have been a world in which the Deity could exercise his power. On the other hand, Origen clearly denied the co-eternity of the visible world with God and argued that, since God comprehends all things, the world must have both a beginning and an end. Henry Chadwick has resolved the apparent contradiction by making a distinction as follows: the eternal object of God's power for Origen was the spiritual world of angels and human souls, whereas the world with a beginning and an end was a world of material bodies.

Basil provided an interesting interpretation of Origen's speculations in his *Hexaemeron*. Before the creation of this present, finite world, he said, there may well have been a spiritual world for the angels to live in. Their world would have been eternal and infinite since purely intellectual creatures are not confined by bodies and hence can comprehend the infinite! So a world could be infinite and still be orderly, according to Basil, but we ourselves can say nothing about such a world since it would transcend *our* comprehension.

On balance, then, we may say that the creationist tradition required the finitude of the present, visible world in both spatial extent and duration, though it could allow the existence of other worlds, beyond out comprehension, that could be infinite and even eternal. The two principle Christian contributors to scientific development in the sixth century stressed the basic idea of finitude. Boethius (d *c* 525), writing in Italy under the Ostrogoths, wrote an influential treatise on arithmetic in which he stipulated that 'nothing which is infinite can be found in science nor can be comprehended in science'. In Alexandria, John Philoponos (d *c* 565) wrote two treatises refuting the idea of the eternity of the world, one against Proclus and the other against Aristotle. Among the arguments presented in the latter was the statement that the present motions of the heavens would be inexplicable if they had no beginning since, in that case, there would be an infinite series which would defy human comprehension. In this, as in other arguments, Philoponos turned Aristotle's principles against Aristotle's conclusions with devastating effect. The inspiration for his critique may, however, be credited to the creationist tradition he inherited from Athanasius and Basil.

The issue of the temporal duration of the cosmos was never quite settled. Neoplatonist Christians continued to adhere to the eternity of the world in spite of Philoponus' refutation, and some later Arab philosophers, like al-Farabi and Ibn Sina (known in the Latin West as Avicenna), were ambiguous, at best, on the issue. On the other hand, al-Kindi and al-Biruni followed the reasoning of Philoponus, the latter arguing against Ibn Sina on this and many other issues. The issue was to become a prominent one again in the scholasticism of thirteenth-century Europe, as we shall see in chapter two.

The principal idea we are tracing, however, is that the natural world is comprehensible because it is circumscribed and because the same Logos that is responsible for its ordering is also reflected in human reason. Enough has been said to show that this idea became deeply ingrained in the Christian tradition, particularly where it was reinforced either by Neoplatonism or, as in the later Middle Ages, by Arab philosophy. Thus, for example, Adelard of

Bath (d c 1150; not to be confused with Peter Abelard, d 1142), often regarded as the first scientific thinker of Western Europe, taught that the visible universe is subject to quantification in that it is limited by its very nature so that there is only a finite number of individuals in any species. Adelard also extolled the arts for their ability to teach the human soul to intuit the divine pattern of things based on her god-given affinity with the divine *rationes*, or seminal reasons implanted within them.

On the point at issue, then, there is demonstrable continuity in the creationist tradition through the twelfth century and, as we shall see, at least through the seventeenth. There was also considerable dissension within the creationist tradition, but that occurred more in relation to other points we shall consider.

3. THE CREATIONIST TRADITION: UNITY OF HEAVEN AND EARTH

We have noted that Basil viewed the heavenly bodies to be hot just like terrestrial fire and denied that they were intelligent like angels or humans. The principal target here was Aristotle who had taught that the heavens were composed of a fifth element, that they were divine, and that the stars and planets moved along with them by virtue of their being alive and having eternal souls. The Pythagoreans and Platonists also viewed the stars as being divine intelligences due to the regularity of their motion. The Epicureans denied that the stars were living, as Anaxagoras had before them, but they did so by denying the apparent regularity of their motion. The Stoics treated both heaven and earth as being permeated by the divine world soul, practically identifying God with the cosmos. They did succeed, however in eliminating the Aristotelian dualism of heaven and earth, and they regarded the substance of the heavenly bodies to be fire like that found on earth.

Old and New Testaments

In the biblical tradition, the sun, moon and stars were believed to move at the command of God (Josh. 10:12ff.; Job 9:7; Ps. 147:4; Isa 40:26; 45:12; Hab. 3:11; Ecclus. 43:5, 10), or in accordance with his laws (Gen. 1:14–19; Ps. 148:3–6; Jer. 31:35f.). Occasionally they were personified in figurative language (Gen. 37:9, Judg. 5:20; Neh. 9:6; Job 38:7; Pss. 19:1–6, 89:9; 148:3f.; Isa 14:12; Ecclus. 16:27f.; Baruch 3:34), or associated with angels (Job 38:7; Dan. 8:10; 12:3; Rev. 1:20; 16:8; 19:17), but terrestrial elements were also personified and associated with angels (Job 38:36; Ps. 104:4,

7ff.; 114:3–7; 148:7ff.; Rev. 7:1ff.; 14:18; 16:1–5, 17 so there was no difference between heaven and earth in this respect. The biblical teaching was not a 'de-animation of the heavens' so much as a non-duality of heaven and earth.

The rending of the heavens and the alteration of its luminaries was a prominent feature in biblical theophanies (Judg. 5:4; 2 Sam. 22:10; Pss. 18:9; 144:5; Isa 24:23; 64:1, Hab. 3:11). The complete destruction of the heavens and the extinction of its luminaries was expected on the great and terrible day of the Lord (Isa. 13:9–13; 34:4; 51:6; Joel 2:1–11, 30f.; 3:14f.; Mark 13:25, 31; 2 Pet. 3:5–12). This was to be followed by the creation of a new heaven and a new earth in which there would no longer be any need for luminaries (Isa. 65:17; 66:22f.; 2 Pet. 3:13; Rev. 21:1, 23f.; 22:5). Another significant feature of the biblical cosmology was that there were waters (just like those on earth) above the heavens (Gen 1:6ff.; Ps. 148:4; Dan 3:60; 1 Enoch xiv.11). In other words, the waters of the cosmos gathered wherever God told them to.

The writers of the New Testament claimed a Lordship for Jesus Christ which was coextensive with that of God the Father. Jesus was thus Lord over all things in both heaven and earth (Matt. 28:18; 1 Cor. 8:6; 15:24–28; Eph. 1:10, 20–23; 4:8ff.; Phil 2:9ff.; Col. 1:15–20; Heb. 1:2f.). In all of these ways, Scripture made it clear that the heavens were not to be accorded any special status and that they were subject to the same laws as the earth and its inhabitants.

The Heavens: Animate or Inanimate?
In the second century AD, Tatian and Athenagoras both criticized Aristotle for limiting providence to the heavens. 'God's eternal providence', said the latter, 'is equally over us all.' Athenagoras also rejected Aristotle's notion that the heavenly substance was divine though he allowed the angels a role in the ordering of both heaven and earth.

The early Christian appropriation and critique of Greek science continued with regularity down to the time of Basil. Here we may note some of the most distinctive contributions.

Origen allowed that the sun, moon and stars were endowed with life and intelligence, a view for which he was later condemned according to the minutes of the Second Council of Constantinople (AD 553). Significantly, he based his conclusion on the biblical facts that the luminaries received commands from God in Scripture and that they were subject to change just like earthlings. Here again, Origen shows us the variation that could occur within the basic outline of the creationist tradition. The notion that mute creatures exhibited a form of intelligence was later revived by the hermetic and alchemical traditions in the Renaissance (section 3.1) and by the spiritualist tradition in the seventeenth century (section 3.3). Although it poses the danger of disregarding the uniqueness of humans, its abandonment by modern science has posed the opposite danger of disregarding the integrity of all God's creatures. The variety of interpretations allowed by the historic creationist tradition thus had some value.

Tertullian and Lactantius adopted the Stoic view that the Spirit of God is diffused through all things (cf. Wisd. 1:7; 7:24), though they rejected the Stoic identification of the world with God. Tertullian pointed out (AD 197) that the sun and moon could not be gods since they undergo change, for example, in eclipses. Lactantius (early fourth century) argued that the stars could not be animate because their motions showed no variation, thus turning the Platonic argument for their vitality on its head.

Athanasius, in the fourth century, picked up on the idea that the Word of God holds all things together (cf. Col. 1:17; Heb. 1:3) and argued that the same act of divine will was responsible for the straight-line motions we observe on earth as for the circular motions we find in heaven. In citing examples of the upholding work of the divine Logos, Athanasius treated celestial phenomena side by side with terrestrial ones.

Basil, then, stood within a well-established tradition in denying any special status to the heavens in his *Hexaemeron*. He seems, however, to have been the first Christian writer to follow the Platonists and Stoics in explicitly denying the existence of a fifth element peculiar to the heavens.

In the late fourth and early fifth century, the issue of the animation of the celestial bodies was still an open one. Theodore of Mopsuestia (in Cilicia) allowed the angels a role in moving the stars. Jerome denied that the stars were alive, as Basil had. Augustine was undecided.

In the sixth century, John Philoponos attacked Theodore's speculations on the role of angels and argued that what was visible must also be tangible, hence the stars could not be angels. He also followed Basil in regarding the heavenly bodies as fire, pointing out that differences in colour and magnitude indicated differences of composition just as with terrestrial fires. Indeed, he went so far as to compare the radiation of stars with that of animals like glow-worms and luminescent fish, thus evoking the charge of 'heresy' from his Neoplatonist contemporary Simplicius. And, again using Aristotelian principles against Aristotelian conclusions, Philoponos argued that celestial bodies must have both form and substance, hence they must be composite and perishable like all other bodies. Thus, on both observational and theoretical grounds, Philoponos established the creationist position of the unity of heaven and earth over against Aristotle. In the estimate of one modern historian (I. P. Sheldon-Williams), Philoponos thereby put the Christian doctrine of creation on a scientific basis.

Islamic and Medieval European Discussions

On the whole, the idea of the unity of heaven and earth was not challenged after the work of Basil and Philoponos though its radical implications for physics were not to be fully realized until the seventeenth century. The issue of the animation of the heavens was still an open one, however. As we have seen in the cases of Origen and Theodore of Mopsuestia, the creationist tradition did not rule out this idea absolutely.

In the East, John of Damascus (d c 750), citing 'the divine Basil' as an authority, regarded the heavens to be corruptible, like all things, 'according to the law of their nature' and declared that the luminaries were inanimate and insensible.

Islamic philosophers and scientists of the ninth through the twelfth century were divided on the issue, however. Although the Qur'an portrayed the sun, moon and heavens as directly subject to the ordinances of God, the rediscovery of Aristotle and Neoplatonism in the ninth century made such an impact that leading thinkers like al-Farabi (d AD 950) and Ibn Sina (Avicenna, d 1037) attempted a synthesis with the teachings of the Qur'an and postulated a hierarchy of intelligences corresponding to the heavens, as a bridge between the unity of God and the multiplicity of the terrestrial world. Influenced by Philoponos and taking a stricter reading of the Qur'an, al-Biruni (d 1048) rejected the vitality of the heavenly bodies, and in the twelfth century, al-Bitruji (Alpetragius) wrote a treatise which attempted to explain the motion of the heavens without recourse to celestial intelligences altogether.

Al-Bitruji's treatise was translated into Latin by Michael Scot in 1217, at the height of the influx of Greco-Arabic learning into Western Europe. In the meantime, the Western tradition had vascillated on the issue as much as the Syrian-Arab world had. Of the two principal scientific writers of the early middle ages, Isidore of Seville (d 636) had allowed for the possibility of the stars having souls, while the Venerable Bede (d 735), perhaps the first critical mind in Western European thought, omitted any reference to these speculations in his revision of Isidore's work.

In the twelfth century the Neoplatonists associated with the cathedral school of Chartres freely speculated on the role of intelligences among the celestial spheres. William of Conches (d c 1150), in particular, held that terrestrial events like the formation of Adam's body (as distinct from his soul) were governed by the stars and the spirits associated with them, rather than directly by God. His synthesis of Scripture with Neoplatonism was attacked by the more fundamentalist William of St Thierry, and he subsequently retracted a few of his more unguarded statements such as the one noted above.

The process of the 'de-animation of the heavens', as Richard Dales calls it, was not completed until the idea of the unity of heaven and earth could be given a mathematical form in which the need for celestial intelligences was unambiguously eliminated. For this we have to wait for the work of Isaac Newton.

4. THE CREATIONIST TRADITION: RELATIVE AUTONOMY OF NATURE

The ideas we have traced so far, the comprehensibility of the world and the unity of heaven and earth, have been widely accepted in Western thought since the time of Basil, despite uncertainty over related issues like the eternity of the world and the animation of the heavens. Our third theme, the relative autonomy of nature has been the cause of far more misunderstanding and dispute. Our discussion, then, will provide an introduction to the contest between science and religion that began in the West in the twelfth century, a contest that we shall be surveying in the following chapters of this volume.

By the 'relative autonomy' of nature, we mean the self-sufficiency nature possesses by virtue of the fact that God has granted it laws of operation. Like all laws, the laws of nature may come to be viewed as enslaving and inflexible, but, in their original sense, at least, they were viewed as liberating (from chaos) and life-giving. The autonomy of nature is thus 'relative' in the sense of being relational (to God), as well as in the sense of not being self-originated or entirely self-determined.

Old Testament and Intertestamental Judaism
Among the texts of the Old Testament contributing to the idea, Genesis 1 is best known. Day and night follow each other automatically once their alternation is established (Gen. 1:5), and new generations of plants and animals succeed each other without interference

through the normal processes of reproduction (Gen. 1:11f., 21f., 24f.). Elsewhere in the Old Testament, lawfulness is attributed to the courses of the sun, moon and stars (Job 38:33; Ps. 19:4ff.; 148:3ff.; Jer. 31:35f.; 33:25), the ebb and flow of the tides (Job 38:8–11; Ps. 104:9; Prov. 8:29; Jer. 5:22), the alternation of seasons (Gen. 8:22), and even to meteorological phenomena like wind, rain and lightning (Job 28:25ff.; 38:24f.; Ps. 148:8).

Within the Old Testament understanding of time, however, wherever the beneficent effect of God's mighty deeds was seen to continue, God's foundational work was also viewed as continuing. Creation once and for all was also continual creation (*creatio continua* or *creatio continuata*). In other words, the order of nature is a dependent order and, like an executive decree, is subject to the regular ratification of God. It is not rigid, but flexible, and it can be altered when its fulfillment in good is at stake (Gen. 6:5–9:17). The natural order is not separate from history and its denouement. It is neither impersonal nor amoral; hence it is not to be set over against the freedom and responsibility humans experience in everyday life (Pss. 19; 93; 104). Any supposed order that might ultimately lead to chaos, anarchy or injustice would not, in the biblical view, be true order. Hence, the upholding of natural order not only allows, but requires its emendation at points where irreversible damage may occur. We shall return to this idea in our discussion of resurrection and healing in the following section.

During the intertestamental period, the Jews developed the idea of the relative autonomy of nature considerably, partly as the result of their dialogue with Greek natural philosophy. In the early second century BC, Jesus ben Sirach, writing probably in Jerusalem and influenced perhaps by the Platonic emphasis on mathematical patterns, gave a stunning description of the ceaseless regularity of natural rhythms:

> The works of the Lord have existed from the beginning by his creation, and when he made them, he determined their divisions. He arranged his works in an eternal order, and their dominion for all generations: they neither hunger nor grow weary, and they do not cease from their labours. They do not crowd one another aside, and they will never disobey his word (Ecclus. 16:26ff.).

The stress here on nature's obedience to God's word was intended as a contrast to the foolishness of humans who disregard God's (moral) law, as the context makes abundantly clear (Ecclus. 16; 17). The contrast between the obedience of the luminaries and the rebelliousness of humans was made even more explicit by a near contemporary of ben Sirach in an early segment of 1 Enoch (ii.1-v.5), and it reappeared in the following century in the Testament of Naphtali, the Psalms of Solomon, and the Dead Sea Scrolls.

Already in the second century BC, however, an indication was given of the notion of mechanical inflexibility that could develop within the creationist tradition. This first occurred with Aristobulus of Alexandria (mid-second century BC), sometimes called the first Jewish 'philosopher' of the Hellenistic period. Aristobulus argued that God had arranged the order of creation (Genesis 1) in such a way that it would last for all time. God would keep it as is and would not make any changes. In spite of his belief in the invariability of the order of nature, Aristobulus did not regard God as being absent or inactive. Indeed the very regularity of natural law was for him a sign of God's presence and activity. This is not deism as we have known it in the modern Western world.

Early Christian Texts

The transmission of the idea of nature's relative autonomy into Christian circles is best illustrated by the Odes of Solomon, composed in Syria or Palestine, probably during the early second century AD. Like Aristobulus, the author reflected on the seven days of Genesis chapters one and two:

And He [the Lord] set the creation and aroused it,
then He rested from his works.
And created things run according to their courses,
and work their works,
and they are not able to cease and be idle.
And the hosts are subject to His word (Ode 16).

A comparison with the passage from Jesus ben Sirach quoted earlier shows a certain degree of dependence. The idea of God's resting from his works, however, must have come from the kind of philosophical interpretation of the Sabbath we find in Aristobulus and Philo.

Moving on to the fourth century, we have several witnesses to belief in the relative autonomy of nature just prior to the time of Basil. Arnobius of Sicca (north Africa), writing during the persecution under Diocletian in the early fourth century, argued that accusations that Christians had disrupted the world were unfounded. Natural events were still in accord with the 'laws established in the beginning' and the 'fabric of this machine and mass [of the universe], by which we are all covered and in which we are held enclosed' remained intact even after the advent of Christianity! There are several allusions here to the work of Lucretius, the Latin Epicurean, but the ideas of laws of nature being established by God at the beginning of time and the finitude of the cosmos are clearly biblical and, if anything, aimed against the physics of the Epicureans, who taught the randomness and unboundedness of nature. The comparison of the universe to a machine was to become a popular theme in later medieval and early modern European thought.

In the East the sufficiency of natural law was taught by Eusebius of Caesarea (in Palestine, *c* 314) who benefited directly from the writings of Aristobulus. One of the first Christian writers to utilize the Greek term for nature (*phusis*), he described Moses as attributing to God the framing of the 'laws of universal nature' as well as those of the nation of Israel. The stability of the firmament, the suspension of the earth, the orbits of the sun, moon and stars, and the alternation of the seasons were all established in the beginning by God's word and law.

Dating from around the middle of the fourth century is a remarkable chapter of Christian cosmic speculation in the Pseudo-Clementine *Recognitions*, which were originally written in Greek and later translated into Syriac and Latin so as to have an extensive influence on subsequent Christian thought in both East and West. As in Arnobius we find phrases like 'machine of the world' and 'fabric of the world' which were current in popular expositions of Epicurean science and well-suited to the expression of biblical faith. The paths of the stars, we are told, are governed by 'fixed laws and periods' and are evidence of divine creation. The reproduction of animals is also regular even though God has ordained a few special cases (like those of the crow, which conceives through the mouth, and the weasel, which brings forth through the ear!) to remind us that the order of the world is due to his appointment rather than to nature itself.

Thus the power of effective causation, for Pseudo-Clement, was present in nature only by virtue of God's creative decree. For example, the germination of seeds and the growth of plants was due to the 'power of the spirit' (i.e., moisture) which God has implanted in water at the moment of its creation. The manner of the germination of seeds, furthermore, was open to rational investigation, at least by the 'worthy and faithful' who understood something of the mysteries of God's ways. Thus the author himself was able to 'prove by fact and example' that the process depends entirely on the power of water by means of a thought experiment in which the amount of earth used is weighed both before planting and after the harvest and is found to be exactly the same. This was perhaps the greatest encouragement any ancient Christian writer was to give to rational scientific investigation.

Basil of Caesarea

We come back then to Basil in the seventh decade of the fourth century AD. In spite of the precedents we have studied, Basil is usually cited as the first major Christian contributor in the creationist tradition, and not without reason. In view of the influence he was to have in both East and West, several passages in his *Hexaemeron* take on great significance for the evolution of our belief in the relative autonomy of nature. His comments on Genesis 1:11 ('Let the earth put forth vegetation . . .') and 1:24 ('Let the earth bring forth living creatures . . .') are particularly striking in this connection. Genesis 1:11 mentions 'vegetation, plants yielding seed, and fruit trees bearing fruit in which is their seed'.

Basil first notes the wisdom of the order: first vegetation (LXX: 'grass'); then trees. This order, he notes, is followed by the earth to this day, and will continue for all time:

> For the voice that was then heard and this command were as a natural and permanent law [*nomos phuseos*] for it; it gave fertility and the power to produce fruit for all ages to come.

As in the Pseudo-Clementine *Recognitions* the power to cause germination is seen to be present in nature by virtue of creation, although, for Basil, that power appears to reside in the element earth rather than in water.

In concluding his homily on this text, Basil returns to the theme of the relative autonomy God grants to nature by his command and, in so doing, gives us the first of two classic examples of what later became known as the concept of impetus or momentum:

> It is this command which, still at this day, is imposed on the earth . . . Like [spinning] tops, which after the first impulse, continue their revolutions, turning upon themselves when once fixed in their centre; thus nature, receiving the impulse of this first command, follows without interruption the course of ages, until the consummation of all things.

Spinning tops were a phenomenon known to every child that strained the basic principles of Aristotelian physics. Belonging to the terrestrial world, they yet moved in circular fashion like the celestial spheres, thus demonstrating once again the non-duality of heaven and earth. Moreover, the relatively stable state of spinning was regarded as 'unnatural' in the Aristotelian view and required the *ad hoc* supposition of a thin layer of air whirling around the top to keep it going. For Basil, the motion of the spinning top was perfectly 'natural', however. It was just like the regular cycle of seedtime and harvest (Gen. 8:22) that one observes in terrestrial nature. In either case there is an initial impulse (the twist of fingers, in one case; the command of God, in the other) the effect of which continues indefinitely even after the original action has ceased. In modern science, the principle exhibited in the case of the spinning top is called the law of the conservation of momentum (in this case, angular momentum) or principle of inertia. For Basil, it was not only tops but all of nature, organic as well as inorganic, that moved in regular intervals in accordance with the command of God.

Basil's second example was that of a rolling ball. Here Basil describes the spontaneous generation of life from earth in response to the command of God in Genesis 1:24 ('Let the earth bring forth living creatures'). He compares it to the way a ball, once set in motion, rolls down an inclined plane without further assistance. The details are not entirely clear, but the original impulse is apparently a small push which brings the ball to the edge of the downward slope. Acceleration occurs as the ball begins to roll down the decline and continues until the ball reaches level ground again and eventually rolls to a stop.

Aristotle's physics could account for the acceleration downwards but had difficulty with the continuation along the horizontal. As in the case of the spinning top, however, the motion described was perfectly natural according to Basil. As the nature of soil and seminal potency in seeds produces the cycle of birth and death once the latter is set in motion by God's word, so the contour of the ground and the spherical shape of the ball produce the familiar pattern once the ball is set in motion. From a modern perspective, the physics is slightly more complicated than that of the spinning top case, involving in modern terms the conservation of energy as well as momentum, but the basic reasoning is the same, and each case reinforces the point of the other.

It would be over twelve hundred years before Galileo, Descartes and Newton would formulate a principle of inertia in mathematical terms that could be used in calculations. However, the idea of relative autonomy that lay behind it was clearly fixed by the time of Basil. Indeed it was deeply embedded in the Hellenistic-Jewish-Christian tradition that Basil inherited, as we have seen. Basil merely gave practical examples from everyday experience to illustrate the principle of the relative autonomy of nature as it had been understood since the time of Jesus ben Sirach and Aristobulus.

Transition to the Middle Ages Surveyed

The idea that motion is conserved and that its quantity depends only on the magnitude of the initial impulse was developed in the sixth century by John Philoponos as part of his programmatic attack on the physics of Aristotle. Through the writings of Philoponos, and also through the Syriac hexaemeral tradition, it was passed on to Arab philosophers of the eleventh and twelfth centuries like Ibn Sina (Avicenna), Ibn Bajjah (Avempace), al-Baghdadi, and al-Bitruji (Alpetragius). The idea recurred, with significant alterations, in the Western scholastics of the thirteenth and fourteenth centuries like Thomas Aquinas, Peter John Olivi, and Francis of Marchia (section 2.3). The degree to which this Western development was stimulated by ideas transmitted by the Arabs is difficult to determine. It may have been an independent development based on the fundamental idea of the autonomy of nature embedded in the hexaemeral tradition.

The alterations in the idea were largely due to the influence of Neoplatonism. Ibn Sina and Ibn Bajjah had reinterpreted the impartation of impetus as a continuously impressed force, thus weakening the basic idea of the autonomy of nature and ruling out the possibility of conservation of momentum in the absence of a continuous force. In this altered form, the idea of an impressed force continued down to the time of John Buridan (mid-fourteenth century) who revived the idea of a conserved impetus by appealing to the efficacy of God's original act of creation, as Basil had done almost a thousand years earlier.

In the meantime, the idea of the relative autonomy of nature had been transmitted to the Latin West and had prepared the way for the medieval developments we just noted. Basil's *Hexaemeron* was paraphrased by Ambrose in 389, and an elegant Latin translation by Eustathius appeared around the turn of the fifth century. Basil's work was also known and used by Augustine, Cassiodorus, and the Venerable Bede. The Pseudo-Clementine *Recognitions* were translated by Rufinus (d 410) about the same time and were influential on both Isidore and Bede.

Augustine of Hippo

Augustine (writing 386–430) developed the idea of the autonomy of nature to an unprecedented degree by stressing the transcendence of God, for whom there was no time as we know it, and explaining the unfolding of nature (and history) in terms of seminal causes that God implanted at creation so as to have their effects in a predetermined sequence. Thus Augustine could account for the fact that heaven and earth were created in the beginning of God's work (Gen. 1:1), yet did not take form as firmament and dry land, respectively, until the second and third 'days' (Gen. 1:6–10). He solved the problem by referring the initial act of creation (Gen.1:1) to the seeds (as well as the unformed material) of heaven and earth. In effect, the seeds of all things were created at once, and the work of the 'six days' in Genesis 1 was really an inventory of the potencies contained in those seeds.

As a result of Augustine's interpretation, the seminal causes, which had been so closely related to the divine world soul in Stoicism and Neoplatonism and to the Wisdom or Word of God in intertestamental Judaism and early Christianity, could now be regarded as distinct from God's (transcendent) essence. Moreover, the beginning of God's rest and of nature's relative autonomy were pushed back from the first Sabbath (Gen. 2:2) to the very first instant of time. This is, therefore, the first clear indication we have of the concept of autonomous nature that was to prevail in the West after the seventeenth century.

Augustine was not a deist in the modern sense, however, for he regarded God's eternal will and power as terminating in time. God's eternal decree functioned as a continuously creative activity by virtue of which seminal causes could produce their respective effects. Still, given the fact of that continuous activity, the inevitability and predictability of cause-effect sequences seemed to follow.

Boethius and Cassiodorus

The sixth century was a pivotal one for the development of Western civilization. Two Italian Christian leaders of that time were instrumental in the formation of medieval European scholarship. Boethius (d c 524) established the format of the medieval curriculum (the three literary arts, or *trivium*, and the four mathematical sciences, or *quadrivium*) and wrote texts on the four sciences (arithmetic, music, geometry, and astronomy). He thus made available the rudiments of Euclid, Nichomachus and Ptolemy to later generations, though most of this was lost and not rediscovered until the late tenth century. He also began a translation programme that was to include the major works of Plato and Aristotle and anticipated the later, more comprehensive, translation programme that began in the twelfth century.

Even if Boethius had lived to complete his great work, it is doubtful whether there was a sufficient market for scientific ideas in his time to have allowed a scientific renaissance of any magnitude. The scientific development of the Greco-Roman era had reached a point of diminishing returns for lack of an adequate social and technological base, and the Christian influence that was to catalyse the next major advance was only beginning to make itself felt.

However, the assimilation of Boethius's works in the tenth and eleventh centuries helped to prepare the West for the rapid assimilation of Greco-Arabic science in the twelfth and thirteenth centuries. As Richard Dales has put it: 'From Boethius's textbooks, the Middle Ages . . . learned to conceive of the world of nature as an ordered whole and to deal with it rationally.'

Though Boethius's philosophical ideas came principally from Neopythagorean and Neoplatonic sources (the compatibility of which with biblical thought at some points, at least, has already been noted), it was his creationist faith and his Christian altruism that motivated his efforts and sustained him through periods of doubt right up until his untimely death.

Boethius's contemporary Cassiodorus (d c 575?) was less of a theoretician, and more of an organizer. Like Boethius, he left his stamp on the scholarship of medieval Europe during its formative stages. The monastic community Cassiodorus founded in Calabria was not influential in itself, but the library he assembled and the advice he gave his monks concerning the importance of the arts and sciences were to encourage the love of learning in the rapidly spreading Benedictine monastic order which inherited them. By playing down the mystical aspects of Neopythagorean mathematics and showing the usefulness of the arts and sciences for an understanding of Scripture, Cassiodorus helped to allay the fears that many devout monks would naturally have about the contamination of pure doctrine with secular ideas.

The impact of monasticism on European culture was to be as much on the social and technological levels as in terms of pure scholarship. One aspect of this impact which relates to the idea of the autonomy of nature was the concern for cosmic time and its measurement for liturgical purposes. The determination of the time of day, the month, and the year had already been an important task of astrologer-priests in the ancient Near East. Some Jewish sects believed that the worship of God was carried on through the night by the hosts of angels in heaven, and the early Christians developed their own prayer cycles as a means of participating in this heavenly cosmic liturgy (Luke 2:13; Heb. 12:22ff.; Rev. 4:8; 7:15). The

Qumran Community (second century BC to second century AD) had developed a common life in which work and study were coordinated with the cycles of worship: human life was thus constructed in the image of the lawful mechanism of the cosmos. Beginning with the fourth century AD the common or cenobite life was adopted and adapted by Christians: Pachomius in Upper Egypt; Eustathius and Basil in Asia Minor; Augustine and Cassian in the West. The sixth century saw the founding of the Benedictine order which was to dominate European history for seven hundred years and lay the foundations of Western science and technology. The rules developed by the monastic fathers specified a certain number of hours (usually six) for work each day in addition to the regular duties of worship.

It is in connection with this more practical side of the creationist tradition that Cassiodorus made his most influential contributions. He provided his monastery with both a sundial and a water clock: the one for sunny days, the other for cloudy days and for nights, '. . . in order that the soldiers of Christ, warned by the most definite signs, may be summoned to the carrying out of their divine tasks as if by sounding trumpets.' This is the first indication we have of the importance time-keeping devices were to assume in the monastic life of the middle ages.

Also significant was the composition (whether by Cassiodorus or by someone commissioned by him) of a revised *computus* (computational tables), keyed to the year 562, for determining the dates of successive Easters. This document was innovative in that it used the nineteen-year (235 month) cycle of Dionysius Exiguus (AD 525), rather than the less accurate eight-year cycle popularized by Pliny in the first century AD.

The Computus Tradition through Bede

From the sixth century to the twelfth, progress in calendrics and astronomy was slow, but the motivation was strong. In the late sixth century, Gregory of Tours (d 594) wrote a treatise on the courses of the stars to enable monks to determine the proper hours for night offices from the positions of the constellations at different times of the year. Isidore of Seville (d 636), writing in what is generally regarded to be the depth of the dark ages, made a clear distinction between astronomy and astrology: the former, which he called 'natural astrology', dealt with the lawful courses of the heavenly bodies (*lex astrorum*), while the latter dealt with personal horoscopes.

At this point, the scene of activity shifted to the British Isles, where a *computus* tradition was already flourishing under the aegis of Celtic monasticism at Iona and Lindisfarne. In the year 668,

Theodore Tarsus was appointed Archbishop of Canterbury, and under his supervision, Hadrian of Africa established a comprehensive curriculum, including astronomy and computation, at the monastery school of Canterbury which became the model for monastic schools founded by Benedict Biscop at Wearmouth (674) and Jarrow (c 681).

It was at Jarrow that the Venerable Bede (c 672–735) grew up and received his training. Bede is recognized as the first indigenous scientist of the West. In an autobiographical note he appended to his *History of the English Church*, he described himself as having been devoted all his life (since the age of seven) to the monastic discipline at Jarrow. But, he said, he found his chief delight in study, teaching and writing. Among other things, Bede's study, teaching and writing included the organization of a cooperative programme for monitoring the tides up and down the English coast ('the establishment of a port') and the writing of two major works on time measurement and chronology, one of which became a standard text for centuries to come.

While basing much of his work on the texts of Pliny and Isidore, Bede was more willing to check inherited wisdom against his own observations than Isidore, and he gave the first clear statement of the sphericity of the earth in medieval times. (The idea was thus well established by Columbus's time.)

In general, Bede presented the following generation of scholars with an ordered universe of cause and effect in which as many phenomena as possible were reduced to general laws. Bede was venerated by the leaders of the Carolingian renaissance half a century later, and his scientific works were still influential at the cathedral school of Chartres in the twelfth century.

The eighth century thus marked a turning point at which the creationist tradition, together with the disciplined monastic life it fostered, gave rise to the earliest stages of Western scientific thought. The turning point was also marked by the fact that, for the first time in the West, a mild conservative reaction occurred.

Boniface's Reaction to Virgil of Salzburg

Around the year 748, Boniface complained to Pope Zachary that Virgil (later to be bishop of Salzburg) held the view that the opposite side of the world (the antipodes) might be inhabited by humans, a teaching generally associated with writings of the classical Epicurean, Lucretius!

We know little of Virgil's background other than that he was born in Ireland or Scotland. It has been suggested that his speculations about inhabitants of the remoter portions of the globe were rooted in Celtic traditions concerning a race of immortals that dwelt underground. If so, his citation of the classical idea of the antipodes was more indebted to folk religion than to empirical science in the modern sense. It was an early attempt of synthesis between science and faith rather than an instance of opposition between the two.

Boniface was a product of Anglo-Saxon Benedictine education and something of a classical scholar himself, though of more a literary than a scientific bent. A humanist by inclination, he worked hard at organization and discipline, helping to establish more than sixty monasteries in Germany (the 'Apostle of Germany') and attempting, almost single-handedly, an extensive reform of the Church in France. So we can readily understand that the pronouncements of Virgil on an issue that had been regarded as highly speculative by Basil, Ambrose and Augustine and was associated with classical Epicureanism and Celtic mythology might elicit his concerns about the re-emergence of paganism. Boniface is still known today for his symbolic act of felling the Oak of Thor at Geismar.

In response to Boniface's complaint, Pope Zachary denounced the idea that the other side of the earth might be inhabited, apparently on the grounds that it implied the existence of a race of beings not descended from Adam and Eve (the equatorial zone was believed to be impassable). Such an idea Zachary declared to be 'in opposition to God' (i.e., contrary to divine revelation; cf. Gen. 10:32; 11:8; Matt. 24:14) and detrimental to Virgil's own soul. The Pope accordingly instructed Boniface to excommunicate and unfrock Virgil on the supposition that his report of Virgil's words was accurate. Apparently no action was taken, however. In fact, Virgil became bishop of Salzburg in 767 (or 755?) and was canonized in 1233.

The brief altercation between Boniface and Virgil in the mid-eighth century was one of the first in what was to become a long series of conflicts between the interests of intellectual inquiry and the moral and spiritual concerns of church order in Western Christendom. We recall that Church leaders of the second, third and fourth centuries (e.g., Irenaeus, Tertullian, and Lactantius) had been overtly critical of much of Greek science, largely for ecclesiastical or pastoral reasons. In the fourth century, Pseudo-Clement (of the *Recognitions*) and Basil took a more positive approach to pagan learning, and this new departure combined with the emergence of monastic discipline to produce the interest in natural phenomena we found in the Venerable Bede.

So the issue between Virgil and Boniface was *not* a conflict between science and religion. Both protagonists were loyal church-men. Indeed, both were missionaries for their faith. Both of their respective viewpoints – belief in the comprehensibility and unity of nature and concern for corporate responsibility – were born and nurtured within the creationist tradition. They may be viewed as representing two wings of that tradition – the one more progressive and the other more conservative. Both viewpoints would prove to be instrumental in the development of modern science. What we have, then, is a tension between two ideals or goods – both sanc-tioned by the Church and both conducive to scientific progress – not a conflict between science and religion as such.

Rabanus, Gerbert and Fulbert

With the work of Boniface and Virgil, the focus of our story shifts from Britain back to France and Germany, where the Carolingian Renaissance was engineered by Alcuin of York (d 804), an educator trained by a former student of Bede. The work of building an indigenous northern European intelligentsia was continued by Alcu-in's student Rabanus Maurus (d 856), who was Archbishop of Mainz and later known as *primus praeceptor Germaniae* ('the foremost teacher of Germany').

As if it had not already been proven that an interest in natural science was no bar to promotion in the Church, the last year of the millennium saw Gerbert of Aurillac, the leading European mathema-tician of the day, become (by appointment of the German Emperor, Otto III) the first French Pope, Sylvester II. Gerbert, trained in the classics by the Benedictines at Aurillac, had travelled to Spain to study Arabic science and had taught astronomy at the cathedral school of Rheims. Using Arabic models, he devised astronomical instruments with which to illustrate his lectures, and was perhaps the first Christian in the West to use Hindu-Arabic numerals instead of the more cumbersome Roman ones. Gerbert thus gives us the first indication of the way in which the creationist tradition of the West produced the kind of demand for scientific knowledge that would pave the way for the major influx of Greco-Arabic learning in the following three centuries.

Gerbert's pupil, Fulbert, was responsible for building the cathedral school at Chartres into a centre of scientific studies in the early eleventh century. It is among twelfth-century Chartrians, stimulated in part by a renewed interest in Neoplatonism, that many historians of science today see the beginnings of the modern scientific outlook. Thierry of Chartres (d *c* 1155) and his students developed the idea of relative autonomy to the point where nature became almost mechanistic in the modern sense. However, the Chartrian Platonists were not the only exponents of the idea of autonomy in the twelfth century: there were also Peter Abelard (d 1142), Adelard of Bath (d c 1150), William of Conches (d c 1150), and Honorius of Autun (d 1152) – all testimony to the fact that the idea had become deeply ingrained in European thought well before the twelfth century, as our survey has shown.

Academic and Ecclesiastical Dimensions of Autonomy

The revival of natural philosophy in the eleventh and twelfth centuries was closely associated with a renewed interest (stimulated by the rediscovery of Boethius's works) in the use of Aristotelian dialectic (logic) to interpret Scripture and organize theological discourse generally. This was the first wave of Aristotelian influence in the Latin middle ages, often referred to as the 'old logic'. The 'old logic' of Aristotle did not include the major corpus of Aristotelian natural philosophy, but it prepared the way for the reception of the latter in the late twelfth and early thirteenth centuries.

Also in the eleventh and twelfth centuries, there was a conservative reaction to both Neoplatonic natural philosophy and Aristotelian dialectic. This reaction was similar to that of Boniface in the eighth century but far more extensive in scope. The use of the word 'conservative' in this context is traditional, but it may be misleading since many of the anti-dialecticians also advocated reforming the Church and ending abuses that stemmed from secular interference in ecclesiastical affairs.

An important alignment of social and theological interests thus came about that was to persist in varying forms for over seven centuries. The freedom of the Church from secular control was associated with the freedom of theological discourse from the constraints of secular (Aristotelian) reason. It was a pattern that was to repeat itself in various ways in the fourteenth, seventeenth and nineteenth centuries. Both sides sought autonomy in their own terms: autonomy of the natural sphere was mirrored in academic privileges, on the one hand; autonomy of the spiritual, sacramental and moral spheres was mirrored in clerical privileges (and the restriction of dialectic to its place as just one of the arts), on the other. What God had joined together was beginning to come apart, at least, as far as Western society was concerned.

God's Absolute Power: Damian, Manegold and William of St Thierry
Peter Damian (d 1072), first and foremost among these critics of
dialectic, had himself taught grammar and rhetoric (the other two
arts in the *trivium*) at Ravenna before being drawn to monastic life.
His skill in dialectic was also amply demonstrated by his devastating
use of the art in arguing against its more zealous advocates.

Damian's basic concern, however, was that the extensive use of
reason to draw inferences in theological matters neglected the sover-
eign freedom of God, or, equivalently, that an increasing emphasis
on the autonomy of the natural order overlooked the biblical basis
of natural law in the divine decree. Consequently, he stressed the
potentia absoluta ('absolute power') of God to alter the course, or
even the existing state, of nature. To take an extreme case: God
could not only reverse the effects of a past injustice, but even cause
it not to have happened in the first place! Such were the lengths
some conservatives felt compelled to go to in order to counter the
threat of an emerging naturalism and rationalism.

Writing a little later than Damian, Manegold of Lautenbach (*c*
1080) shared many of his concerns. The natural philosophers, he
complained, were so concerned with the physical nature of things
that they could no longer conceive of a substantial being existing
beyond the natural order.

William of St Thierry (d 1148), one of the greatest medieval
mystics, was a friend of Bernard of Clairvaux. He wrote to Bernard
against both Peter Abelard and William of Conches, succeeding in
the former case in inducing the more famous churchman to take up
his own pen. The grounds in that instance seem to have been purely
theological, resting, of course, on the underlying issue of the value
of dialectic. The case against William of Conches, however, concerned the latter's radically naturalistic interpretation of Genesis, as
well as theology. It would not be fair to say that William of St
Thierry was opposed to science itself, however, for he wrote a
treatise of his own *On the Nature of the Body and the Soul*, which
was based on some of the latest medical ideas. Indeed, one of his
principal concerns was to affirm the unity of body and soul against
the dualistic tendencies of William of Conches and other Platonists.

Such was what is sometimes called the 'conflict between religion
and science' in the eleventh and twelfth centuries. The episode has
been noted by recent historians as marking the first time since
antiquity that the problem of scientific versus religious thinking
received serious attention. This observation represents a great
advance over the earlier tendency to view the problem as having
arisen in the seventeenth, or even the nineteenth, century. Yet, as

we have noted, the roots of the problem go back to the second century BC and as far back as the eighth century AD even within the confines of West European history.

Moreover, the issue was not one of religion and science, so much as of two different emphases within the creationist tradition. As we shall see in later chapters, the left wing of the creationist tradition gradually abandoned its theological orientation and the right wing eventually lost its interest in science. But the process of divorce was not completed until the emergence of the specialized professions of the nineteenth century. In the meantime, we are dealing with two opposing interpretations of creationist theology, not with an opposition between science and theology as such.

Still, those historians who date the problem from the eleventh or twelfth century are partly right, for it was during that period that the dichotomy between the natural and the supernatural, so ingrained in modern Western thought, had its origin. The scholastics (after Anselm and Peter Lombard) began to make a systematic distinction between the regular power (*potentia ordinata*) of God, reflected in the normal sequences of cause and effect, and his absolute power (*potentia absoluta*) at any time to suspend or alter those sequences – a distinction that was quite useful in the interpretation of Scripture. But, already in the eleventh and twelfth centuries, the normal sequences of nature were viewed as due to a power delegated to nature by God, and the distinction became an opposition that was quite foreign to the sense of Scripture. In place of a *relative* autonomy of nature based on the efficacy of God's creative word, one then had an impossible choice: either an autonomous world, created by God but virtually independent of his continued presence and power; or else a world so utterly dependent on God's will moment by moment that all rational, scientific investigation became impossible. In effect, we have the beginning of the dissolution of the creationist tradition itself, even though the total demise of the tradition took seven centuries to complete.

The Order of Nature: Adelard and William of Conches

Two examples of the problem will suffice: first, Adelard of Bath, who wrote in the late 1120s. In his *Natural Questions*, Adelard tried to defend his interest in Arabic science against an attack by conservatives by equating the work of God with the miraculous and contrasting it with the work of nature. The wording of his defence shows how the separation of God and nature came about:

I take nothing away from God, for whatever exists is from Him

and because of Him. But the natural order does not exist confus-
edly and without natural arrangement, and human reason should
be listened to concerning those things it treats of. But when it
completely fails, then the matter should be referred to God.

The underlying ideas cited in this passage – the creation of all things
by God, the consequent order and rationality of the cosmos, and
the power of human reason – all stem from the Judeo-Christian
creationist tradition, dating back at least to the second century BC.
What was new was that Adelard set the natural order and the work
of God, rational investigation and Christian faith, over against each
other as alternatives ('. . . when human reason fails, *then* the matter
should be referred to God').

The consequence of this polarization was that, for Adelard, God
was removed from the natural order in such a way that natural law
became inflexible and impersonal:

> Truly, whoever thinks to abolish the innate order within nature
> is mad . . . For he who disposes is most wise and, consequently,
> is least of all either willing or even able to abolish the fundamental
> order in nature . . . and among [natural] philosophers it is agreed
> that any upsetting of this order is least likely to occur.

The belief that God does not normally alter his established order
(*potentia ordinata*) had been an essential part of the creationist tradition since Genesis, but, for earlier theologians like Aristobulus
and Augustine, the natural order itself was upheld by God (through
his word, will or power). For Adelard, on the other hand, the
only sort of properly divine action envisioned was his abolition or
upsetting of that order (*potentia absoluta*), and even this was deemed
to be unlikely. The order of nature was so fixed that God was neither
'willing nor even able' to alter it!

William of Conches, our second example, began teaching at Paris
and (possibly) at Chartres at just about the same time that Adelard
was writing (1120s) and was the most influential master of the time
until he was forced to retire around 1144. In one of his later works,
his gloss on Plato's *Timaeus*, William made a similar differentiation
between the work of God and the work of nature:

> It must be recognized that every work is the work of the Creator
> or of Nature, or the work of a human artisan imitating nature.
> The work of the Creator is the first creation without pre-existing
> material, for example the creation of the elements or of spirits,

or it is the things we see happen contrary to the accustomed course of nature, as the virgin birth and the like. The work of nature is to bring forth like things from like through seeds or offshoots, for nature is an energy inherent in things and making like from like.

This statement is, if anything, more extreme than Adelard's: Adelard had at least attributed the ordering, as well as the creation of the elements, to God. For William, however, the ordering of nature was due to the inherent properties of the elements, and only the creation of the elements (and spirits) and their properties was due to God's agency. Consequently, the ordering described in Genesis was itself subject to rational scrutiny and could not be accepted as authoritative.

William went so far as to reject the statement of Genesis 1:7 about the existence of waters above the visible heaven as unnatural and contrary to reason. The difference is not just a matter of degree. Basil and other early representatives of the creationist tradition believed in the order of nature *as* the work of God, whereas William believed in it as self-ordering and self-perpetuating. The work of nature was autonomously 'to bring forth like things from like', and any act of God subsequent to the first moment of creation ('the virgin birth and the like') was '*contrary* to the accustomed order of nature'. Here we have the idea of 'miracle' as a violation of the laws of nature that was to become popular in the seventeenth and eighteenth centuries (e.g. David Hume).

We should note the effect the differentiation between the natural and divine orders had on William of Conches' epistemology. The consistent testimony of the Church fathers up to and including the Venerable Bede, whom William and others of his time greatly admired, had been in favour of the existence of supracelestial waters almost without exception. So William was forced to limit the authority of the fathers (and, by implication, that of Scripture) to matters of religious faith and morals. This resulted in a clear dichotomy in modes of knowing correlated with the ontological dichotomy between God and nature. In matters concerning the work of God, now limited to the initial impetus of creation and occasional miracles, the authority of Scripture and the Church was to be taken on faith. With regard to the workings of nature, however, reason alone was to be followed. Moreover, these two procedures were mutually exclusive and antithetical. Given this view of the alternatives, already expressed in the mid-twelfth century, it is no wonder that many creative modern thinkers have become sceptical about theology and about matters of faith generally!

Finally, we should note the dualism that emerges in William of Conches between two spheres of human existence: (1) the moral and spiritual, now relegated to the jurisdiction of the Church; and (2) the technological and natural, based on human art and science. On one hand, William's dichotomy between faith and reason, noted above, left the realm of human traditions and values ('the establishment of custom') on the side of pure faith. On the other hand, his dichotomy between the work of God and the work of nature left human technology ('the work of an artisan imitating nature') on the side of nature, based on human bodily needs and a knowledge of the structures of nature.

The resulting antithesis of ethical mores and technological skills was probably not intentional in William of Conches, but it was an immediate implication of his thought. It also reflected and was reinforced socio-politically by the increasing autonomy of the secular order from the Church as witnessed by the rapid development of lay guilds during this period and the growth of mercantile capitalism.

Still, while we have used terms like natural as opposed to supernatural, reason as opposed to faith, secular and technological as opposed to moral and ecclesiastical, it should be kept in mind that we are really talking about two strands of the same creationist tradition, two strands that were beginning to unravel in the twelfth century. If the two seem so separate to us today, we must remember that we in the West are the products of the history here described, and that 'from the beginning it was not so' (Matt. 19:8). Our thesis will receive further support as we consider the rationale for Western medicine and technology that developed out of Christian moral and spiritual values prior to the split in the creationist tradition in the twelfth century.

Our Definition of the Creationist Tradition Defended

At this point, we are in a position to note the differences between the definition of the 'creationist tradition' we have offered, going back to the biblical and patristic periods, and the definition Richard Dales offers in his studies of developments in the twelfth century. The features that characterized the 'creationist' (or 'transcendent-creationist') tradition according to Dales are a gulf between God and the world, the de-animation of nature, creation *ex nihilo*, the consequent goodness, self-sufficiency and rationality of nature, and a tendency to view nature in mechanistic terms. Dales' conclusion is that the creationist tradition was inherently unstable and tended toward modern atheism.

For comparison, our own definition has consisted thus far of the rationality of nature (with or without the stipulation that it be finite), the commensurable rationality of the human mind (hence the comprehensibility of nature to humans), the unity of heaven and earth (with or without the association of the heavens with ruling angels), and the relative autonomy of nature based on God's creative word and power. In other words, the creationist tradition, does not entail (*pace* Dales) a gulf between God and the world or a de-animation or mechanization of nature in the modern sense. Such an emphasis did begin to enter the tradition with Augustine's separation of the seminal causes from God's consubstantial Word and Spirit, but it was not essential to the tradition itself. The idea of the complete autonomy, or even mechanicity, of nature did not enter until the gulf opened by Augustine widened to the point of suggesting a dichotomy between God's ordering of nature and his absolute power, or even between nature itself and God. This did not happen until the eleventh or twelfth century. In our view, then, it was not the original biblical and patristic tradition, but a distortion of it, that tended toward the determinism, reductionism and atheism that characterizes so much of modern Western thought.

5. THE CREATIONIST TRADITION: MINISTRY OF HEALING AND RESTORATION

Thus far we have concentrated on the theoretical aspects of the historic creationist tradition, which were given coherence by Basil in his sermons on Genesis 1. Three principal themes of this tradition – the comprehensibility of the world, the unity of heaven and earth, and the relative autonomy of nature – can be traced through the centuries in both East and West, as we have found, until they are seen to converge in Western Europe during the twelfth century and find their place at the foundations of modern Western science.

But the creationist tradition and Basil's contribution, in particular, were not just theoretical in nature. They had strong practical components that were closely related to the theoretical, but took on a life of their own and influenced the history of science just as much, if not more, than the theoretical. We have already discussed the importance of the liturgical concern for time and the regulation of monastic life as vehicles for the sense of regularity in the rhythms of the cosmos. In this section we turn to the healing and helping ministries of the early Church, rooted in the biblical beliefs of creation, resurrection, and the possibility of the miraculous, which, through the work of Basil and his contemporaries, gave rise to the Christian traditions of medical science and technology in the middle ages. Much of what we discuss here relates to the histories of medicine and technology.

Jewish and Greek Assessments of Technology

What evidence we have for the Old Testament and intertestamental attitudes towards technology is rather paradoxical. The Israelite monarchy, dating back to the time of David and Solomon (tenth century BC), was made possible by the development of an iron-based technology competitive with that of the Philistines and Canaanites (Josh. 17:16; Judg. 1:19; 4:1ff.; 4:13ff.; 1 Sam. 13:19–22). The early monarchy was thus a time of major growth for all the arts and crafts needed to maintain a small oriental dynasty (1 Kgs. 5–10; cf. Exod. 31:1–11). On the other hand, the association of human fabrication with the manufacture of idols and with political repression gave rise to a lasting suspicion of the manual arts, particularly among the working classes, from the time of Solomon onwards (1 Kgs. 5:13–18; 9:15–23; 11:1–8; 12:25–33; 16:31–34; Isa. 2:7f.; 17:7f.; Jer. 22:13–17; Hos. 8:4f.; 13:2).

This reaction intensified during the Babylonian exile when the Jews were confronted with a superior technology in alliance with a polytheistic religion (Isa. 40:19f.; 41:6f.; 44:9–20; *passim*). Babylonian, and later Greek, technology were thus associated, in certain strata of the apocalyptic tradition, with the antediluvian fall of the angels and the beginnings of warfare and immortality (e.g., 1 Enoch vi–xi, of the late third century BC or earlier). This occasionally negative attitude in the post-exilic period must be interpreted in the light of the clear association of technology with oppression and persecution by foreign powers, however.

In other words, the Jewish position was neither for nor against technology as such: it was for relief from suffering and oppression, and all technology was assessed in terms of that criterion (Isa. 25:1–5; 61:1–7; cf. Wisd. 7:16–22; Jubilees iv.15–19; 1 Enoch lii). What we are about to trace is a thousand-year development through which technology once again (as in the days of David and Solomon) became associated with the relief of human misery, a development which contributed to the social basis needed for the growth of modern Western science.

The fundamental belief of the Jews was in God as the Creator of all things (Gen. 1; Pss. 33:6–9; 139:13–16; 148:5f.; Prov. 8:22–31;

Jer. 10:12; 51:15). In dialogue with schools of Greek philosophy that posited a pre-existent substratum of unformed matter, the Jews affirmed creation *ex nihilo*: God was the Creator even of the matter of which all things consist (2 Macc. 7:28; Letter of Aristeas cxxxvi; 2 Enoch xxiv.2; 2 Baruch xlviii.8; Genesis Rabbah i.9). The corollary of this belief was that things can be changed. Things do not have to continue as they now are because their existence depends on a God who created them beginning with nothing, who can therefore transform them as he will, and who has promised that such a transformation will take place through the power of his Spirit (Pss. 104; 146; Isa. 40:27–31; Jer. 33; Ezek. 37; Wisd. 19:6–12; 1 Macc. 7:28).

A comparison with the classical Greek outlook is useful at this point. The Greeks were able to maintain a tradition of political independence through much of their history even during the period of Persian hegemony. Even under later Roman rule (after 146 BC), Greeks enjoyed the privilege and status of providing the dominant cultural ambience. So it is not surprising to find that technology, especially the technology of warfare, was widely praised and patronized among the Greeks.

On the other hand, the Greek philosophers, almost without exception, viewed matter as eternal and uncreated. If there was a God, he had to do the best he could with the prescribed properties of matter. In other words, the Greeks did not believe in the *possibility* of radical change, partly because they did not experience the *need* for radical change. As Ludwig Edelstein has put it: 'The world was there to live in, not to be used or to be made over.'

So there was a paradox at the heart of both Jewish and Greek thought alike. The Greeks, following the Babylonians and Egyptians, had developed the rudimentary techniques of engineering, but their outlook precluded them from sensing the full value of those techniques. The Jews, on the other hand, due to their faith and their social condition, understood the need for physical redemption even though they failed (after David and Solomon) to see the potential of technology in the fulfilment of that need. The development of Western technology required both of these contributions and, therefore, required an outlook on life that could bring them together. This integrated outlook was provided by the early Christian church.

The New Testament Church: Healing Power and Social Benefit
The distinctive contribution of the New Testament was the belief that the power and love of the Creator had been poured out on humanity through the ministry of Jesus and his disciples. The

outpouring of God's Spirit had empirical correlates in the relief of the oppressed, the healing of the sick, and the raising of the dead (Matt. 8:1–10:8; Mark 1:9–45; Luke 4:14–19; 6:17ff.; Acts 3:1–16; 5:29ff.; *passim*). Indeed, these works of the Spirit were regarded as the principal signs or evidences that promises of the Old Testament had been fulfilled and that the message of the disciples of Jesus was trustworthy (Matt. 11:2–24; 12:15–32; Luke 7:21f.; 13:32; Acts 3:17–4:22).

The display of healing power was regarded as evidence of the Spirit's presence, but it was not sufficient evidence in itself. No people of antiquity were more aware of the possible misuses of power than the Jews. Even the Jewish apologists who portrayed Moses as a great king in Hellenistic terms stressed the idea that he did not use his power for personal advantage, but rather for the benefit of others. The New Testament writers insisted on the same criterion for the assessment of spiritual gifts. The powers of prophecy and exorcism, even accompanied by the name of Jesus, were not to be trusted if used for evil or selfish ends (Matt. 7:21ff.). Christians whose gifts were recognized were not to use them for their own advantage or to regard themselves as superior to others. Everything was to be done as Christ had done it, for the edification or benefit of others (Mark 10:42–45; Rom. 12:16; 14:13–15:6; 1 Cor. 10:23–11:1; 14:1–33; Phil. 2:3–7; 1 Thess. 2:1–8; 1 Pet. 4:10f.).

To sum up: the early Christians believed in the possibility of healing and restoration that would truly benefit the needy. Underlying this belief was faith in a God who had created and could restore, a Messiah who had initiated God's final rule over both the forces of nature and the structures of society, and a Spirit who had been poured out on the believers enabling them to carry on the work of Jesus and to extend it to all nations.

Two Streams in the Second Century: Apocryphal Acts and Apologists
During the second century the ideas we have documented from the New Testament divided temporarily into two streams and merged again in the writings of Irenaeus and Pseudo-Clement.

The first stream, that of the apocryphal books of acts, stressed the healing power of the apostles and related it to their faith in a God who created all things. Of particular interest is a document known as the Third Epistle to the Corinthians (Acts of Paul viii.1–3) which dates from the late second century and was later included in the Syriac and Armenian canons of the New Testament. In the context, Paul was preaching against the Gnostics who denied that the body was God's creation and that there would be a resurrection.

Claiming that God had created the body, together with all things, and would not forsake his creation when it was lost, Paul explained that Christ had come in the flesh, had died, and had been raised in the flesh in order to secure the salvation of all flesh.

In the sequel (preserved in the Coptic Heidelberg Papyrus) Paul and a young woman named Frontina were thrown down into a pit and Frontina was killed. When Paul saw the grief of Frontina's mother, he prayed to the Lord Jesus Christ for deliverance. Thereupon, Frontina was restored to life, and the crowd cried out with one voice: 'One is God, who has made heaven and earth, who has given life to the daughter . . .'

The story is, of course, apocryphal, but it gives us an idea of the healing ministry of the Church as it was understood in the second century and shows the close connection between Christian faith and practice. Belief in creation meant the possibility of healing and restoration to life. Similar incidents can be found in the Acts of Peter (late second century), the Acts of John and the Acts of Thomas (both of the third century), though the connection of healing power with the doctrine of creation is not made so explicit.

The second stream of thought in the second century is found in the major Christian apologists: Justin, Athenagoras and Theophilus. Since these writings are apologetic rather than narrative in character, we would not expect to encounter the same emphasis on the mighty deeds of the apostles that we found in the Apocryphal Acts. We do find arguments for the future resurrection based on a belief in God as Creator (cf. 2 Macc. 7:28; Rom. 4:17; Heb. 11:3, 19), but these are not clearly related to the present healing ministry of the Church.

More significantly, we find polemical arguments against Greek philosophy and science to the effect that the philosophers were primarily motivated by a desire for personal fame, in contrast to the prophets and apostles who served the people without any expectation of rewards. Here, for the first time, the Judeo-Christian concern about the misuse of power was developed into an effective critique of the privileged status of intellectuals in the classical world. There was no question of Justin or the other apologists being anti-intellectual themselves for they regarded Greek philosophy highly and borrowed from it freely. Yet they were also concerned about the uses to which philosophy was put, and thus they introduced an element of social assessment that has played an important role in Western thought ever since.

Two Streams Rejoined: Irenaeus and Pseudo-Clement

The two streams came back together in the late second century in the work of Irenaeus of Lyons. In his treatise *Against Heresies*, directed primarily against the Gnostics, Irenaeus argued that the possibility of resurrection followed from the fact of creation, and also that the possibility of healing followed from the fact that the Creator had become flesh and performed healings when his handiwork had become impaired. Christian ministers continued to perform healings by calling on the name of the Lord Jesus Christ who had made all things in the beginning. Indeed, the reason the Gnostics were unable to raise the dead was that they did not believe in either the creation or the resurrection of the body. Irenaeus's thought here is identical to that of the Apocryphal Acts noted above.

But Irenaeus did not reduce the controversy with the Gnostics to a contest of power as the Apocryphal Acts tended to do: like the Apologists, he also dealt with the matter of motivation and its effect on the persons being healed. Simon Magus and his followers, he argued, would perform miracles for personal reward, not for the well-being of those whom they treated. The Christians, on the other hand, took no payment for their services but gave what little they had to the needy and, like Jesus, were exclusively concerned with the welfare of others:

> It is not possible to name the number of the gifts which the Church throughout the whole world has received from God in the name of Jesus Christ . . . and which she exerts day by day for the benefit of the Gentiles, neither practicing deception upon any, nor taking any reward . . . Nor does she perform anything by means of angelic invocations . . . but, directing her prayers to the Lord, who made all things, in a pure, sincere and straightforward spirit . . . she has been accustomed to work miracles for the advantage of mankind, and not to lead them into error.

Whether the Church of the second century entirely lived up to Irenaeus's standard or not, the ideal itself was clear, and, given the recurrence of popular mistrust towards science and technology through the centuries, it was an ideal without which the social support needed for the development of modern science in the West could not have emerged. However, Irenaeus could not have claimed the ideal with any credibility unless the Church of his time at least approximated its realization. Both ideal and example, then, were to have an important effect on the development of Western civilization.

The combination of the two streams, emphasis on the possibility of healing and the criterion of human benefit, is also found in writings of the third century like those of Pseudo-Clement. Being a dramatic narrative with extensive dialogue based on the alleged teachings of Peter, the Pseudo-Clementine *Homilies* could bring together the narrative style of the Apocryphal Acts and the theological arguments of the Apologists even more forcefully than Irenaeus did. Thus we find Peter prefacing the healing of a crippled old woman with the words: 'If I be a herald of truth, in order to [confirm] the faith of the bystanders, that they may know that there is one God, who made the world, let her straightway rise whole.' Conversely, when he was told that Simon could perform prodigies like making statues walk and flying through the air (both associated with technological feats in the ancient world as today), Peter pointed out that such wonders were designed to astonish and deceive rather than to heal and to save. In contrast, '. . . the miracles of compassionate truth are philanthropic, such as you have heard that the Lord [Jesus] did, and that I after him accomplish by my prayers . . .'

Early Monastic Medicine

Enough has been said to show how the New Testament beliefs and values were translated during the second and third centuries into an effective ministry of healing and restoration that was seen as a viable alternative to the claims of Greek science and technology. All of this took place while Christians were a persecuted minority in a pagan empire. The following centuries saw a distinct shift in outlook, though not in the underlying faith, as a new generation of Christian leaders attempted to meet the challenges that came with religious recognition and responsibility for secular affairs. Here again the key figure was Basil of Caesarea, but the larger movement in which Basil participated was the rise of cenobite (communal) monasticism.

The fourth century saw the rise of the monastic movement and the beginnings of public hospital care, two movements which were to be closely related throughout the middle ages even though we do not generally associate them together today. In fact, it was the early cenobite communities that were responsible for converting the miracle-based healing ministry of the post-apostolic period into a systematic program for health care that could be made available on a regular basis. Some modern writers like Leslie Weatherhead have argued that this transition entailed a weakening of Christian faith and a capitulation to Greek science. Undoubtedly, a new source of tension was introduced into the Church, and, of course, the development of modern medicine does suggest a gradual dilution of the specifically religious element, but the transition of the fourth century itself was a legitimate extension of early Christian faith and practice into new areas of responsibility, as we shall see.

The problems of maintaining a minimal degree of health care came to the fore in the first cenobite communities organized by Pachomius in Upper Egypt where the rigours of asceticism were monitored and kept within strict limits. Illness was a frequent occurrence and required special allowances for diet and for rest. Then, too, people would come from miles around to be healed of their various infirmities. In such cases, neither Pachomius nor his chief disciple Theodore claimed any special powers, but they affirmed their faith in the possibility of healing, as the early Christians had, on the basis of the fact that God was the creator of all things. As we shall see, this monastic ministry was an important component in the background of Basil.

Basil's Ministry of Medical Care

Basil was uniquely suited to promote a synthesis of this simple Christian faith with Greek medicine at this juncture in history for three reasons. First, Basil had received his early training under Libanius (at Antioch or Constantinople, c 349). Libanius was a classical rhetorician and undoubtedly helped imbue Basil with the late Stoic ideal of philanthropy as an ordinance of God's providence or natural law, essential to the welfare of civilization. The Stoic concept of philanthropy tied in nicely with the Judeo-Christian ideal of selfless service and provided Basil with a simple conceptual scheme for applying the latter to the needs of fourth-century Greco-Roman society.

Secondly, Basil studied the classical sciences (astronomy, geometry and arithmetic) at Athens (c 350–55) and took a special interest in the art of medicine. According to his companion Gregory of Nazianzus, he had a sufficiently good grasp of the mathematical disciplines 'not to be baffled by those who are clever in such sciences', yet he refused to devote himself to them entirely since they did not contribute to spiritual development. Medicine, on the other hand, was useful to Basil in dealing with his own delicate condition, and in serving the monks under his care in later years. Accordingly, 'he attained to a mastery of the art, not only in its empirical and practical branches, but also in its theory and principles.'

Thirdly, Basil had gained firsthand acquaintance with the monastic way of life during a tour he made (356–7) of Syria, Mesopotamia, Palestine, and Egypt following in the steps of Eustathius of

Sebaste. Here he came into contact with the cenobite ideal of mutual service and the ministry of helping and healing to the surrounding community, ideals which were later reflected in the monastic rules Basil drew up for the communities under his own supervision in the Pontus and at Caesarea. Eustathius had founded a hostel for the poor in his diocese of Sebaste in Armenia, and Basil himself organized a small network of hospitals under his care in the vicinity of Caesarea.

Our principal source of information about the work of Basil at Caesarea is Gregory of Nazianzus's panegyric (*Oration* XLIII) written about two years after Basil's death (AD 379). Gregory's testimony is invaluable to us not only because it tells us what Basil did, but because it gives us the shared understanding of the theological meaning of those actions. Since Basil and Gregory worked so closely together we may take Gregory's comments as if they were Basil's own: as Gregory puts it, their friendship was so close that they were of one life and one nature like 'one soul, inhabiting two bodies'. The consistency of Gregory's comments with Basil's thinking is substantiated at various points by the text of Basil's recorded sermons.

There were two particularly notable instances, according to Gregory, in which Basil worked to 'benefit the people' of Caesarea: during the famine of 369 and in the construction of a public hospital a few years later.

Basil's Relief Work During the Famine of 369

During the famine of AD 369, Basil (then still a presbyter) appealed to the merchants of Caesarea to donate some of their stores of grain to feed the poor. Then he gathered as many of the victims of the famine as he could and, together with his monks, fed and cared for them 'imitating the ministry of Christ'.

The theological rationale for this public ministry had two aspects, according to Gregory, corresponding to the two streams of thought we have traced from intertestamental Judaism to the fourth century. First, Basil believed in the possibility of radical change, a belief which, as we have seen, was based on the idea of God as creator of all things. But, whereas previous instances concentrated on the miraculous element, Basil related this faith to the practice of charity he had learned from the monastic tradition. Gregory explained this development by noting three ways in which Basil's work could be compared to that of Moses, Elijah and Jesus: (a) it was based on the same power of God (available through Christ); (b) it was inspired by the same faith; and (c) it had the same results of feeding the hungry. The only difference was that Moses, Elijah and Jesus altered the nature of the elements themselves, as was proper for 'their time and its circumstances', whereas Basil had to sway the hearts and minds of the rich – no small feat in itself!

The second aspect of Basil's theological rationale was the Judeo-Christian ideal of selfless service. Gregory explains that unlike Joseph, who made grain available to the poor in Egypt in the hope of personal advancement (Gen. 41), Basil neither gained nor expected any personal profit from the venture: his services were entirely gratuitous. The point we wish to make here is that there was a continuity of ideals between the biblical ministry of miracles and Basil's ministry of social service despite the changes in circumstance and strategy. Those, like Basil, who ministered to the needy saw their service as a direct expression of their Christian faith.

Basil's Public Hospital

A few years later (c 372), after he had been appointed Bishop of Caesarea, Basil, no doubt, sensed the need for a more permanent form of ministry to the needy. Again using funds solicited from the wealthy, he founded what modern scholars regard as history's first hospital (or infirmary) open to the public on a regular basis. The significance of this event for the historical development of medicine has been pointed out by others. What needs to be stressed here is that the same twofold faith we have been tracing as part of the creationist tradition was again cited by Gregory as the theological basis for Basil's action: (a) as in the case of the famine of 369, he viewed his medical care as the functional equivalent of the healing miracles Jesus had been able to perform by a mere word; and (b) he founded the hospital for the support of the poor rather than for personal fame. Again the shift from miracle to method in medicine was viewed as an appropriate response to changing conditions and new responsibilities. Basil still believed in the possibility of miraculous cures, and he was credited on more than one occasion, with having been granted such a miracle in response to his prayers. Whether healing came with or without visible means, God was the author of the healing power, so faith and prayer were essential to the process in any case.

We have followed the progress of the New Testament belief in the possibility of radical change and the ideal of selfless service in the ministry of healing and restoration up to the pivotal work of Basil of Caesarea. We must now briefly trace the tradition of medical care up to the twelfth century and then say a few words about the cultivation and theological interpretation of the other manual arts and the significance of all this for the development of modern Western science.

Early Medieval Medicine: Three Lines of Transmission

There is evidence for a growing tradition of medical care in Syria and Mesopotamia following the time of Basil. During a famine in Edessa in 372–3, Ephraim of Syria appealed to the rich for funds and, following Basil's example, established an infirmary with some three hundred beds which was made open to the public, native and foreigner alike. Subsequently, in the fifth century, Edessa became a medical centre with teaching facilities. When the Byzantine emperor Zeno closed the school of Edessa in 489, many of its faculty moved to Nisibis in Sassanid Persia and helped to establish that city as a major centre of learning. Then, in the mid-sixth century, the Sassanid ruler Khusro I (r 531–79) built up a medical school at Gunde-Shahpuhr (Arabic: Jundishapur) with the help of Christian physicians from Nisibis. In the late eighth and early ninth centuries, Christian physicians of Gunde-Shahpuhr were employed in turn by the Abbasid Moslem caliphs for the translation of ancient Greek scientific treatises into Arabic and the founding of a hospital and a medical school at Baghdad. Thus the Syrian medical tradition, dating back to the examples of Basil and Ephraim, was instrumental in establishing the foundations of Islamic medical science and thereby contributed to the beginnings of medieval Western medicine through the translations of Constantine the African (c 1065 to c 1087) and the school of Salerno in southern Italy in the eleventh century.

Before considering the theological aspects of this development, we should note two other lines of transmission from Basil to the medieval West. First, in the eastern Roman (Byzantine) Empire there was a succession of Christian physicians, beginning with Caesarius, (d c 373), brother of Gregory of Nazianzus, who served the Byzantine court under a succession of emperors, and culminating in the work of Alexander of Tralles (d 605) and Paul of Aegina (fl. Alexandria, c 640). Both of the latter wrote medical treatises which were influential among the Arabs and the school of Salerno.

The third line of transmission of medical knowledge was in the Latin West. Under the guidance of Gregory's friend and pupil, Jerome, wealthy Roman Christians contributed to the founding of public hospitals in the late fourth century. Augustine also encouraged the practice in northern Africa during the early fifth century. A long succession of popes, prelates and Christian princes could be added to this list.

Cassiodorus's efforts to found a medical facility at Cassiacum (southern Italy) in the sixth century are of special interest in that they were inspired by the example of the Syrian school at Nisibis. Cassiodorus advised his monks to study herbs and medicine and specified that they read the classical Greek medical works (in Latin translation). He thereby encouraged the development of medical practice within the monastic movement of Western Europe that was just beginning its greatest expansion with the work of St Benedict.

The spread and development of medicine in Western Europe was closely associated with Benedictine monasticism through the early middle ages. Constantine the African spent his last and most fruitful years (c 1077–87) translating Greek and Arabic medical works from Arabic into Latin at Monte Cassino. At this point the Eastern (Greek, Syrian, Arabic) and Western (Latin) medical traditions came together and contributed to the medical science of the eleventh and twelfth centuries.

Like any broad historical survey, this sketch of three lines of transmission might take on a certain air of inevitability, especially since it leads up to the background of our own cultural milieu. However, there was nothing inevitable about any of the three lines of development we have just traced. Each of them depended on the peculiarities of local conditions and the motives and efforts of numerous individuals. Theological convictions would be just one of the factors involved at any given point. So a thorough investigation of the interactions between theology, social conditions, and the progress of medical science from the fourth to the twelfth century would require considerable additional research. Indeed, this is a fruitful area for those who may wish to pursue the subject and make a contribution to the field. Here we may note a few of the more salient points we know something about at present.

Early Medieval Medicine: The Role of Creation Theology
In the case of Basil and Gregory of Nazianzus, belief in the value of medical care was closely related to belief in creation and the ethic of selfless service, as we have seen. This close relation between faith and practice seems to have continued into the fifth and sixth centuries, but it is more difficult to trace after that, at least with regard to the Christian healing ministry associated with medicine.

Ephraim of Syria (d 373) was an admirer, perhaps an acquaintance, of Basil. His best-known work in theology was his hymn-writing campaign against the Gnostic disciples of Bardaisan in which he argued for the creation and future resurrection of the body. He is also reported to have performed healing miracles in the name of

Christ, and his theological understanding of that ministry can be inferred from his defence of the inclusion of Third Corinthians (Acts of Paul viii. 1–3) in the Syriac canon. If Ephraim was familiar with the account of Paul's raising Frontina, he may well have made the same association between the doctrine of creation and the ministry of healing found in the Acts of Paul. In any case, the basic constellation of ideas with which he worked was the same as that from which the medical philosophy of Basil and Gregory had emerged.

Ephraim's influence on Syriac Christianity was great, but it is difficult to tell whether the significance of the healing ministry was still understood in theological terms after his time. In the fifth century the exegetical and theological works of Theodore of Mopsuestia (d 428) introduced an emphasis on Aristotelian logic into the Nestorian schools of Syria and Mesopotamia, and the influence of Ephraim apparently diminished. The extant autobiographical fragments of Hunayn ibn Ishaq (d c 877), the Nestorian physician who organized the first systematic translation of Greek philosophical treatises into Arabic, give no indication of any awareness of the theological motifs we have considered. However, it could also be that those motifs were taken for granted as common ground with Moslem antagonists and so did not call for special discussion as much as beliefs peculiar to Christians which Hunayn so ably defended.

In the West, the development was slightly different. Jerome had consulted with Gregory of Nazianzus in 381 while the latter was Bishop of Constantinople. The matters they discussed largely concerned the exegesis of difficult texts, but the issue of medical care as an expression of Christian service may also have come up. In any case, Jerome was familiar with the cenobite monasticism of Pachomius – he translated the Pachomian rules into Latin – and he would have learned of the healing ministry, if not of its theological legitimation, from that source. In his letters, he exhorted wealthy Roman Christians who were providing care for the poor to do so in an attitude of humility as Christ had done.

The three principal founders of Western monasticism were John Cassian, Cassiodorus, and Benedict of Nursia. After making an extensive tour of the Egyptian monasteries (385–99) and returning to Marseilles, Cassian compiled his findings in Latin for the Western brethren (420–30). His treatment of the spiritual gift of healing recorded the fundamental Christian belief that persons could be healed and even raised from the dead as a demonstration of the power and mercy of God (especially in contrast to the philosophical dialectics used by heretics) but emphasized the primary value of love, humility and personal holiness. Cassian, however, did not emphasize medical care or ministry to the poor.

Cassiodorus (d c 575) and St Benedict (d c 550) both made special provisions for the care of the sick in their instructions to monks. Cassiodorus was influenced by Syriac Christianity and possibly also by the monastic rules of Basil. At any rate, his affinity with Basil is particularly striking in the moving paraphrase of Ecclesiasticus 38 in his *Introduction to Divine and Human Readings:*

> Learn, therefore, the properties of herbs and perform the compounding of drugs punctiliously; but do not place your hope in herbs and do not trust health to human counsels. For although the art of medicine be found to be established by the Lord, it is He who without doubt grants life to men who makes them sound [Ecclus. 38:4–8].

The essential connection between the trustworthiness of the Creator ('He who without doubt grants life to men') and the rationale for medical care was appreciated by Cassiodorus in the same sense that it had been by Basil and Gregory of Nazianzus.

Gregory the Great (pope 590–604) was second to none in his advocacy of justice for the poor and his efforts to relieve their distress. However, Gregory's advice to clerics on admonishing the sick was to encourage resignation rather than to hold out any real hope of healing. Gregory regarded health as a gift from God that could be withdrawn but said nothing about its restoration.

The study of medicine was touched on in the monastic-school curriculum of Isidore of Seville (d 636) and given more prominence in the Carolingian curriculum designed by Alcuin of York (d 804). Cassiodorus's understanding of its theological significance continued to have influence until at least the tenth century, but there was little development until the rise of the cathedral school of Chartres in the late tenth century.

The Scholastic Reinterpretation: Earthly versus Heavenly Medicine
Fulbert (d 1028) became principal of the school around 1005 and established its general direction. As one of the early champions of Aristotelian dialectic, Fulbert differentiated two distinct kinds of medicine: earthly, natural medicine, which was based on the use of herbs (accompanied by prayer to Christ for healing); and heavenly or supernatural medicine based on miraculous powers like those of Christ who could heal the sick and raise the dead by a mere word.

Fulbert's dichotomy of two types of medicine was closely related to the scholastic differentiation of two powers of God, *potentia ordinata* and *potentia absoluta*, which was also coming into general use in the eleventh century (section 1.4). Whereas Basil, Gregory of Nazianzus, and Cassiodorus had seen the creative power of God realized in the properties of herbs and the skills of the physician, the medieval West began to view the two as antithetical.

As in the case of the two powers of God, the dichotomization of the idea of medicine had an institutional parallel: the development of professional secular medicine and spiritual care as separate disciplines. Practicing physicians relied increasingly on the processes of nature as something quite distinct from the immediate creative activity of God (though the older, more integrated tradition also persisted through the seventeenth century). At the same time, as part of the Gregorian reform of the Church, clergy ordained to the major orders were officially discouraged from practicing surgery or attending the sick except as spiritual directors.

The rapid influx of new medical ideas from the Arab world during the eleventh and twelfth centuries accelerated this trend toward a dichotomization of health care. Although there may have been a strong faith motivation behind Islamic medicine, that faith was perceived as foreign by Europeans and was left behind as scientific and philosophical texts were translated and adapted to Western needs.

The Twelfth-Century Assessment of Technology: Hugh of St Victor

At the same time that clergy were defining themselves in opposition to professional physicians, however, the monasteries were taking an increasing interest in the development of water-powered technology, a mechanical art no less 'earthly' than medicine itself. As an example, when Arnold of Bonneval described the rebuilding of Clairvaux (1136), he was so enthusiastic about the new water-powered machinery that he neglected to mention the church! Another monastic writer adopted a more theological perspective when he thanked God that the new machines could alleviate the oppressive labours of both humans and animals (a classical motif).

The idea that various technologies or mechanical arts were God-given means of alleviating human suffering was popularized by Hugh of St Victor's overview of the arts and sciences (the *Didascalion*) in the 1120s. Each branch of philosophy, Hugh argued, has one of two ends: 'either the restoring of our nature's integrity or the relieving of those weaknesses to which our present life lies subject'. The restoration of the divine likeness in human nature was of eternal consequence. It was accomplished by the theoretical sciences (theology, mathematics and physics), which remedied human ignorance by promoting the contemplation of the truth, and also by the practical disciplines (ethics, economics and politics), which remedied human vice by promoting the practice of virtue. The relief of human weakness, on the other hand, was accomplished by mechanical arts like fabric making, armament, commerce, agriculture, hunting, medicine, and theatre; the mechanical arts ministered to the necessities of this life rather than the next.

So, by the twelfth century, technology had come to be viewed in the West as a positive, potentially liberating force in society, much as it had been in the early days of the Israelite kings, over two thousand years earlier. At the same time, it began to be understood as a purely human endeavour, based on an understanding of the workings of nature, rather than a sacred one, related to the creative and recreative work of God. We have already traced the development of this characteristically Western way of thought in the special case of medicine. A few notes will suffice to bring us up to date with regard to the other mechanical arts.

Background of the Twelfth-Century Assessment

We recall that technology was viewed mostly negatively by the Jews in the late Old Testament and intertestamental periods, largely because it was associated with idolatry and the oppressive power of foreign nations like the Babylonians, Greeks and Romans. This critical assessment continued for some time particularly in the writings of Western culture-critics like Arnobius and Augustine. At the same time, writers like Methodius and Lactantius began to speak of human fabrication as analagous to, or even participating in, the all-creative power of God.

Basil utilized several popular Platonic and Stoic themes in developing the theological meaning of the mechanical arts in his sermons on the Hexaemeron. Addressing an audience of artisans on their way to and from work, he described architecture, working in wood and brass, and weaving, and compared the products of these 'creative arts' to the world that had been fashioned by the 'supreme Artisan'. The arts, Basil explained, were given to humans by God after the fall of Adam to alleviate the harshness of nature. In providing a theological meaning to the mechanical arts, he anticipated Hugh of St. Victor's interpretation by over seven hundred years.

The two principal founders of Western monasticism, Cassiodorus and Benedict of Nursia (in the sixth century), both placed a high value on the machines and tools used by their monks. Like many of the monastic fathers before him, St Benedict required his followers to spend at least six hours a day in manual labour.

Many historians today regard this monastic emphasis on work as having been a major stimulus to the development of Western technology, but there is some disagreement as to the exact reason why. Lynn White, Jr. has argued that the Benedictines placed a high value on manual labour itself, even making it the practical equivalent of prayer. Jacques Le Goff, on the other hand, argues that work was viewed as a form of penance and that the monks welcomed any opportunity to reduce its burden so as to devote themselves more to prayer and to study. From the ninth century on, at least, the recurring tendency was to turn the more menial forms of labour over to the lay brothers (*conversi*) and serfs and to reserve the choir monks for spiritual exercises, a dichotomization similar to that we have already seen in the case of medicine (earthly and heavenly, secular and spiritual). In any case, the end result of the monastic enterprise was the development of labour-saving machinery and the positive assessment of the potential of technology we find in the twelfth century. The theological views of Basil, Cassiodorus and Benedict thus provided much of the basis for the Western appreciation of the value of technology as well as medicine.

Like the idea of the relative autonomy of nature, the positive valuation of technology was promoted by the creationist tradition going back to the Old Testament and intertestamental periods. It originated in the belief that God had created all things and that out of compassion for his fallen creatures he had poured out his creative Spirit on the followers of Jesus. It was also constrained by the social criterion that power should be used for the benefit of others rather than in personal self-interest. By assessing technology in this light and giving it a positive value, Christians provided it with a theological legitimation that it had not enjoyed in either the Greek or the Jewish world. Since the middle ages was a time when the laity was emerging as a self-conscious class in Western society, technology was thus provided with a strong social base without which neither it nor modern science could have developed as they have in the last seven centuries.

The close association between Western Christianity and technology has, however, to be qualified in at least two ways. First the dichotomy of earthly and heavenly callings that evolved in the eleventh and twelfth centuries was foreign to the outlook of early Christians like Basil who viewed medicine and the other arts as the expression of the creative power of God in Christian service. And, second, the underlying Christian commitment was to the healing and restoration of the human race in accordance with God's creative intention. Technology was to be assessed – and, if need be, reassessed – in terms of its overall contribution to that public ministry. In the eleventh and twelfth centuries, technology appeared to be a force for liberation both for an artisan class emerging from a feudal society and also for Western Europe as a whole emerging as a new power in a world dominated by other, more highly developed cultures. All of this was to change in succeeding centuries with the institutionalization of technological power and the beginnings of Western imperialism. The problem of identifying a distinctively Christian attitude toward the mechanical arts was, accordingly, to become more complex.

FOR FURTHER READING

Chadwick, Henry, *Early Christian Thought and the Classical Tradition* (New York, 1966).

Chenu, M.-D., *Nature, Man, and Society in the Twelfth Century* (Chicago, 1968), chaps. 1, 6.

Clagett, M., *Greek Science in Antiquity* (revised ed., New York, 1963).

Dales, R. C., *The Scientific Achievement of the Middle Ages* (Philadelphia, 1973).

idem, 'A Twelfth-Century Concept of the Natural Order', *Viator* 9 (1978) pp. 179–92.

idem, 'The De-Animation of the Heavens in the Middle Ages', *Journal of the History of Ideas* 41 (1980) pp. 531–50.

Edelstein, L., *Ancient Medicine* (Baltimore, 1967) pp. 205–46.

Gask, G. E., and Todd, J., 'The Origin of Hospitals', *Science, Medicine and History*, ed. E. A. Underwood (London, 1953) pp. 122–30.

Hengel, M., *Judaism and Hellenism* (2 vols., London and Philadelphia, 1974).

Le Goff, J., *Time, Work and Culture in the Middle Ages* (Chicago, 1980).

MacKinney, L. C., *Early Medieval Medicine* (Baltimore, 1937).

Marty, M. E., and Vaux, K. L., *Health/Medicine and the Faith Traditions* (Philadelphia, 1982), chaps. 3, 4.

Miller, T., *The Birth of the Hospital in the Byzantine Empire* (Baltimore, 1985).

Robbins, F. E., *The Hexaemeral Literature* (Chicago, 1912).

Sambursky, S., *The Physical World of the Greeks* (London, 1956).

Stiefel, T., 'Science, Reason and Faith in the Twelfth Century', *Journal of European Studies* 6 (1976) pp. 1–16.

idem, 'The Heresy of Science', *Isis* 68 (1977) pp. 347–62.

Weatherhead, L. D., *Psychology, Religion and Healing* (London, 1951), pp. 70–88.

White, Lynn, Jr., *Medieval Religion and Technology* (Berkeley, 1978).
Zilsel, E., 'The Genesis of the Concept of Physical Law', *Philosophical Review* 3 (1942) pp. 245–79.
idem, 'The Genesis of the Concept of Scientific Progress', *Journal of the History of Ideas* 6 (1945) pp. 325–49.

2

THE MEDIEVAL CHURCH AND ARISTOTELIAN SCIENCE
(thirteenth to the fifteenth century)

1. THE RECEPTION OF ARISTOTELIAN SCIENCE

The history of medieval Western European science is largely the story of the translation, assimilation and criticism of newly discovered Greek and Arabic texts, particularly the philosophical works of Aristotle and his commentators. We have already discussed the extensive influence of Greek science on intertestamental Jewish, early Christian and early medieval thought. So a moment of reflection may be required to see why so much of Greek science should have been perceived as something radically new in thirteenth-century Europe.

It is true, as we have seen, that the early Church reflected a wide spectrum of Greek philosophic thought: Pythagorean, Platonic, Aristotelian, Epicurean, Stoic, Cynic, and Hippocratic ideas were all considered and selectively adapted. But, for the most part, this interaction took place at the level of ethical and theological considerations. There was not a great deal of interest in the specifics of Greek scientific theories mainly because the pursuit of such esoteric matters was perceived to detract from the spiritual and social objectives that Jews and Christians held to be primary. We argued in section 1.5 that this temporary check on the pursuit of scientific speculation was salutary for scientific and technological development in the long run. None the less, it resulted in the postponement of serious consideration of scientific theories for a thousand years in the Latin West.

It was a very different story in the Greek and Syriac East. There, partly due to the greater accessibility of Greek texts and partly due to the prestige associated with philosophic pursuits in Greek culture, a strong scientific tradition survived and progressed well into the middle ages. While 'pre-scientific' by modern standards, this tradition was sufficiently authoritative to impress the leaders of Arab civilization, particularly the Abbasids of Baghdad, who became the heirs of much Greek and Syriac culture after the seventh century AD.

In order to assess the situation in Western Europe, it is helpful to compare the Abbasid Moslems with the Carolingian Franks of the late eighth and early ninth centuries. The Arabs and the Franks were both tribal peoples, initially dominated by warrior classes, who had conquered and settled in the territories of earlier civilizations. Both were fiercely proud and sensitive to indications of their cultural and technological inferiority to older civilizations. Any attempt to understand the progress of natural science (whether in the middle ages or today) must take into account the feelings and energies of peripheral peoples like these who suddenly move into the mainstream of history. On balance, however, the Abbasid Arabs were culturally superior to the Franks, and, whether or not that superiority was really due to the assimilation of Greek science in any degree, a connection between the two indicators was clearly made in the mind of the Latin West. Any significant development in Western civilization beyond the Carolingian level of the ninth century would have to include a mastery of the science of the Greeks which had been neglected for so long. One major effect of Arabic civilization, as far as the West was concerned, was to make that point abundantly clear.

From this review of the broad sweep of world history, we must now shift our focus to the actual conditions and attitudes that prevailed in the Latin West as Greek and Arabic texts began to be translated. The work of translation was a massive project carried on by many individuals of varying nationality and with varied motivation. Most of the work was done in Spain, southern Italy and Sicily (all former Arab colonies newly reconquered by Europeans) during the last three quarters of the twelfth and the first three quarters of the thirteenth century. A complex interplay of intellectual curiosity, personal ambition and perceived market conditions (translations were in demand) helped to produce the impressive results of this project.

What was the role of the Church in the initial stages of translation and assimilation? It must be said that the Church neither initiated nor encouraged the process directly. In fact, a series of ecclesiastical bans from 1210 to 1263 attempted to prohibit the public reading of Aristotle's books on philosophy and their commentaries in the liberal arts curriculum at Paris. The modern reader, conditioned by hundreds of years of disestablishmentarian rhetoric, must be careful, however, not to draw too simplistic a picture of the situation. For one thing, the Church had been instrumental in the founding and staffing of the major Western universities, particularly those in France, Germany and England. It was to be expected that its judicatories would make rulings concerning the arts curriculum, which was standard preparation for higher studies in theology as well as in law and medicine. Indeed, most of the determinations were made with the advice and consent of representative arts masters, so it was not a violation of 'academic freedom' in the modern sense.

Secondly, it has been pointed out by a number of recent historians that the more rationalistic aspects of Aristotelian science, particularly those stressed by the Averroists, were actually detrimental to open scientific investigation. The latest trend in scholastic matters could easily become dogmatic in its own right, and, in the circumstances of the Middle Ages, it could only be checked by authoritarian measures on the part of the Church.

Moreover, the influence of the Church should not be judged merely on the basis of official pronouncements and regulations which tend, by virtue of their function, to be restrictive. Gregory IX renewed the ban of 1210, but also in 1231 appointed a commission to expurgate the prohibited books where necessary so that they could be used for pedagogical purposes. Urban IV, who again renewed the ban in 1263, was the very pope whose court (at Viterbo and Orvieto) brought together William of Moerbeke, the greatest translator of the time, and Thomas Aquinas, the greatest theologian, with the result that William was encouraged to carry out a systematic translation of the Aristotelian corpus in the early 1260s. Since William was made chaplain and confessor to the pope in 1272 and Archbishop of Corinth in 1278, his well known activity as a translator can hardly be said to have been done in opposition to the Church!

Finally, it should be noted that only a century later, in 1366, the legates of Urban V were requiring a knowledge of all known works of Aristotle for the license to teach the liberal arts at the University of Paris. Initial opposition to the translation and assimilation of Aristotle's philosophical works had thus been reversed and replaced by official approval. Indeed, present-day historians are more likely to fault the medieval Church for its near canonization of Aristotle in the fourteenth century (leading up, of course to the condemnation of Galileo in the seventeenth century) than for its earlier opposition. From a twentieth-century viewpoint, what needs to be explained is not so much the Church's earlier attempt to ban the philosophical works of Aristotle as its capacity to assimilate the Aristotelian corpus and to harmonize it with its own theology.

The ability of the Church to synthesize the new science with its traditional ideas is, therefore, the most remarkable feature of the thirteenth century. It is best exhibited in the masterful 'summae' (comprehensive treatises) of Thomas Aquinas, written in the third quarter of the century. But it appears quite clearly among the very earliest theologians of the period. William of Auvergne (d 1249), for example, accepted the mechanistic (Aristotelian) astronomy of Alpetragius (al-Bitruji) and the formal distinction between essence and existence made by Avicenna (Ibn Sina) while, at the same time, rejecting some of the metaphysical aspects of Aristotle and Avicenna that appeared to conflict with teachings of the Church. Since William is generally regarded as one of the more traditional, 'Augustinian' theologians of the period, his attitude is indeed remarkable. It represents quite an advance in sophistication beyond the more recalcitrant stance toward natural philosophy exhibited by twelfth century theologians like Bernard of Clairvaux and William of St Thierry.

Indeed, William of Auvergne combined much of the naturalism of twelfth-century philosophers like Adelard of Bath and William of Conches with the religious conservatism of their critics. It is as if the centrifugal tendencies of the twelfth century and the initial breakdown of the creationist tradition had evoked an effort toward greater equilibrium and comprehension. None the less, the lines were clearly drawn between Church and state, revelation and reason, God and nature. The fact that the Church could sanction efforts towards synthesis and make room for Aristotelian philosophy within subordinate spheres of thought could not reproduce the harmony of all things under the sovereignty of God that was portrayed in the Psalms and was taught by many of the early church fathers. The underlying bifurcation was temporarily transcended, but the strain was to prove too great, and hostilities reminiscent of those of the twelfth century were to break out again in the last third of the thirteenth century. We shall return to this matter in the following sections of this chapter as we discuss the effect the newly discovered science had on the development of medieval theology and the subsequent influence of theology on medieval science.

2. THE IMPACT OF ARISTOTELIAN SCIENCE ON SCHOLASTIC THEOLOGY

We have just seen that Aristotelian philosophy was perceived as something radically new in thirteenth-century Europe. Of course, it was understood that this material had been known to the Greek East for over fifteen hundred years, but aside from a few logical treatises (the 'old logic' of Aristotle, Porphyry and Boethius) it had not been available in the Latin West. The seriousness with which the new ideas were treated must be understood against this background.

What was the impact this new wave of thought had on Christian theology? The most important fact was that, for the first time since the days of the early Church, theologians had to defend their faith as being true in a thought-world in which their right to specify the criteria for truth was no longer uncontested. In spite of growing pluralism in both Church and society, however, Europeans of the Middle Ages would not have appreciated the compartmentalization and relativism we experience in the modern world. Truth was believed to be one: any suggestion that there could be two or more separate truths was repugnant so the challenge of the new alternative could not be ignored.

For over a millennium the Church had championed a tradition in which the world was held to have been created by an all-wise God in such a way that its operations were lawful, natural, and open to human comprehension, at least in principle. Here now was a massive body of texts that provided an actual account of the cosmos as a rational, naturally ordered system. On the other hand, it also contained ideas like the eternity of the world that appeared to conflict with the creationist tradition. Was Aristotelianism then the fulfilment of the Christian worldview or its nemesis? From our perspective in the modern world, the science of Aristotle is outdated, but the challenge it raised is perennial: how can one reconcile a science which seemingly owes nothing to Christian faith, and may conflict with it at any point, with a faith which encourages belief in the possibility of science and values its benefits, yet cannot sanction its teachings or its applications without further scrutiny? The various ways in which medieval theology adapted to meet this challenge were, of course, closely related to the specifics of Aristotelian science, but, as we shall see, they set important precedents for similar modes of adaptation in later periods of our history.

There are basically two areas in which medieval theology adapted to meet the challenge of Aristotelian science. One area was the concept of revelation and its study, which is the discipline of theology. The other was the concept of God, who is the primary object of theology. It was principally issues in the medieval doctrine of God that, in turn, impacted on the development of natural science as we shall see in section three.

Revelation and Reason: Theology and Science

The principal problem confronting medievals was the fact that there now appeared to be two distinct bodies of knowledge, both of which had to be taken seriously. The relatively limited body of Aristotelian logic and science available before the thirteenth century (the 'old logic') had not presented such a problem for theologians because the principal source of human science in this case was pure reason. Augustine had already in the fourth to fifth century effected a successful synthesis of pure reason and revelation, by portraying both as forms of illumination from God: there was a direct analogy, even a partial correlation, between the two. Sense perception, particularly vision with the aid of physical light, could also be given a role at a subordinate level in this scheme with little or no threat to the hegemony of revelation. The early thirteenth-century scientist Robert Grosseteste (d 1253) worked out a system based on the light-metaphysics of Augustine in which some account could be given even of non-visual phenomena like heat, astrological influence, and mechanical action.

Significant problems like the motion of projectiles and the trans-mutation of the elements, however, had been treated in detail by Aristotle and his commentators, and there was no possibility here of visual analogues or an epistemology of illumination. In fact, Aristotle's scientific epistemology, in sharp contrast to that of Augustine (and Plato before him), was based on the abstraction of concepts and principles from sense data.

The creationist tradition of the twelfth century had already shown strains between the concepts of God and nature, revelation and reason, even within the overall harmony of Augustinian metaphysics. The idea of abstraction, set alongside of that of revelation, now threatened to introduce a complete bifurcation in both subject material and method.

The shift is significant. Rather than having to maintain an overall unity, one had to effect a totally new synthesis. Augustine had been able to choose his own ground, so to speak. Of the various schools of Hellenistic thought available, he decided to choose Neoplatonism because it came closest to meeting his spiritual needs (as it did for most other Christians of his age) and because it seemed to agree with Christian teaching at several points. The thirteenth-century scholastics did not exactly choose Aristotle, however. Through the selective interests of the Syrian Christians and Arab Moslems, Aristotle had emerged from the pack of Greek philosophers as 'the Philosopher', and it was the Arabs, as we have seen, who set the standard for Europeans of the high Middle Ages.

Thirteenth-Century Syntheses

How, then, could one formulate a synthesis between the two bodies of knowledge, one derived from sense perception by way of abstraction and the other derived from revelation by way of illumination and faith? There was no unanimously favoured solution to this problem, but one can define four characteristic positions on a spectrum depending on the degree to which reason and revelation were integrated. At one extreme was Siger of Brabant, the Latin Averroist, who, as an arts master in the 1260s, expounded various points of Aristotelian philosophy which had implications, like the eternity of all species and the substantial unity of all human minds, which appeared directly to contradict the teachings of the Church. The problem was that Siger made no effort to harmonize or synthesize these conclusions with official theology. His views were opposed by theologians like Bonaventure and Thomas Aquinas in the late 1260s and early 1270s and were condemned by two important sets of articles promulgated by the bishop of Paris, Stephen Tempier, in 1270 and 1277.

A position clearly to the right of Siger, yet still making a very sharp differentiation between reason and revelation, philosophy and theology, was that of Albert the Great (d 1280). Philosophy, he held, was based on human reason unaided by God. There was a definite sphere of truth that it could establish without recourse to revelation. For instance, reason could demonstrate the existence of God as First Being, but neither his attributes nor the fact that he had created the world in time (i.e., that the world was not eternal). It could treat the intelligences Aristotle described as movers of the celestial bodies, but not the angels who were described in Scripture as intermediaries between God and humans. It could investigate those things that happen 'on the ground of causes inherent in nature', but not those miracles by which God freely chooses to manifest his power. As a general rule, according to Albert (here following William of Conches), one should follow the apostles and fathers of the Church in matters of faith and morals, but follow the Greek natural philosophers in matters of medicine and physics.

Thomas Aquinas (d 1274) was a student and associate of Albert's around the middle of the century (1245–52). Though it is difficult to tell to what extent his differences from Albert were deliberate, the fact that Thomas intentionally worked towards a greater correlation between philosophy and theology suggests that he was concerned to avoid the dichotomy that might be inferred from the writings of his mentor.

On the more positive side, Thomas sought to develop his theology along apologetic lines that could be used in missionary efforts to convert the Moslems. Aristotelian philosophy was useful here in that it provided concepts and methods that could be turned against the very people from whom the Latins had first learned them! Similar strategies were suggested by Roger Bacon and Raymond of Penafort (d 1275). In fact, it may have been the latter who suggested the idea to Thomas.

For Thomas, then, a clear distinction could be drawn between philosophy and theology with respect to their methods and starting points, but there was considerable overlap in their principles and conclusions. Philosophy starts with what can be known about the world, and follows reason towards divine things (such as God and the angels) as principles that must be posited in order to account for the existence and behaviour of natural things which are their proper effects. Theology, on the other hand, begins with divine things, as revealed in Scripture, and follows the rule of faith towards their effects in nature and history.

But, while this overall synthesis seems harmonious enough, there are indications of underlying tension and even suggestions of dichotomization. For one thing, the 'divine things' posited as principles by reason are not coterminous with the 'divine things' of revelation. Some theological dogmas like the Trinity, the creation of the world in time (finite age), and the future consummation were completely beyond the reach of reason and, hence, found no place in philosophy. Therefore, one had to differentiate between revealed theology, which treated these particular dogmas, and natural theology, which treated those beliefs that could be established by reason without the aid of revelation. The latter category included the existence of God, divine attributes like unity, and the dependence of the world on God for its existence and consummation. So Thomas allowed reason and revelation to overlap to a degree whereas Albert had kept them quite separate.

Even this limited overlap between reason and revelation has to be qualified, however, by the fact that, for Thomas, it was impossible to have both knowledge (by reason) and faith concerning the same theological truth at the same time. Once one was able to demonstrate a particular truth by reason, one ceased to hold it, in the proper sense, by faith. So truths like the existence and unity of God were not properly articles of faith, but rather a preamble to faith. On the one hand, this allowed those who lacked skill in philosophy to hold them in simple faith, while, on the other, it allowed the Christian apologist to impress intellectually-minded Moslems and others with the philosophical credentials of at least some of the teachings of Christianity. While these few teachings were not sufficient to establish the truth of Christianity as a whole, they did help to defend the veracity of the Christian Scriptures which were held by Moslems to have been corrupted from the original versions.

A theologian who sought a more thorough integration of faith and reason was the Franciscan, Bonaventure (d 1274, the same year as Aquinas). Using a less formal, more Augustinian notion of reason, he concluded that reason and revelation could be seen to interpenetrate almost entirely. On the one hand, theological truths like the creation of the world in time were demonstrable by means of reason alone. On the other hand, due to the effects of sin, even those truths that Aquinas allowed as accessible to reason were not fully or properly understood if they were not viewed in the light of revelation. Thus, the unity of God, for instance, was not properly apprehended if it was thought to exclude the Trinity (as it was by Moslems). It followed, then, that the same truth could be held by means of both faith and reason at the same time. Indeed the cooperation of the two human faculties was essential to full understanding of any truth.

Bonaventure illustrated this relationship with the image of two books. By virtue of its being created by God and its exemplifying God's ideas ('exemplarism'), nature was a book in which one could discern the divine attributes. Human ability to read this book properly had been vitiated by sin, however, so a second book of God, Holy Scripture, was needed to provide reliable knowledge of ethical and theological matters.

The image of the two books of God can be traced back to the theologies of Augustine and Francis of Assisi. After Bonaventure, it was taken up by Raymond Lull (d c 1316) and Raymond Sebond (d c 1436). It was to be used even more widely in treatments of science and theology in the Reformation and early modern periods.

For those who took the effects of human sin and the necessity of divine grace seriously, the image of the two books proved to be quite effective. Raymond Lull believed that he had been granted a vision of all truth, both scientific and theological, through divine illumination. On the basis of this vision, recorded in his *Ars magna* (c 1274), believers could see the reproductive energies in plants and trees as an image of the eternal generation in God through which the Father engendered the Son. The study of nature thus elevated the mind to the understanding and love of God. Here there was no conflict between the relative autonomy of nature and the all-sufficiency of God.

On the other hand, the image of the two books could also be used to argue for the complete autonomy of science based on natural reason. In that case, Scripture might be viewed as superfluous or even inferior to human reason. This tendency for the creationist tradition to undercut its own presuppositions became apparent already with Raymond Sebond's *Book of Creatures* of 1436 and was to contribute to the rise of rationalism and deism in the seventeenth century. Even Bonaventure's more unitive view, it appears, harboured an underlying dichotomy of reason and revelation, or of nature and grace. None the less, it provided a model for the mutual questioning of reason and revelation that soon bore fruit in the natural philosophy of Franciscans like Peter John Olivi, William of Ockham, and Francis of Marchia (section 2.3).

Concept and Method of Theology

We have reviewed four characteristic ways in which thirteenth-century scholastics (Siger of Brabant, Albert the Great, Thomas Aquinas, and Bonaventure) handled the issue of the relation between reason and revelation, or science or theology. Clearly this new concern had an effect on the concept of theology and of its method. One could no longer assume that theology in the proper sense was simply an exposition of the traditional articles of faith (e.g. those of the Apostles' Creed) for most of the first article ('I believe in God the Father Almighty, Maker of heaven and earth') was now held to lie within the province of reason and even to constitute, for Thomas, at least, a preamble to faith. Thomas's system was extremely influential: he became the official doctor of the Dominican order in the early fourteenth century, and his teachings were declared normative for all Roman Catholics at the Council of Trent (1545–63). The general approach of Thomas, if not all his teachings, was also influential in Protestant scholastic circles of the late sixteenth and early seventeenth centuries.

The net effect of the synthesis with Aristotelian philosophy on the procedure of theology was threefold. First, the order in which topics were treated tended to proceed from those truths that were thought to be accessible to reason – a 'general revelation' available to all humans – to those truths that were known only on the basis of biblical revelation – a 'special revelation' unique to Christian faith. This procedure was followed by Thomas in his two great '*summas*'. But the procedure was not peculiar to Thomas: it appeared in a variety of theological systems though the location of the line between truths of natural reason and those of revelation varied widely.

The second effect of the scholastic synthesis was a heightened emphasis on rigorous deduction within the treatment of revealed theology itself. In natural theology, as we have noted, one could use the abstractive method of the sciences; that is, one could begin with what is known empirically and reason inductively toward principles that must be posited in order to account for the known facts. The model here was Aristotelian natural philosophy. In revealed theology, however, another model became influential, that of Euclidean geometry. In Euclidean geometry, first principles were posited as self-evident and deductions were made in keeping with strict rules. The way had been prepared by the use of Aristotle's logic or dialectical method (the 'old logic'), which had been known in part since the tenth century and had already influenced the procedure of rational theologians like Anselm of Canterbury (d 1109). This trend towards rigorous deduction was reinforced, however, by various translations of Euclid's *Elements of Geometry* in the twelfth and thirteenth centuries and by the overall challenge of the newly available corpus of Aristotelian philosophy which we have been describing.

The presentation of theology had always been closely related to the function of teaching, and with the rise of the universities in the thirteenth century, it had to establish a role for itself in relation to the new curricula. Before undertaking the study of theology, a student had to master the arts and sciences, including both Aristotelian science and Euclidean geometry. The expectations of the graduates who went on to theological studies and the questions they subsequently raised for their instructors must have had quite an impact on the way theology was taught. Was revealed theology a science? If so, in what sense? If it was not a science, at least not in the normative sense, how could it be presented in a way that would command the respect of students trained in the new disciplines? The exact definition of science was to some extent a matter of semantics, but the result for theology was the same in any case. One had to stress certain foundational principles, derived from Scripture and the rule of faith, from which one could make inferences that would decide the pertinent theological questions of the day.

Take, for instance, the procession of the Holy Spirit, an issue that divided the Christians of the West from the Eastern Orthodox.

In his *Summa against the Gentiles*, Aquinas presents a series of arguments. In the first of these, he begins with Romans 8:9 which refers to the 'Spirit of Christ' and proceeds to show (a) that the Spirit is 'of Christ' as Christ is the natural son of God and (b) that the Spirit must be 'of Christ' in the sense of having its origin from Christ because the only relations found within the Godhead are relations of origin (IV.24.2). The rigour of demonstration here was not quite up to the standards of Euclid and Aristotle, but the style of presentation was similar enough, one may presume, to carry weight with students who had been trained in the arts and sciences.

The third effect of the scholastic synthesis was the subdivision of theology into distinct 'loci' as topics for consideration. To some extent, this process had already been begun with the rational procedure of Anselm and the systematic collection of texts from Scripture and the fathers by Peter Lombard (d c 1160). Lombard's *Book of Sentences* became the principal text for the study of theology in the thirteenth century. The division of its material under the four main headings of God, creatures, the work of Christ, and the sacraments and last things, provided the model not only for numerous commentaries and 'quaestiones', but also for the 'summas' of later scholastic theology.

The parallel development of commentaries and 'quaestiones' on the works of Aristotle during the thirteenth century contributed to this subdivision of topics in two ways. First, the fact that both theologians and their students had to master the Aristotelian texts and be able to comment on the specialized issues involved, elevated the standards of questioning and refuting alternative views in the theological faculty. Secondly, the treatment of specific issues like the potential eternity of the world and the providence of God in relation to second clauses (to be discussed below), issues raised or heightened by the assimilation of Aristotelian science, called for additional sections and subdivisions in any credible presentation of theology. Separate consideration was required for what could be shown by pure reason and what was known by revelation, for what could be said with respect to God's normal activity (*de potentia ordinata*), what could be said of his special acts of power (*de potentia absoluta*), and what must be said of his omnipresence irrespective of any action at all. The result, as one might expect, was a fragmentation of theological doctrine into highly specialized issues with practically no possibility for students to integrate the separately derived conclusions into a cohesive whole.

In summary: scholastic theology adapted to meet the challenge of the new Aristotelian science by defining and attempting to correlate the respective roles of human reason and divine revelation within an overall synthesis. The placement of revelation in the synthesis, which corresponded to the place of theology in the university curriculum, had the effects of:

(1) establishing the order of the theological curriculum as proceeding from natural theology to revealed theology;

(2) encouraging the use of rigorous deduction in the treatment of revealed theology;

(3) increasing the isolation of distinct theological 'loci' as topics for consideration.

It is easy to see why Renaissance and Reformation theologians reacted so strongly against the scholastic synthesis, and our own attitudes will very likely be critical as well. It would be best to reserve final judgement, however, until we have reviewed the struggles of modern scholars to achieve a new synthesis and the consequences of their failures. The scholastic model survived well into the eighteenth century and even continues to provide a framework for integrative endeavours for many believers to this day.

God and the World

In chapter one we described the origins and early development of the creationist tradition and found certain paradoxes emerging that threatened to split the tradition into two camps already in the late eleventh and early twelfth centuries. One party stressed the supernatural or absolute power of God (*potentia absoluta*) in both creation and providence, while the other stressed the autonomy of nature as created and ordained by God (*potentia ordinata*).

As we have seen already in this chapter, leading administrators and theologians of the Church managed temporarily to transcend these differences and to effect a new synthesis in the thirteenth century. Still, the comprehensive naturalism of Aristotelian science was bound to intensify the underlying problems. During the first three quarters of the century, theology showed a marked tendency to accommodate itself to the naturalism of Aristotle. To some extent, this tendency was a continuation of the naturalistic and secularizing trends of the twelfth century. A distinct shift took place during the 1270s, however when the supernaturalistic side of the creationist tradition made itself felt, and there was a massive reaction against certain aspects of Aristotelian science. This reaction, in turn, led to new directions in scientific thought in the fourteenth century, as we shall see in section three.

The creationist tradition had generally pictured God as having given all creatures being at a particular point of time (the 'beginning' in the Greek and Latin translations of Gen. 1:1) in such a way that their subsequent behaviour was ceaselessly obedient to specific laws or commands. While continuously subject to God's ratification and amendment (where needed to fulfil moral purposes), these laws provided natural beings with a degree of autonomy that made prediction and rational investigation possible. Though it may seem paradoxical to us, the world was relatively autonomous, yet God was in direct control.

The naturalism of Aristotle was really quite different. To begin with, Aristotle was more concerned with natural change and its causes than he was with natural behaviour and its laws. Every event was seen as the realization of a certain potency in nature under the activating effect of an agent. The agent had to be contiguous with the effect both spatially and temporally, but, in general, it was also prior in time or higher in space. If one could follow the chains of causation that lay behind terrestrial events, one would be led either backward in time (for efficient and material causes) or upward through the celestial spheres (for formal and final causes). From this vantage point, we can see three problems raised for Christian theology:

(1) the suggestion that the temporal sequence of cause and effect was eternal;

(2) the location of God at the outermost sphere of the cosmos as Prime Mover or First Cause;

(3) the problem of God's absolute power in the world of second causes.

Potential Eternity of the Universe

For Aristotle, time and change were endless, hence the chain of causation in the temporal sense (material and efficient causes) was potentially infinite, though it could not be demonstrated to be actually infinite. Hence, there was no first moment or 'beginning' of time. The world was completely stable and potentially eternal.

As one might expect, most Christian theologians in the thirteenth century rejected any notion of the actual eternity of the world. They differed, however, as to whether the contrary ideas of creation and the finite age of the universe were demonstrable by reason or whether they could be known only by revelation. Franciscan theologians like William of Auvergne and Bonaventure gave what they saw as compelling reasons for rejecting the eternity of the world and affirming a beginning of time. Albert the Great also offered an argument for the finitude of time, but claimed that this sort of reasoning was only 'probable': philosophy alone could not demonstrate that God was the cause of the existence (as distinct from the essence) of the world.

Thomas Aquinas disagreed with all of the above. Against Albert, he held that God could be shown by reason to be the efficient cause of the world's existence. But he also argued against more conservative theologians like Bonaventure that the dependence of the world on God for its existence did not entail its finite age, so that the latter was known by revelation alone after all.

To some extent, the issue of the demonstrability of the finite age of the universe was simply a matter of defining the respective spheres of natural and revealed theology as discussed above. But, even if the world was believed by all parties to be temporally finite on the basis of revelation, the fact that it was allowed by some to be potentially eternal so far as rational science could determine, was a significant innovation in the theological conception of nature. The paradox of potential eternity along with actual finitude was one aspect of the underlying tensions of the creationist tradition. On the one hand, God was believed to have created the world, presumably, as Genesis 1:1 seems to indicate, a finite time ago. On the other hand, the regularity and lawfulness with which God was believed to have invested the world, made it virtually impossible for reason to discover any actual 'beginning' for the processes of nature.

The creationist tradition could thus be interpreted as sanctioning the scientific quest for a natural cause behind each cause without end. Thus, William of Conches and members of the school of Chartres had attempted a naturalistic explanation of the creation account of Genesis in the twelfth century (section 1.4). Indeed, Origen and Basil had allowed for an eternal world of spiritual, if not material, creatures in order to do justice to their belief in the infinite power of God (section 1.2). When viewed against this background, the speculations of Albert and Thomas can be seen as legitimate developments of the creationist tradition and not simply as accommodations to Aristotle. On the other hand, the potential infinity of the chain of natural causes as determinable by reason would not have been articulated so tantalizingly, as it was by Thomas, if it had not been for the impact of Aristotelian science.

What happened to the idea of the potential eternity of the world after Aquinas? The list of 219 theses condemned under Bishop Tempier of Paris in 1277 included over twenty propositions dealing with various aspects of the eternity of the world. Four of these articles condemned the idea that the eternal existence of the world could be inferred directly from God's eternity and infinite power.

Two others condemned the idea that the chain of natural causes could be extrapolated back indefinitely into the past. Since both of these ideas were well represented within what we have called the historic creationist tradition, it should be clear that the condemnation of 1277 did not represent that tradition as a whole, but was rather an attack, or counter-attack, of one wing of the tradition on the other. In fact, the 1277 condemnation represented that wing of the creationist tradition most often identified as 'conservative' or 'orthodox'.

In any case, the condemnation of 1277 did not stop speculation on the potential eternity of the world. In general, it encouraged belief in the absolute power of God and made people more aware of the incongruities that might arise when the results of pure reason were compared with the truths of revelation. This left the door wide open for fourteenth-century philosophers like William of Ockham, Nicholas of Autrecourt, John of Ripa, and Nicole Oresme to argue that the most probable conclusion of rational investigation was that the natural order is eternal even if this was overruled by the Catholic faith. Finally, in the fifteenth century, Nicholas of Cusa (d 1464) concluded that the world must be indeterminate in both beginning and end if it is to reveal the eternal God who created it. Cusa served the Church as bishop and cardinal, and though highly original, he was hardly unorthodox. In this matter as in others to be discussed, his ideas give us a good indication of the tendencies in the creationist tradition at the end of the middle ages and the beginning of the Renaissance.

God as First Mover and Clockmaker

The feature of the new science that had the greatest influence on the doctrine of God was the Aristotelian cosmology of homocentric spheres as modified by the Arabic natural philosophers, Thebit (Ibn Qurra) and Alpetragius (al-Bitruji). As a rule there were thought to be nine or ten celestial spheres surrounding the earth: seven for the sun, the moon and the five known planets; an eighth sphere containing the stars; an optional ninth sphere to allow for anomalies (either precession of equinoxes or 'trepidation') in the motion of the stars in the eighth, and an outermost sphere responsible for the daily rotation of the heavens.

God was located, in some sense, at the boundary of the outermost sphere. According to Aristotle's *Metaphysics*, God was the First Mover, that is, the ultimate formal and final cause, whose very presence was enough to activate the rotation of the outermost sphere of the cosmos. The latter was, therefore, the 'first moved sphere' (*primum mobile*), the only object with which God was in any kind of immediate relationship and, therefore, the one that was most active. Inner spheres were moved by virtue of their proximity to outer ones thus forming a chain of (gradually weakened) influence extending to the innermost sphere of the moon and even to the cycle of generation and corruption on earth.

The Aristotelian cosmology could be grafted onto the traditional Christian cosmology simply by increasing the number of heavens. The principal authority on the subject prior to the thirteenth century had been the Venerable Bede (d 735), who held that there were five visible, corporeal heavens (air, ether, Olympus, the fiery realm, and the stellar firmament). Beyond these were the 'waters above the firmament' (mentioned in Gen. 1:7; Ps. 148:4), the angelic abode (later known as the 'empyrean' or outermost created heaven), and the ultimate heaven of the Holy Trinity itself. Readers of Aristotle in the thirteenth century had only to replace the four lower heavens of Bede with the four sublunar elemental zones (earth, water, air, and fire) and subdivide the stellar firmament into the nine or ten celestial spheres described above (the supra-celestial 'waters', generally thought to be crystalline, were sometimes located in the ninth sphere). The result was an up-to-date cosmological model, combining the best insights of both science and theology, with a total of four sublunar elemental zones and nine or ten celestial spheres (below the empyrean).

Since God was located, symbolically, at least, beyond the outermost created heaven, the effect of the Aristotelian cosmology with its nine or ten heavens was that his action should appear to be rather more remote from terrestrial events than was traditionally thought to be the case. We speak here only of the normal mode of God's activity (*de potentia ordinata*), not of the occasional use of God's absolute power (*de potentia absoluta*) in miracles, which we shall discuss below. Indeed, the incorporation of the Aristotelian cosmology into the older Christian worldview would not have been possible if such a distinction had not previously been worked out in the twelfth century, as we have seen.

In Jewish and Christian cosmologies of the intertestamental and New Testament periods, there had been a number of heavens between God and humanity, ranging from three to ten in number. But there were strictly angelic heavens, which defined the spiritual chain of command from God to the physical world and the mystic path of ascent from the world to God. They were not spatial spheres within the physical world itself. Even Bede's more naturalistic cosmology of the eighth century contained only two distinct levels (the stellar firmament and the waters above the firmament) between the elemental zones around the earth and the spiritual heavens of God and the angels.

So with the influx of Aristotelian thought a spatial gap threatened to open up between the regular activity of God and events on earth. Grosseteste, for instance, held that the diurnal rotation of the first moved sphere was communicated to it by God in such a way that its motion was transmitted to the lower spheres and finally to the earth. The same idea appears in Roger Bacon, William of Auvergne, Bonaventure, Albert the Great, and Thomas Aquinas in the thirteenth century.

The remoteness of God's providence suggested by the new cosmology, of course, had to be counterbalanced, even with respect to the normal mode of God's activity, if Aristotelian science was to be acceptable to Christian faith. This was done in several ways. Bonaventure, Albert and Thomas all attempted to restore the balance by limiting the influence transmitted through the celestial spheres to the physical, secular aspects of life. For example, the configuration of the heavens was responsible for the creation of worms and insects from putrefaction, and the radiation of the sun would influence the birth and death of higher animals, all, of course, under God's ultimate control. There were two channels open, however, for the more immediate influence of God in human life under normal conditions: God could enlighten the soul or affect the will directly, and he could, and regularly did, infuse grace through the seven sacraments, particularly through the Eucharist.

In effect, the normal, everyday life of medieval humans was viewed as taking place on two levels: one of nature, in which God's providence was mediated through the hierarchy of celestial spheres; and one of grace, in which God's power was mediated, for the most part, by the hierarchy of the Church. Thus, one of the most commonly cited features of high medieval thought, the dichotomy of nature and grace, can be understood partially as an indirect result of the impact of Aristotelian science. The cosmology of Bede allowed an interpenetration of the two, as God and the angels were within two or three heavens of the tallest mountain (Olympus). The extensive spatialization of the normal God-world relation brought about by the assimilation of Aristotle's cosmology, however, forced an intensification of the God-soul relation in order to legitimize piety within the new worldview. And at a time when the gap between secular life and ecclesiastical tradition was widening, the Church had to consolidate its control over the channels of grace in order to counteract the apparent stranglehold of the new science over the realm of nature.

What happened to the idea of the restricted immediacy of God's normal action after Aquinas? The condemnation of 1277 did not address this issue directly. In fact, Bonaventure, who was the principal theological influence behind the 1277 condemnation, was a strong proponent of the idea. As a true Augustinian, Bonaventure was content to view the natural order as exemplifying or reflecting the attributes of God from a distance and seeking direct access through mystic ascent and sacramental grace.

The Aristotelian cosmology maintained its hold on Western European thought well into the Renaissance. The development of mechanical clocks in the late thirteenth and early fourteenth centuries provided the new image of clockmaker for God to take the place, or, at least, to supplement, the image of sphere-mover, but the consequences for the doctrine of God were much the same. Two figures who illustrate the transition are Nicole Oresme (d 1382) and Henry of Langenstein (d 1397).

In his commentary on Aristotle's treatise *On the Heavens* (1377), Oresme discussed at some length the question of how God could be said to be in heaven while at the same time being omnipresent. The reason for the apparent discrepancy, he concluded, was that a cause is properly said to be present where its action is most evident, and, since the heavens are the most evident effect of divine providence, God is properly said to be located in (or just beyond) them although, strictly speaking, he is everywhere.

How do we know that the heavens are the most evident effect of God's providence? Oresme listed a number of indications including their great size, their permanence, their influence on terrestrial events, their orderly arrangement, and their ceaseless, regular movement. In connection with the latter two features – arrangement and movement he introduced Cicero's analogy between the cosmos and a clock, saying that the regular movement of the heavens must depend on the power of some higher intellect just as that of a clock does even though a clock does not have spiritual beings like angels as part of its machinery the way the real cosmos does.

Oresme went onto describe how God imparted motion to the heavens at creation as follows:

> . . . the situation is much like that of a man making a clock and letting it run and continue its own motion by itself. In this manner did God allow the heavens to be moved continually according to

the proportions of the motive powers to the resistances and according to the established order [of regularity].

One can almost visualize a master craftsman balancing the wheels and weights of a fourteenth-century town clock as one reads this passage.

Oresme's idea of a quantity of motion imparted to the heavens once and for all was a relatively new one in fourteenth-century Europe and was at variance with the idea of continuously-caused motion in Aristotelian physics. We shall return to this idea in section three. The idea of the remoteness of God's action from human affairs suggested by the clockwork image, however, was a direct inheritance from the thirteenth-century hierarchy of celestial spheres which combined elements of the creationist tradition with the newly discovered cosmology of Aristotle.

Henry of Langenstein's *Lectures on Genesis* provide us with a representative synthesis of science and theology at the end of the fourteenth century. Though preferring Aristotle's account of the motion of the spheres to the newer idea of impetus, Henry, like Oresme, used the image of clockmaker to describe the normal action of God in relation to the world. Just as the craftsman assembles all the parts of a clock and then sets it all in motion by moving just one part, so God set the entire world in motion just by energizing the angels, who in turn moved the heavens. The whole system thus formed a 'golden chain' (*catena aurea*) of efficient causes extending all the way from God to the natural phenomena that occur on earth. Again the connection is quite clear between the cosmology of Aristotle and the clockwork image that was gradually taking its place.

Thus the modern world was to inherit from the middle ages one of its basic images for describing the relationship between God and the world (the image of the two books being another). The revolution that occurred in the Renaissance did not introduce the idea of mechanism: what it did was to destroy the medieval idea of the cosmos as a spatial hierarchy between humans and God.

Already in 1440, in his treatise *On Learned Ignorance*, Nicholas of Cusa had maintained that the cosmos had neither centre nor circumference (though it still had celestial spheres) for all creatures were equally proximate to the deity who was their true centre and circumference. In so doing he restored the sense of the unity of heaven and earth found in the creationist tradition of the early Church (section 1.3) and signalled the end of the hold Aristotelian cosmology had had on the Western mind for over two centuries.

None the less, the restricted immediacy of God's normal activity that characterized thirteenth-century thought continued to be a factor in the post-Aristotelian world. By dissolving the matrix of thought out of which the image of God as clockmaker was born, Cusa allowed the clockwork metaphor to live on in a world in which it could be applied directly to the terrestrial sphere, and even to life on earth, as well as to the heavens. So, while Cusa's intent was to portray every creature as a 'created god', the eventual result of his revolution was the reduction of every creature to a clocklike mechanism.

As we pause on the threshold of the mechanistic philosophy of the modern Western world, we are in a position to review the key steps that led up to this point. In chapter one we traced four stages of the creationist tradition:

(1) the ancient Near Eastern view (shared by the Old Testament) of the cosmos as subject to divinely ordained laws;

(2) the beginnings of the idea of the relative autonomy of nature under the impact of Hellenistic thought in the intertestamental and early Christian periods;

(3) the greater emphasis on the transcendence of God and the deterministic course of nature that began with Augustine and the cultural shift from the Hellenistic East to the Latin West;

(4) the dichotomy between God's normal role (*potentia ordinata*) and his occasional displays of supernatural power (*potentia absoluta*) that arose in the late eleventh and early twelfth centuries.

In this chapter we have traced two further stages in the development:

(5) the quasi-spatial distancing of God's normal activity under the impact of Aristotelian cosmology in the thirteenth century;

(6) the emergence of the idea of the clockwork mechanism along with the first extensive production of weight-driven clocks in the fourteenth century.

On the whole, there was continuity in the portrayal of the ceaseless regularity of the cycles of nature. What changed was the understanding of God's relationship to natural causation. From the ancient Near Eastern ideal of kingship to the Neoplatonic and Augustinian concept of transcendent Being, to the Aristotelian First Mover, to the late medieval Clockmaker, the idea of God's normal activity became gradually less immediate to the events of the world, leaving the relatively autonomous cycles of nature to take on the appearance of a completely autonomous mechanism.

The Problem of God's Absolute Power
The problem of God's absolute power (*potentia absoluta*) was not new with the thirteenth century. Augustine had struggled with it intermittently, and it had played a significant role in the conflict between the two wings of the creationist tradition in the twelfth century (section 1.4). The impact of Aristotelian naturalism in the thirteenth century was bound to intensify the problem, however, particularly as it was incorporated within an overall synthesis rather than championed exclusively by one party as twelfth-century naturalism was.

In our discussion of 'God as First Mover and Clockmaker', we saw that the assimilation of Aristotelian cosmology led to a greater sense of the remoteness of God's normal activity. This assimilation would not have been possible if there had not been a clear distinction in the Western European mind between the normal activity of God and his occasional miraculous displays of power, a distinction that was forged in the eleventh and twelfth centuries. Christians of the thirteenth century could assimilate the naturalism of Aristotle precisely because there was always the possibility of reverting to God's absolute power when the ideas of the potential eternity of the world and the hierarchy of natural causes threatened to compromise the sovereignty and freedom of God.

Among the first to experience the tension was Roger Bacon (d c 1292), an early advocate of scientific research. While God normally worked through the medium of second causes for the sake of order, he argued, one must allow for his absolute power, for which no ulterior cause or reason can be sought, both in his creation of the world at the beginning of time and in his acting without the medium of second causes at various subsequent times in history.

Thomas Aquinas stressed the normal activity of God through the agency of celestial spheres and their angelic movers 'according to the order of nature'. Yet, at the same time, he tried to dispel the notion that such regularity in any way compromised God's ability to act 'apart from the order of nature' at any time or place. In fact, the order of nature was, for Thomas, doubly contingent. In the first place, God could have ordained an entirely different (normal) order by virtue of his being its Creator. But, secondly, God is not bound, even now, by the order he has established and which we normally observe. He can either produce ordinary effects without the precedence of their normal causes, or he can produce unprecedented effects within the normal order of things.

Unfortunately, for many churchmen of the late thirteenth century, the carefully balanced statements of Thomas were insufficient protection against the unrestrained speculation of arts masters like Siger of Brabant. As mentioned earlier, there was a massive reaction in the years after 1267, culminating in the condemnation of 219 Theses by the Bishop of Paris, Stephen Tempier, in the year 1277. The articles of condemnation that stressed God's absolute power as Creator held that the order of the natural world was freely chosen by God and that a plurality of worlds (presumably with a plurality of 'natural' orders) could just as well have been created. Articles that stressed God's absolute power even within the established order held that God can do things that are impossible according to the order of nature, e.g., that he can move the heavens in a straight line (as well as circularly) thus leaving a vacuum, and that he can act directly in nature without the mediation of second causes.

The articles affirming the possibility of a vacuum and the possibility of a plurality of worlds were of particular importance. Both possibilities were ruled out by Aristotelian natural philosophy. Hence, the condemnation encouraged the exploration of new, non-Aristotelian hypotheses in fourteenth-century natural philosophy as we shall see in section three. For the moment, we need only note that the condemnation of 1277 was a conservative reaction to the naturalism of Aristotle as it affected the concept of God in the thirteenth century. As such, it stood in a long line of such reactions among the people of God. We have already discussed the opposition to Hellenistic culture within conservative Jewish circles in the second century BC, the critique of Greek philosophy by Irenaeus and Tertullian (second to third century AD), the reaction of Boniface to Virgil of Salzburg in the eighth century, and that of William of St Thierry to William of Conches in the twelfth. As in these earlier cases, the condemnation of 1277 was not an attack of theology against science, but rather an attack of one wing of the creationist tradition – with its own ideal of science as well as religion – against another.

The condemnation of 1277 had an immense influence on subsequent theological thought. In some quarters, particularly among Franciscan theologians like Duns Scotus and William of Ockham, it contributed to an increasing emphasis on the absolute power and will of God, partially at the expense of the predictability of natural processes and the reliability of human reason. Among Dominicans, on the other hand, it seems to have precipitated a reverse reaction in the adoption of Aquinas's theological synthesis as official doctrine. The net result was the well known fragmentation of scholastic theology into opposing schools (Thomists, Scotists and Ockhamists), that characterized late medieval thought.

Still, we find scientist-theologians like Henry of Langenstein in the fourteenth century trying to sort out the alternatives as best they could within an Aristotelian framework. God established the normal order of cause and effect at creation, Henry reasoned, but he could change that order at any time as he did, for instance, in the great deluge of Genesis. For the most part, scientific reason could determine the causes of natural phenomena, but, when a problem proved recalcitrant to reason, one could always appeal to the absolute power and inscrutable will of God. For example: how could the elements have passed through the lower celestial spheres (understood as physical entities, after Aristotle) on their way to the eighth heaven in order to form the stars? By a supernatural act of God! Why do the stars twinkle while the planets do not? Because God made them that way!

In other words, even though Henry's universe was mechanical like a clock, there were gaps in the natural order which could only be filled by an appeal to the direct action of God. Fortunately, there were enough gaps to allow a certain credibility to the occasional exercise of God's absolute power. Four centuries would have to pass before mathematics and physics developed to the point where there would no longer appear to be room for God's direct action in nature. But the framework of thought in which God's working through second causes (*potentia ordinata*) and his acting directly (*potentia absoluta*) were viewed as antithetical was already well established in the Middle Ages. The almighty God of Scripture was well on his way to becoming a 'God of the gaps'.

3. THE INFLUENCE OF MEDIEVAL THEOLOGY ON NATURAL SCIENCE

The most important effect medieval theology had on the development of natural science was its legitimation of efforts to study the newly discovered texts and to assimilate their contents within the Christian worldview (discussed in section one). In spite of its shortcomings from a modern perspective, Aristotelian science was the only available body of knowledge that treated nature comprehensively and sytematically. If Western science was to develop at all, it had to start somewhere, and there was no better place to start than with Aristotle. Consequently, had the theological tradition of Western Europe been such that the assimilation of the new ideas were impossible or counterproductive, it is difficult to see how any progress could have been made at all.

On the other hand, had the theological tradition of Western Europe been such that there were no adequate basis for an effective critique of Aristotelian thought, then the scientific standards of the Greeks and Arabs might have been equalled, but they could never have been surpassed. Our task in this section will be to identify those theological determinants in medieval thought that may have assisted in the development of a post-Aristotelian science.

There are basically two ways in which medieval theology affected the development of science. One was its influence on the concept and method of natural science. The other was its influence on the late medieval concept of the cosmos as God's creation which pointed beyond the cosmology of Aristotle.

The Concept and Method of Natural Science

The degree to which the modern understanding of the concept and method of natural science was already developed in the middle ages has been one of the most debated subjects of recent historical studies. The present consensus is that several preliminary contributions were made during the medieval period. These include:

(1) the relative autonomy allowed to the sciences in relation to theology;

(2) the value assigned to mathematical method and quantification;

(3) the importance of observation and experiment.

On all three of these points, the theological input had a mixed effect.

The Relative Autonomy of Natural Science

The principal contribution of thirteenth-century theology was its effort to construct an overall synthesis that gave a place to the sciences alongside of theology itself. In general, the sciences were means to religious and social ends, just as undergraduate studies in the arts and sciences were normally followed by postgraduate studies in theology, law or medicine.

Still, there were variations in emphasis. Since there was no universally accepted way of constructing a synthesis, there was no universally accepted understanding of the role of the sciences. Dominicans like Albert the Great and Thomas Aquinas leaned toward a greater degree of autonomy of the sciences within their own sphere, though the ultimate goal assigned was the improvement of life and the strengthening of faith. Franciscans of the thirteenth century like Bonaventure and Roger Bacon, placed more stress on spiritual and social ends. Bacon even suggested that the pope exercise a measure of control over scientific research in order to prevent its benefits from falling into the wrong hands and being used for anti-social (or anti-Christian) purposes.

The condemnation of 1277 was a reaction to what appeared to be too great an autonomy for science as conceived by Latin Averroists like Siger of Brabant and Dominicans like Thomas Aquinas. Paradoxically, however, its effect may have been to intensify the distinction between scientific and theological considerations. The propositions condemned for the most part dealt with the theological aspects of Aristotelian science that seemed to contradict Christian faith. They were concerned with metaphysics, or what we would term the presuppositions of science. The result was that matters of theology were reserved as the special province of trained theologians.

There was no restriction on the freedom of scientists to explore the workings of nature, however. In fact, the rejection of various Aristotelian propositions clearly encouraged speculation in this area. In the fourteenth century, consequently, we find philosophers who were influenced by the condemnation, like William of Ockham and John Buridan, making a clear distinction between the methods of natural science and those of theology. Gradually, the two wings of the creationist tradition were turning into two separate professions or disciplines, each with its own subject matter and methodology, though the actual separation of science and theology was still a distant prospect in the late Middle Ages.

If it is difficult to achieve a clear definition of the autonomy allowed the sciences in the Middle Ages, it is even more difficult to reach an assessment of the result. Is a high degree of autonomy for the sciences a good thing? Or should spiritual and social goals be made primary and science treated as a means? Different assessments of the attitudes of medieval theologians often reflect the values of the contemporary historian as much as those of the historical subject.

Perhaps the fairest thing that can be said is that medieval theology allowed the vigorous pursuit of scientific questions while, at the same time, holding out the hope that progress on these matters would be beneficial both to the individual scientist as a person and to Western civilization as a whole. In a society where the most ambitious youths were motivated partly by a desire for truth and partly by a desire for glory – glory for themselves and for their homelands – nothing could have provided a greater impetus for scientific development than this.

THE MEDIEVAL CHURCH AND ARISTOTELIAN SCIENCE 79

Mathematical Method and Quantification

Historians like A. C. Crombie hold that one of the most significant contributions of the Middle Ages to the development of the natural sciences was its belief in the power of mathematics for the understanding of natural processes. The emphasis on mathematics came in a series of developments culminating in the fourteenth century. In the background was the creationist belief in the comprehensibility of the world epitomized in the frequently cited text of Wisdom 11:20: 'Thou hast arranged all things by measure and number and weight.' The Latin West inherited its belief in the mathematical structure of nature through the Christian Neoplatonism of Augustine and Boethius which was revived in the eleventh and twelfth centuries, particularly at the cathedral school of Chartres, and passed on through Robert Grosseteste and others in the early thirteenth century.

The principal contributions of the thirteenth century to the mathematization of natural science came from Robert Grosseteste (d 1253) and the so-called 'perspectivists', including Roger Bacon, John Pecham, Witelo of Silesia, and Theodoric of Freiburg. These writers excelled in their investigations of the laws of the reflection and refraction of light and their applications to the optics of lenses and to the rainbow. In contrast to Aristotle and his commentators, the perspectivists were concerned more with structures and laws in nature than with efficient, formal and final causes.

Concurrent with the perspectivists, yet working more within the Aristotelian methodology, were Albert the Great and his student, Thomas Aquinas. Albert seems to have been influenced directly by Grosseteste, particularly in his treatment of the rainbow, even though he rejected the subordination of natural science which he sensed in the writings of certain 'friends of Plato', who may have included Roger Bacon. The influence of Grosseteste, or, at least, of Neoplatonism, was partly responsible for Albert's allowance for an 'incipient actuality' (*incohatio formae*) in prime matter, which, according to Aristotelian principles, was supposed to be pure potentiality.

Aquinas steered even further away from Platonism than Albert and insisted on the pure potentiality of matter. Yet, in order to avoid making nature appear to be recalcitrant to formative influence from above, he ascribed to it a 'capacity for obedience' to God's command (*potentia obedientialis*), a capacity instilled at creation by God himself. The implication for Aristotelian philosophy was that matter was susceptible to quantitative determination, that very susceptibility being educed from the pure potentiality of prime matter by an efficient cause. The historian, Max Jammer, has argued that Aquinas's significant modification of the Aristotelian notion of matter thus opened the way for the modern quantitative concept of mass. Jammer has also described how Aquinas's attempts to analyse the transubstantiation of the elements in the Eucharist and the nature of the resurrection of the body played a role in this development.

The principal contributions to the mathematization of natural science in the fourteenth century came from Thomas Bradwardine (d 1349) and his associates and successors, known as the 'Oxford calculators', at Merton College. In his treatise *On the Proportions of Velocities in Motions*, which was written in 1328 as he began his postgraduate studies in theology, Bradwardine used the latest algebraic methods to define the concept of instantaneous velocity and to work out a new law for its dependence on motive power and resistance. 'Bradwardine's law', as it came to be known, was widely used until the seventeenth century, when it was replaced by the more accurate law of Galileo.

It is not clear whether Bradwardine was influenced by Grosseteste and the thirteenth-century perspectivists to any extent. Two direct theological influences that may have contributed to his appreciation for mathematics, however, were the writings of Augustine and twelfth-century hermetic treatise called *The Book of the Twenty Four Philosophers*. The latter reintroduced the idea of God as limiting and containing all things that was so prevalent in intertestamental and early Christian thought and was to be popularized again in the fifteenth century by Nicholas of Cusa.

It has been suggested that Bradwardine's faith in the power of mathematics to determine the laws of nature influenced John Buridan (d *c* 1360) in his attempt to give quantitative measure to the idea of impetus. If so, then both of the major trends toward the mathematization of natural science in the fourteenth century could be seen as parts of a coherent process rooted in the creationist tradition. The work of other physicist-theologians of the later Middle Ages like Nicole Oresme (d 1382), Henry of Langenstein (d 1397) and Nicholas of Cusa (d 1464) gives us further evidence of the continuing vitality of the creationist belief in the power of mathematics in the period leading up to the Renaissance and the scientific revolution of the sixteenth and seventeenth centuries.

Observation and Experiment
The medieval attitude towards observation and experiment was less developed than that towards the value of mathematics. The thir-

teenth and fourteenth centuries were a period of great technological progress: some of the instruments that were later to play a role in the scientific revolution (mechanical clock, pendulum, scales, magnifying lens, and magnetic compass) received their basic forms during this period. However, on the whole, these developments were not sufficiently advanced as yet to allow a precision of experimental testing comparable to the precision of the mathematical laws that were being worked out theoretically. The thirteenth and fourteenth centuries were also a period of great advance in military technology, mining, medicine, alchemy, and navigation. For the most part, however, the new facts and ideas being discovered in these productive 'arts' were not yet incorporated into the theoretical sciences.

It should not be concluded, on the other hand, that medieval writers did not attribute great value to the practical and productive disciplines in principle. If they were falling behind the times in failing to make use of the results of new technological developments, they were often ahead of their times in suggesting new projects of invention and reform. The problem, in short, was that the theoretical and experimental wings of science were not well coordinated.

Traditional practical concerns of the creationist tradition like the need for calendar reform and the benefits of medicine were exhibited by Robert Grosseteste and Roger Bacon in the thirteenth century. Of particular interest from our perspective is Bacon's attempt to redeem the practical magic arts as a source of potential benefit to society. The early Church opposed these arts, he argued, only because they had been used by the pagans to deceive and defraud people. Once the faith of Christ had been accepted, however, the fraudulence of magic could be purged and the arts could be put to good use. Here is a typical example of the belief in the possibility of restoration tempered by the criterion of social benefit which we have found to be an integral part of the creationist tradition (section 1.5). It should be noted, however, that the possibilities of human art were, for Bacon, limited by the effects of the fall of Adam. Thus medicine, for instance, could prolong life, but not beyond the years of our first parents. The reversal of the effects of the Fall and the attainment of immortality must await the general resurrection.

In contrast to the rather limited notion of scientific experiment, the medieval aptitude for the observation of nature was impressive. In fact, the greatest scientific advances were made with respect to atmospheric and celestial phenomena that were subject to direct observation.

This aptitude for observation can be seen as the culmination of a tradition reaching back to the work of Bede in the eighth century and mediated by the naturalism of the school of Chartres in the twelfth century. The thirteenth century provided two new stimuli, however, that must be given due credit.

The first stimulus was the Christianized Aristotelianism of Albert the Great and Thomas Aquinas. Here, the emphasis on the normacy of God's providential action through second causes promoted the idea of the relative autonomy of natural processes and encouraged the study of nature for its own sake. This was particularly true of Albert whose personal observations in biology, botany and geology were among the first independent achievements of Western European science. Albert studied the embryological development of insects, fish, chickens, and mammals; he dissected crickets and crabs. He observed the effects of local floods and decided (against Aristotle!) that the Milky Way was a configuration of stars rather than a sublunar vapour. His characteristic manner of certifying his conclusions was to say 'I was there and I saw it for myself'.

The second stimulus to the observation of nature in the thirteenth century came from the mysticism of Francis of Assisi (d 1226). In part a reaction to the mercantilism of his native city, in part a revitalization of the cosmic scope of the language of the Psalms, Francis's love of nature showed Western humanity for the first time how to celebrate creation as the garment of God. Though Francis himself was suspicious of science, his sense of the presence of God in nature was given philosophic credentials by Bonaventure and Raymond Lull and may have inspired subsequent generations of Franciscan scholars to take the scientific study of nature more seriously.

It is difficult to determine whether these stimuli had any direct influence on the scientist-theologians of the fourteenth and fifteenth centuries. The Oxford calculators were purely theoreticians. John Buridan (d c 1360) based many of his ideas on observations involving arrows, bellows, pendulums, water wheels, and grindstones, but whether these were actual observations or merely thought-experiments is difficult to say. Henry of Langenstein has been credited with pursuing the study of nature for its inspirational value, but his actual observations were limited to ones such as the fact that the stars twinkle while the planets do not.

In the mid-fifteenth century, Nicholas of Cusa described experiments (or 'games') with spinning tops and globes and also with weights on a balance scale. His account of one experiment designed to demonstrate the conservation of matter by weighing a quantity of earth before planting and after harvesting was actually carried out by Helmont in the mid-seventeenth century. But Cusa's own description of the experiment closely follows a literary convention going back to the Pseudo-Clementine *Recognitions* of the fourth century (section 1.4).

The most that can be said is that the ideals of observation and experiment were well developed in the late Middle Ages and that this was partly the result of the creationist tradition, but that the realization of the ideals had to await the Renaissance. Only in areas like alchemy and medicine do we find medieval followers worthy of the traditions of Roger Bacon and Albert the Great.

Arnold of Villanova (d 1311), one of the first physicians in the Latin West to recognize the importance of alchemy for medicine, had studied theology under the Dominicans and was later associated with the Spiritual Franciscans. In the tradition of Jesus ben Sirach (Ecclus. 38: 1–8), he taught that medicine was a gift from God and that the true physician needed divine illumination, as well as human reason, in order to diagnose and treat diseases even when the causes were natural. Arnold's writings were foundational to Paracelsus and his chemical philosophy in the sixteenth century.

Guy de Chauliac (d c 1370) also studied under the Dominicans and under the Franciscan, Raymond Lull, and served as private physician to three popes. He was noted for his firsthand description of symptoms of the bubonic plague and for his advice that all surgeons study anatomy based on post-mortem dissections.

Guy's contemporary, John of Rupescissa, was, like Arnold of Villanova, a Spiritual Franciscan who applied the experimental techniques of alchemy to medicine. He specialized in the art of extracting the spirit or essence (technically, the fifth essence) of minerals and herbs in order to render them more effective as pharmaceuticals. John's alchemical writings show clear indications of experimental procedure and careful observation. He explicitly described the steps required to extract the essences of antimony and mercury. And, in recommending one of his prescriptions, he called on his readers to 'believe one who has tried it because I have tested it'.

Not until the sixteenth century were experimental techniques sufficiently advanced to realize the possibilities inherent in the programs of observation and experimentation suggested by Roger Bacon and Albert the Great. The works of alchemist-physicians like Arnold of Villanova and John of Rupescissa were studied as classics for centuries, however, and helped paved the way for the rise of early modern chemistry.

Beyond the Natural Philosophy of Aristotle

We turn now to examine various ways in which medieval Christian theology may have challenged the physics and cosmology of

Aristotle in such a way as to lead science beyond it. It should be realized at the outset that Aristotelian science was a comprehensive account of natural phenomena that was rather well suited to reality as it was experienced at the level of technology characteristic of the ancient and medieval world. Consequently, the actual replacement of Aristotle's cosmology could only take place in the event that (a) developments in instrumentation opened the way to a new 'perception' of the natural world and (b) a new account of natural phenomena could be devised that was as suited to the new perception of reality as Aristotle's was to the old.

In other words, there was no question of theology causing a scientific revolution by itself. The most it could do was to suggest alternative hypotheses and to sanction the efforts of some of the more creative scientists of the day. As we saw in our discussion of the relative autonomy of natural science within the medieval synthesis, theology in the thirteenth and fourteenth centuries was in a position to do just that. In fact, it was in a better position than it had been before the thirteenth century or would be after the Renaissance. Before the thirteenth century there had not been a sufficiently coherent and autonomous body of scientific knowledge in the Latin West for theology to interact with. After the Renaissance, the autonomy of natural science would be much greater and the credibility of theology much less.

A second point must be kept in mind. Despite an ordinance of the University of Paris in 1272 aimed at preventing arts masters from disputing theological questions, theology was not yet the special preserve of trained theologians any more than natural philosophy was the special preserve of a class of trained specialists in science. Even arts masters like John Buridan, who were not trained in the higher faculty of theology, were believing Christians, and their understanding of the faith was a determinant in their handling of scientific questions in spite of the fact that they were not allowed to address the theological questions in their own right. This working arrangement in the universities was the functional equivalent of the medieval synthesis in which science and theology overlapped to a degree while each maintained its autonomy within its own sphere.

There were three basic developments in late medieval science that show the direct influence of theological doctrines such as creation and the omnipotence of God. They are:

(1) the possibility of a void;

(2) the gradual articulation of the idea of impetus;

(3) the suggestion of alternatives to the geocentric cosmology of Aristotle with its dualism of heaven and earth.

It is important to note the logical connection between these three developments as viewed against the background of Aristotelian physics: in the order we have stated them, they are directed against progressively more foundational tenets of the latter. A brief review of the logic of Aristotle's natural philosophy, beginning with the most foundational tenet, will show this.

The key to the Aristotelian system of natural philosophy lay in the concept of natural place. Each of the four terrestrial elements had a natural place, with earth at the centre since it was the heaviest. The celestial bodies had no weight but were kept in their orbits by an attraction towards higher spheres culminating in God, the Unmoved Mover. The celestial bodies were thus different from sublunar ones: they were composed of a fifth element, and they showed signs of intelligence and desire, evidence of the role of spiritual beings in their motions. This foundational picture had become deeply embedded in the scholastic synthesis, as we saw in section two, and it would be the hardest aspect of Aristotelian physics to dislodge.

From the Aristotelian notion of natural place we get the idea of natural (intrinsically caused) motion and its opposite, forced (extrinsically caused) motion. Celestial bodies naturally moved in circles (epicycles could be added to account for anomalies). But sublunar bodies, at least simple ones composed of just one element, remained in their natural place, and naturally moved back to that place if displaced. Any motion away from a sublunar body's natural place must, therefore, be continuously forced. Hence, the late medieval idea of impetus, which meant that unnatural motion could be sustained in the absence of an external force, undermined the distinction between natural and forced motion and even called into question the concept of natural place that lay behind it.

On the basis of the ideas of natural place and forced motion, Aristotle denied the idea of a void space which had been posited by the Greek atomists. Among the many paradoxes that the existence of a void would lead to was the thought that any body in a void, once set in motion, would move to infinity. Moreover, it would have to move at infinite velocity since there would be no medium to resist it. Not only were these results counter-intuitive, but they contradicted the rules of natural and forced motion mentioned above. So, if one wanted to attack the Aristotelian system as a whole, one way to start would be to insist on the possible existence of a void.

The Possibility of a Void

One of the earliest contributions to the discussion was made by Thomas Aquinas. Thomas did not allow the existence of a void, but he did contend that the natural motion of a body in a hypothetical void would not be instantaneous. Even in the absence of a resisting medium, the quantitative magnitude (*corpus quantum*) which was educed (along with its natural form) from the pure potentiality of matter in the body would be enough to constitute a resistance. As we have seen, the theological idea that lay behind Aquinas's interest in the quantification of matter was the absolute obedience of all things to the determination of God as exemplified in the transubstantiation of the eucharistic elements and the resurrection of the body.

A more direct challenge to the Aristotelian denial of the void came from the condemnation of 1277. As noted earlier, the condemnation was a reaction of the conservative wing of the creationist tradition to the assimilation of Aristotle's cosmology in the scholastic synthesis. One of the articles explicitly stated that God could move the world in a straight line thus leaving a vacuum or void. Another stated that God could create a plurality of worlds; this also suggested the possibility of a void space between the separate worlds. The theological motive behind these bold suggestions was the desire to acknowledge the absolute power of God and the contingency of the natural order: God could have created a different order than the one he did, and he was not bound by the present order but could alter or even annihilate and recreate any portion of it.

It is a well documented fact that the condemnation of 1277 influenced a number of scientists, as well as theologians, to speculate on the possible existence of a void. Just to give some idea of the variety of speculation, one should mention the following: Henry of Ghent (d 1293) argued that if God created a body outside our world (i.e., beyond the outermost celestial sphere) there would be an intervening three-dimensional vacuum. Thomas Bradwardine (d 1349) inferred from the fact that God could move the world that the divine nature must exist beyond space and time in an uncreated, dimensionless infinity which is itself the 'place' of the world. John of Ripa also started from the fact that the world could be moved, but concluded instead that it must exist in a created void space of infinite proportions: even though infinite and distinct from God this void space would be infinitely exceeded by the immensity of God!

All three of these examples concern the possibility of an extra-cosmic void, whether spatially extended or dimensionless. Albert of Saxony (d 1390), university rector and bishop, speculated also on the possibility of a void space *within* the cosmic order based on the power of God to annihilate any or all of the matter within it.

It should be noted that emphasis on the omnipotence of God could also lead to the opposite conclusion: Duns Scotus (d 1308) argued (against Thomas Aquinas) that God could produce an effect at a distance and, therefore, that his omnipresence was not prerequisite to the exercise of his absolute power. Consequently, one could not assume the existence of an infinite void simply on the basis of God's ability to create (or move) the world wherever he might please! For these, or similar, reasons, the majority of scholastics affirmed the absolute power of God, and hence the possibility of an infinite void, yet concluded either that such a void was unnecessary or else, like John Buridan, that there was no evidence to support it.

Not until Nicholas of Cusa (d 1464) did anyone suggest that the universe itself might be potentially infinite (from the point of view of God's unlimited power) since this more radical step required the rejection of the fundamental Aristotelian notions of natural place and a geocentric cosmos. In the meantime, medieval speculations on the possibility of a void weakened the hold of Aristotle and made possible the discussion of the concept of a permanent impetus of motion.

The Idea of Impetus

Terrestrial motion that was 'natural' in the Aristotelian view required no explanation beyond the object's tendency to return to its natural place. The cause was purely internal to the body, or, perhaps, relational between the body and its natural place. There was no significant change on this issue in the late Middle Ages.

Motion that was either circular or away from a natural place did require an explanation, however. There had to be some means by which a force could be continuously applied as long as the circular or 'unnatural' motion lasted. The cause was, therefore, purely external to the body in the Aristotelian view. In the case of a projectile, for example, the initial thrust lasted for only a very short time. Hence, for Aristotle, the continuing upward motion of the projectile was due to an external agency like the surrounding air which was itself set in motion along with the projectile by the initial thrust.

Behind this Aristotelian physics, lay the metaphysics of matter and form. Matter was purely passive in itself. The characteristics of a body came exclusively from its natural form. Hence, a body could contribute nothing to the determination or sustenance of an unnatural motion.

Thomas Aquinas exemplifies the Christian Aristotelian of the thirteenth century. He accepted the matter-form metaphysic of Aristotle and the consequent distinction between natural and forced motion. He introduced two slight deviations from Aristotle, however, that paved the way for future developments. First, for Aquinas, the heavens were continuously moved by God (as efficient cause): they did not simply move by desire for him (as final cause). Thus he opened the way to direct comparison between the motion of the heavens and cases of forced motion on earth (e.g. spinning wheels).

Second, Aquinas attributed to matter a susceptibility for quantitative determination and magnitude (*corpus quantum*) based on his belief in the sovereignty of God and the properties of the Eucharist and the resurrection body. While adhering to the letter of Aristotelian metaphysics, this deviation violated the spirit of Aristotle enough to provide new insight into the possible contribution of a body to its own (unnatural) motion: the conception of an inherent quantity of matter was fundamental to the later idea of an inherent quantity of impetus.

An alternative way of working around the Aristotelian categories was offered by Robert Kilwardby (d 1279), a Dominican like Aquinas who was, however, an Augustinian in the theological tradition of Grosseteste and Bacon. Kilwardby developed the idea of God as the efficient cause of the motion of the heavens to the point of denying that he was the immediate, present mover of the heavens (as formal cause). God had set the heavens in motion in the beginning in such a way that they now continued their respective motions 'by their own inclinations and tendencies'. The motion of the heavens was, in fact, as spontaneous and natural as the motion of sublunar bodies moving to their natural places. Kilwardby thus attributed an even more active role to bodies (celestial bodies, at least) than did the stricter Aristotelian Aquinas.

One of the first medieval scientist-theologians to challenge the Aristotelian view of projectile motion was the Spiritual Franciscan, Peter John Olivi (d 1298). Olivi's own position is difficult to determine with precision, but his speculations give some insight into the intellectual and spiritual dynamics that were changing ideas about the natural world in the late thirteenth century. For one thing, he reported the opinions of others (other Spirituals?) that projectile motion was due to an 'inclination' or 'species' (in the Augustinian sense of a secondary form) that was impressed on the moving object directly by the initial thrust of the mover. This impulse along the direction of initial thrust apparently continued until it was overcome by the tendency of the object to return to its natural place. In response to this position, Olivi suggested an even more radical view, arguing that motion required no cause at all! Motion was simply a 'mode of being situated' just like being at rest. This was very close to the germinal idea behind the law of inertia as formulated by Galileo and Newton in the seventeenth century.

Olivi exemplified a characteristic of Franciscans in the tradition of Bonaventure in that he attacked the Aristotelian framework, motivated in part by his faith, but also gave reasons for his rejection and did not appeal exclusively to faith. William of Ockham (d c 1350), perhaps influenced by Olivi, also denied that an object required a continuously impressed force to keep it in motion: God could, by his absolute power, produce an effect without any mediating cause at all. Ockham also gave scientific arguments to refute the idea of a mediating force, however. For example, if projectiles were kept in motion by the surrounding air currents, then two arrows moving in opposite directions and passing in mid-air would interfere with each other's motion. The falsity of the conclusion implied the falsity of the premise.

Another Franciscan contribution was made by Francis of Marchia around 1320. Drawing on an analogy between God's setting the heavens in motion and the infusion of grace through the sacraments (from Bonaventure), Marchia reasoned that an impressed force should remain (temporarily) in a projectile even after its initial thrust just as a residual power to confer grace remained in the Eucharist even after the moment of consecration. Hence, like Olivi and Ockham, though for different reasons, he rejected the Aristotelian idea that air currents kept the projectile in motion.

The Dominican and Franciscan speculations we have mentioned might have led nowhere if they had not been drawn together and reformulated by an arts master like John Buridan. Like Kilwardby, Buridan returned to the ancient creationist idea of God setting the heavens in motion once and for all by imparting an impetus that would keep them moving indefinitely. Like Olivi, he also treated the forced motion of sublunar objects in terms of impressed force or impetus. Impetus was defined as the product of the quantity of matter in motion times its velocity and was viewed as lasting until it was overcome by a contrary tendency to return to a natural place. Like Olivi and Ockham, Buridan cited the power of God to maintain unnatural motion even in the absence of a mediating cause, and, like Ockham, gave reasons for rejecting the need for air currents to keep a sublunar object in motion: a millwheel, for instance, once set in motion, would continue to spin even if it were surrounded by a closely fitted cover to keep the surrounding air away.

Aside from these insights from earlier workers, Buridan's own distinctive contribution was twofold. First, by developing the analogy between the rotating heavens and a spinning millwheel on earth, he elevated the idea of impetus to a general principle that cut across the Aristotelian dichotomy between heaven and earth. Second, he realized that the idea of a hypothetical vacuum, discussed above, implied that an impetus once imparted would last forever if there were no counteractive tendency to return to a natural place. For the first time in Western European history, it was realized that a body could theoretically maintain its state of motion by itself, without any external force and without any supernatural act of God to keep it moving.

As we saw in section 1.4, the basic idea of impetus had deep roots in the creationist tradition of the intertestamental and early Christian periods. But it only began to come to scientific fruition with the work of Buridan in the fourteenth century. Buridan's concept of a permanent impetus based on the idea of God's setting the heavens in motion like a spinning millwheel was reformulated by Albert of Saxony (d 1390). Albert's works were later published in the early sixteenth century and had a formative influence on Galileo who developed the idea of inertia that lies at the basis of modern Newtonian mechanics.

While the late medieval concept of impressed force or impetus had its roots in the creationist tradition, there is at least one significant difference between the two that should be noted at this juncture: in the biblical and patristic literature, the seemingly perpetual motions of nature had their origin in the word or command of God rather than in a mechanical thrust. Basil had used the illustration of a spinning object later taken up by Buridan, but he used it to illustrate the power of God's word as exhibited in all the cycles of nature (section 1.4). With the establishment of Aristotelian cosmology in thirteenth-century Europe, the idea of God as the efficient cause of the motion of the celestial spheres gained prominence as we saw in section two. As a result, the late medieval idea of impetus was a good deal more mechanical, and the corresponding notion of God was a good deal more deistic than in the earlier period.

Moving Heaven and Earth
The basic cosmology of Aristotle was largely untouched by speculations on the void and on impetus. The earth was still assumed to be at rest at the centre of the cosmos; the heavens were still assumed

to be rotating concentric spheres made of a substance unlike anything found in the sublunar realm. The initial challenge to this outlook came in the form of a revival of ancient Greek speculation on the possibility of many worlds, which, in Aristotelian terms, meant many centres of gravity or many earths.

Already in the early thirteenth century, at the time of the first major influx of Greco-Arabic ideas, Michael Scot reported that some philosophers (presumably contemporaries) held that God could make other worlds, even an infinite number of them. Michael Scot, William of Auvergne, Roger Bacon, and Thomas Aquinas all argued against this possibility as implying the existence of a void space between the worlds. In fact, the assimilation of the Aristotelian cosmology into the more traditional Christian worldview led to the entrenchment of the geocentric, geostatic outlook during this period.

The condemnation of 1277 not only affirmed the possibility of a void, based on the idea that God could move the cosmos, but it also insisted on the possibility of a plurality of worlds based on the absolute power of God in creation. Fourteenth-century natural philosophers like Bradwardine, Buridan and Oresme were all directly influenced by this decision in their speculations.

Among later medieval philosophers who argued for the possibility (not the actuality) of a plurality of worlds on the basis of God's omnipotence were Henry of Ghent (d 1293), Richard of Middleton (fl. c 1294), William of Ockham (d c 1350), John Buridan (d c 1360), Nicole Oresme (d 1382), and Henry of Langenstein (d 1397). This line of reasoning culminated in the speculations of Nicholas of Cusa (d 1464) in which the cosmos was unbounded and had no unique centre or circumference.

A second line of reasoning was developed by Nicole Oresme based on the idea that God could move the entire cosmos in a straight line and the associated idea of an extracosmic void. If the centre of the cosmos moved, Oresme asked, what would be the reference point for defining motion? It would have to be the infinite, immovable void space beyond the cosmos which is none other than the infinite immensity of God. Consequently, the definition of local motion did not require a fixed earth at the centre of the cosmos as Aristotle had supposed. Although Oresme still concluded that the earth was fixed at the centre of the cosmos, his speculations opened up new possibilities, and, less than a century later, Nicholas of Cusa could dispense with the idea of a fixed reference point for motion almost entirely.

But perhaps the most powerful corrosive to the Aristotelian cosmology was the development of mathematical laws and physical models that cut across the dichotomy of heaven and earth. The unity of heaven and earth had been one of the basic tenets of the creationist tradition as we saw in section 1.3. But opinion was divided with regards to the possible role of angels in directing the motions of the heavens. With the assimilation of the Aristotelian cosmology in the thirteenth century, the case for intracosmic angels was virtually secured: Aquinas, for one, identified the immediate movers of Aristotle's celestial spheres with one of the hierarchies of angels described by Pseudo-Dionysius. This, together with the Aristotelian idea of a fifth element unique to the heavens, made a unified physics of heaven and earth virtually impossible.

The first effort towards a more unified view came from the mathematical physics of Thomas Bradwardine, which we discussed earlier. In his treatise *On the Proportions of Velocities in Motion*, composed in 1328, Bradwardine attempted to develop an abstract algebraic formula that would be applicable to all types of motion, whether linear (as on earth) or circular (as in heaven). It was probably not just a coincidence that Bradwardine became a theological student about that time for his theological writings of later date stress the ubiquity of God's providence as the coefficient of *all* natural events. This sense of the immediacy of God's normal activity had been lost under the impact of Aristotelian cosmology in the thirteenth century as we saw in section two. Thomas Bradwardine signalled a process of recovery that was to continue with fifteenth-century theologians like Cusa and culminate in reformers of science and theology in the sixteenth century.

John Buridan developed his concept of impetus based on the analogy we have discussed between the rotation of the heavens and the spinning of a millwheel on earth. In doing so, he developed the beginnings of a unified dynamics of heaven and earth to correspond to the more mathematical kinematics of Bradwardine and his successors at Oxford. One consequence of this treatment was that there was no longer any need for angels to direct the movements of the celestial spheres.

Of Buridan's successors, Albert of Saxony followed faithfully in dismissing the angels, while Nicole Oresme retained them as a means of providing a kind of inertia to prevent the celestial bodies from moving too fast! So the angels made it into the early Renaissance, but not by much. Their role was severely restricted by Henry of Langenstein (d 1397) and was completely ignored by Nicholas of Cusa (d 1464). Langenstein and Cusa also affirmed the unity of heaven and earth in another way by rejecting the idea of a fifth element and positing the universality of the four primary elements for both heaven and earth.

This concludes our review of ways in which theological considerations influenced the development of natural science in the late Middle Ages and prepared the way for the rise of modern science in the Renaissance. There have been enough points of contact to indicate that theological ideas associated with the ancient creationist tradition were a real factor both in the assimilation and in the revision of Aristotelian science in Western Europe.

4. SUMMARY AND ANALYSIS

We are in a position to offer the following summary of the interaction between theology and science through the Middle Ages. In the biblical and patristic periods, nature was conceived as governed by laws that were authored and administered by God and, hence, were subject to divine ratification and amendment as a matter of course. This picture was transmitted to the Latin West, though with significant changes, as we saw in section 1.4. A sharp differentiation between the absolute creative power of God and the normal course of nature arose in the twelfth century, partly as a response to the rise of an increasingly naturalistic science. That differentiation, in turn, facilitated the assimilation of Aristotle's cosmology in the thirteenth century by a Church which might otherwise have been so resistant as to make further progress impossible.

The result of the medieval synthesis was twofold. On the one hand, considerations of God's normal exercise of providence through second causes led to a replacement of the biblical image of God as Cosmic Legislator by the idea of God as First Mover (the sense of the latter shifting meanwhile from formal to efficient cause of motion). This modified creationist image of God as setting the heavens in motion once and for all was, in turn, instrumental in the development of the late medieval ideas of impressed force and impetus that provided the background for early modern classical mechanics.

On the other hand, a conservative reaction to the naturalism inherent in the new synthesis led to a renewed emphasis on God's absolute power both in establishing the normal course of nature and in superseding it at any time. Specific assertions like the possibility of the cosmos being moved, the possibility of a vacuum, and the possibility of other worlds, challenged the authority of Aristotle in natural philosophy and encouraged efforts to develop a unified mechanics applicable to both heaven and earth.

Even a brief summary such as this one will show that the historical relationship between theology and science was not one of direct causation. Theology neither impeded nor caused the rise of modern science. Rather, the two interacted with changes in each making changes in the other more feasible. We may speak of certain scientific ideas like impetus or the unity of heaven and earth having their roots in the creationist tradition, but we must not think of that tradition as being unchanging over the centuries. It provided a continuity of ideas, but it was not constant. It adapted to meet the challenges of science in the twelfth and again in the thirteenth and fourteenth centuries. Adaptations in the creationist tradition, in turn, provided insight and inspiration to natural philosophers for whom theological belief was still an important part of life.

Even allowing for variability and adaptation, it is difficult to say to what degree the creationist tradition was responsible for the progress of natural science through the Middle Ages. We have argued that the Aristotelian paradigm was the most comprehensive system of natural philosophy available, hence, that the creationist tradition served the progress of science well both in making the assimilation of Aristotle possible and in stimulating constructive criticism that could lead beyond Aristotle.

We do not know whether modern science could have been built on any other historical base or even whether a different kind of modern science could have been developed on the same base. Any real understanding of the role of the creationist tradition in the development of science must await the outcome of efforts in non-western cultures to graft modern science on their traditions and the subsequent contributions of those traditions to the further progress of science.

History is the best exegesis of theology. So the full meaning of our beliefs will not be completely determined until history reaches its own conclusion. In the meantime, those beliefs will continue to be needed in the interpretation of history and the anticipation of future developments.

FOR FURTHER READING

Crombie, A. C., *Robert Grosseteste and the Origins of Experimental Science* (Oxford, 1953).

idem, *Augustine to Galileo*, 2nd ed. (2 vols., Oxford and Cambridge, Mass., 1961).

DeKosky, R. K., *Knowledge and Cosmos: Development and Decline of the Medieval Perspective* (Washington, 1979).

Gilson, E., *The Spirit of Mediaeval Philosophy* (London and New York, 1936), chap. 18.

Grant, E., ed., *A Source Book in Medieval Science* (Cambridge, Mass., 1974).

idem, *Physical Science in the Middle Ages* (Cambridge, 1977).

idem, *Much Ado About Nothing: Theories of Space and Vacuum from the Middle Ages to the Scientific Revolution* (Cambridge, 1981).

Jammer, M., *Concepts of Mass in Classical and Modern Physics* (Cambridge, Mass., 1961), chap. 4.

Knowles, D., *The Evolution of Medieval Thought* (London, 1962).

Lindberg, D. C., ed., *Science in the Middle Ages* (Chicago, 1978).

Steneck, N. H., *Science and Creation in the Middle Ages* (Notre Dame, 1976).

Weisheipl, J. A., *The Development of Physical Theory in the Middle Ages* (Ann Arbor, 1959).

Wildiers, N. M., *The Theologian and His Universe* (New York, 1982).

3

RENAISSANCE, REFORMATION AND EARLY MODERN SCIENCE
(fifteenth through the seventeenth century)

1. RENAISSANCE SCIENCE THROUGH COPERNICUS AND PARACELSUS

The sixteenth century stands out in the history of the Western European church as a time in which Christians tried to get back to the basic truths of their faith. Its importance for our study stems from the degree to which basic creationist themes were rediscovered and reaffirmed.

The Protestant Reformation was one aspect of this broader movement – we shall turn to it in the following section (3.2). In this section we shall look briefly at the influence of fundamental theology on the development of natural science up to the middle of the sixteenth century, a period during which the outlook of the principal figures was clearly still independent of the teachings of the Protestant reformers. Several of the modern sciences took their basic form during this period or, at least, were tending in the direction we recognize today as 'modern'. The fully modern features of natural science were completed in the seventeenth century – based on a synthesis of influences from the Renaissance and Reformation of the fifteenth and sixteenth centuries. We turn to that synthesis in section 3.3.

The fifteenth and sixteenth centuries are generally called the 'Renaissance' because they witnessed a rebirth and a new growth in the arts and sciences that raised Western civilization from a cultural backwater to a dominating force in world events. It was a period of world exploration and of scientific experimentation. It was also the period during which the invention of printing allowed the wide dissemination of scientific works, both old and new. Exploration, experimentation and printing together opened up an unexpected wealth of natural history to the reading public and provided the framework for significant advances.

The history of natural science during the Renaissance is far more complex than that during the Middle Ages. In place of a relatively stable data base derived from common experience and shaped by literary tradition, we find a growing body of new data based largely on individual observation made possible by the development of new technologies. In place of a single dominant philosophical tradition like Aristotelianism, we have an interweaving of several classical traditions together with new currents of thought that disavowed speculative philosophy altogether. Even in the relatively conservative field of theology there were new developments in theosophy and mysticism as well as a renewed interest in traditional doctrines.

In spite of all this novelty, the reader who is familiar with the basic themes in the creationist tradition and the medieval mutations of those themes will find little that is completely new in the Renaissance other than the sheer variety of ideas brought to focus at one time. Ancient traditions were celebrated without any sense of their being out of date because in many cases they were being rediscovered or refined in a way that made them provocative of new insight. Here we shall discuss three major Renaissance traditions – the scholastic, the Neoplatonic and the experimental. All three of these had roots in the Middle Ages and have been described in chapter 2. We shall look here for the theological factors that may have contributed to their revitalization and fruitfulness during the Renaissance.

The Scholastic Tradition to Vesalius

The Renaissance has so often been portrayed as a reaction *against* the scholasticism of the Middle Ages that we are liable to overlook the important contributions made, particularly in Italy, France and Switzerland. Since most of the ideas involved have been treated in chapter two, they need only be mentioned briefly here. But due recognition of their existence is needed in order to establish the importance of continuity with the middle ages, particularly in issues for which Copernicus is often regarded as being revolutionary.

There was an ongoing discussion of questions concerning scientific method in the tradition of Latin Averroism and the Parisian school of John Buridan, particularly at the University of Padua and the College of Rome. Buridan's idea of impetus was also developed by Leonardo at Milan and by Calcagnini at Ferrara. Independently of

Copernicus, Calcagnini argued (c 1530) that it would be perfectly natural for the earth to rotate on its axis.

Marliani (d 1483) revised the law of motion originally formulated by Thomas Bradwardine and also spoke of experiments that refuted Aristotle's earlier version of the laws of motion. Bradwardine's speculations on the possibility of a void and the 'mean-speed theorem' of the Oxford calculators were thoroughly discussed in the school of John Major (1469–1550) at Paris. A Spanish participant in Major's circle of students, Domingo de Soto, concluded correctly (1551) that acceleration should be uniform for a freely falling object and that the speed of fall should be proportional to the time elapsed after the onset of free fall.

In the field of astronomy, Italian scholars like Fracastoro (1535) tried to carry out Aristotle's original programme for representing the motion of the heavens in terms of rotating spherical shells. This modelling programme ruled out the use of either the eccentrics or the epicycles introduced by Ptolemy in the second century. It indicates an imperative for simple geometry and realistic physics – an imperative similar to the one that led Copernicus to his revolutionary hypothesis – yet coming directly out of the scholastic tradition.

In the fields of anatomy and surgery, the traditional ideas of Galen continued to be studied by Vesalius and his successors at Padua and by Felix Platter and Theodore Zwinger at Basel. Vesalius's treatise, *On the Fabric of the Human Body*, published the same year as Copernicus's major work on astronomy (1543), was the first substantial correction of Galenic ideas and is generally regarded as the foundation of modern anatomy.

Theological Motifs in Renaissance Scholasticism

Even from this brief survey one can see that the technical expertise of late medieval scholasticism continued to be scientifically fruitful in at least half a dozen different ways. But what of the theological motifs which, as we have found, played such a large role in medieval scholasticism?

In some cases traditional theological motifs were clearly in evidence. John Major, for instance, based his speculations on the existence of a void space on the power of God to create or destroy matter anywhere even beyond the known stars. He argued that God could even create an infinite number of worlds beyond our own. Another example is Domingo de Soto, who combined his scientific research with theological studies as Bradwardine had done two centuries earlier.

Those like Leonardo and Calcagnini, who were attracted to the

idea of impetus, were influenced, as were their late medieval predecessors, by the traditional idea of God having imposed laws on the
world at the very moment of creation. Calcagnini's references to the
source of these laws as 'Nature' or 'Providence' and Leonardo's
references to 'Reason' as the helmsman of nature suggest that this
creationist idea had been taken over with very little sense of its
biblical origins. On the other hand, it should be kept in mind that
the convenience of defining nature as distinct from God, and reason
as distinct from revelation, was by this time a venerable theological
tradition dating back to the eleventh and twelfth centuries (section
1.4). So Calcagnini and Leonardo could still be taken to represent
the creationist tradition, at least, in its more radical, secularized
wing.

Of the scientists listed, Fracastoro and Vesalius seem to exhibit
the least theological motivation in their work. Fracastoro served
Pope Paul III and was appointed official physician (1546) to the
Council of Trent. Yet it has been said that there is little or no trace
of religious motivation in his scientific work. Vesalius described the
human body as the product of divine craftsmanship, and it has been
claimed that this belief was an important factor in the passion with
which he pursued his dissections. But his references to the 'Great
Artificer of all things' may simply have been a formality, particularly
in his dedicatory letters addressed to monarchs. On the other hand,
Fracastoro's concept of a unifying principle of 'sympathy' in nature
and Vesalius's idea of design in the fabric of the human body clearly
indicate their creationist roots. It is not until we reach the eighteenth
century that we find anything like a genuinely secular, non-theological tradition of science.

The Neoplatonic Tradition to Copernicus
The Neoplatonic tradition is distinguished from the scholastic in
that it was not based on the works of Aristotle and his commentators. Although it received new attention in the Renaissance, its
roots go back to the days of the early Church – long before the
major impact of Aristotelian thought. In fact, up to the thirteenth
century, it was the dominant force in Western European thought.
Even during the two centuries (the thirteenth and fourteenth) of
Aristotelian ascendancy there was a strong Neoplatonist movement
among the Franciscans, particularly among the followers of Robert
Grosseteste, and during the fifteenth century there were several new
schools of thought that brought it back into the forefront. We shall
look briefly at two of these, the Florentine perspectivists and the

hermetic-cabalist tradition, as background for a study of Nicholas Copernicus.

The Florentine Perspectivists

Paolo Toscanelli (1397–1482) was the founder of this movement; Brunelleschi (1377–1446) and Alberti (1404–1472) were his most important students and collaborators. Continuing the work of the medieval perspectivists (e.g., Bacon, Pecham, Witelo) and inspired by the practical mathematical emphasis of Cusa, these mathematician-artists pioneered a geometrical mapping of space that affected all areas of science and technology from crystallography to geography and astronomy, and from painting to architecture and city planning.

The Florentine perspectivists provide background for the work of Copernicus in at least two ways. First, Toscanelli's astronomical studies led him to express dissatisfaction with the equants and eccentrics of Ptolemy. The departure from perfectly circular motion did not accord with his Platonic ideal of simplicity. One of the chief representatives of this Neoplatonic approach to astronomy was Domenico Novara (1454–1504), Copernicus's professor at Bologna during the last years of the fifteenth century.

The second way in which Florentine perspectivism may have influenced Copernicus was in its uniform, non-hieratic conception of space. Rather than representing things from a transcendental viewpoint in which spatial location and magnitude were determined by intrinsic value, artists began systematically to portray objects as they appear from a particular point of view on a level with the landscape itself. It has been suggested that this practice of perspectival representation prepared the way for Copernicus's perspectival shift from a geocentric to a heliocentric representation of the heavens.

Even aside from the question of its impact on Copernicus, the work of Toscanelli, Brunelleschi and Alberti was clearly revolutionary in its effect. Although it was an effort conceived in largely secular terms, it would be useful to have a detailed examination of its theological aspects. The shift from a hieratic to a uniform conception of space undercut the traditional concepts of sacred location and preferred direction which lay at the root of traditional religion, so the work of the Florentine perspectivists can hardly be regarded as lacking in theological significance.

One way to try to assess the perspectivists revolution theologically would be to look at its background; another would be to look at its effects. As to the former, even the brief historical sketch given above shows that there was significant theological input. The medieval perspectivist tradition was rooted in the idea that God created all things in accordance with measure, number and weight (Wisd. 11:20). While this notion is usually referred to as Neoplatonic or Neopythagorean, it should not be forgotten that it was championed and cultivated by Christians who also saw it as profoundly biblical.

Also in the background was the influence of Nicholas of Cusa, a contemporary of Toscanelli – in fact, the two knew each other as students at Padua (c 1420). Cusa's vision of nature as a book of God written in the language of mathematics and his non-hieratic view of the cosmos were also rooted in the idea of creation as we saw in chapter two. Even Alberti's apparent disavowal of metaphysics in favour of the mechanical arts was very much in the spirit of Cusa's pitting the wisdom of the uneducated artisan against the university-trained scholastic – an ideal (or anti-ideal) derived from the Franciscan tradition of the thirteenth century. If Francis of Assisi, Roger Bacon, Raymond Lull, and Nicholas of Cusa may be said to have laicized Christian spirituality, then Alberti may be said simply to have carried the process a step further and secularized it.

What then were the theological effects of the perspectivist revolution? Did the process of secularization destroy the very spirituality it worked on as critics have often said? Not exactly. It would be more accurate to say that the desacralization of space required the interiorization of spirituality rather than its destruction. The locus of ethical and spiritual value shifted from the object to the subject. However, interiorization was a tendency present in Christian Neoplatonism from as early as the fourth century, and the pressure towards secularization was clearly in evidence as early as the twelfth century. So whatever epistemological difficulties there may be in the subject-object dichotomy of modern Western thought, they are not simply the result of the perspectival revolution of the fifteenth century itself. The positive results that come from that revolution – the more realistic representation of nature, the more accurate mapping of the continents, and the vision of well-planned cities – can hardly be said to be lacking in theological value as far as the creationist tradition is concerned.

The Hermetic-Cabalist Tradition

In contrast to the naturalism of the Renaissance perspectivists, the numerology of the Renaissance cabalists may appear to be mystical and entirely unscientific. We could clearly state the scientific importance of the work of Toscanelli and Alberti; the question we have to ask is whether it had any theological content. In contrast, the ideas of Ficino, Pico, Reuchlin, and Agrippa were clearly theological. The question is whether they had any scientific impact in their time.

The founders of Renaissance cabalism were Marsilio Ficino (1433–99) and Pico of Mirandola (1463–94) whose careers, like those of the perspectivists a generation earlier, centred in the Republic of Florence. They and their associates are often referred to as the 'Florentine Neoplatonists'. Whereas the Florentine perspectivists were influenced primarily by Western Neoplatonism in the traditions of Grosseteste and Cusa, the Florentine Neoplatonists drew much of their inspiration from newly discovered hermetic and cabalistic texts purporting to contain wisdom so ancient that it even antedated that of the Greeks.

Ficino's major contribution was the translation of the Greek Hermetic writings (the *Corpus Hermeticum*, also known as 'Poimandres' or 'Pymander') that had been presented to the Florentine financier, Cosimo de' Medici, around 1460. Pico enriched this Neoplatonic-hermetic mixture by introducing the ideas of the Jewish Cabala (or Kabbalah) and correlating its numerological ideas with Pythagorean mathematics. The result was a heady concoction of mathematics and magic, mysticism and machinery, that has challenged the analytical skills of historians of our generation for explanation and assessment.

As far as the creationist tradition is concerned, the rediscovery of hermetic texts did not really introduce anything new. In fact, hermetic ideas were known in the Middle Ages and were particularly influential with Bradwardine and Cusa as we have seen. What Ficino's work did do was to revitalize non-Aristotelian ideas that had been peripheral and to give them respectability in some Christian circles. We shall mention a few of these.

The principal feature in Ficino's hermeticism was an hierarchical model of the cosmos that was not a strictly spatial hierarchy and that made the influence of spiritual entities much more immediate to human concerns than Aristotle's did. In contrast to later cabalist models (Pico *et al.*), Ficino's cosmology was rather simple. From top to bottom it consisted of:

(1) the divine Mind with its eternal ideas;

(2) the world soul (*anima mundi*), which contained the seminal principles or causes;

(3) the world (*mundus animatus*), which was itself a (spatial) hierarchy extending from the material heavens to the earth.

The entire Aristotelian system of sublunar zones and celestial spheres fits within this third category so Ficino's cosmology was definitely weighted toward the invisible and spiritual rather than toward the material and spatial as Aristotle's had been.

Within this hermetic cosmology the positions of the sun and of humanity took on particular significance. In the standard medieval cosmology the earth was at the centre of the cosmos, but the sun also had a strategic location in that its sphere was the fourth, midway between the moon (the nearest 'planet') and Saturn (the farthest), or, equivalently, midway between the earth and stars. Moreover, the sun's light illuminated all the other planetary bodies. Indeed it was frequently viewed as a key symbol of God's reign over the created world.

Ficino's hermetic cosmology gave the sun an even greater role in terms of spiritual influence. From the standpoint of the world soul, the location of the sun was central; it mediated the influence of the world soul, and through it the influence of God and the angels, to all the visible world. It is true that the earth was still at the centre in the spatial sense, but the sun could now be viewed as central in dynamical terms. In fact, the hermetic idea of the world soul was not so far away from the later Newtonian notion of universal gravitation. On the other hand, it should also be noted that Ficino's 'natural magic', with its use of solar talismans and hymns addressed to the sun as a lesser god, could only arouse hostility in orthodox Christian circles and prejudice church officials against the notion of heliocentrism even when it was offered as a purely scientific hypothesis. Like many theological ideas, Ficino's hermeticism could work for and against science at the same time.

The central role of humanity in the cosmos was also heightened in Ficino's cosmology. For one thing, human beings were viewed as participating in all three levels: human intellect corresponding to the divine Mind; soul (or subtle, astral body) corresponding to the world soul; and material body at the mundane level. In other words, there was a direct parallel between the macrocosm (the cosmos) and the microcosm (humanity). Such a parallel had been discussed by Church fathers as early as Clement of Alexandria and Gregory of Nyssa, but it had been weakened by the impact of Aristotelian cosmology in the Middle Ages. Ficino's hermeticism helped to bring it back into vogue.

Another way in which Ficino heightened the role of humanity was with respect to its creative role in the cosmos. As one who participated in all levels of existence, even the divine (as intellect), humanity could, in principle, know all things and create all things. The dynamical hegemony of the sun in the order of nature was paralleled in the technological potential of human arts. Humanity was the true vicar of God upon whom the freedom and responsibility of restoring and completing the work of creation fell.

While such utopian ideas are sometimes regarded as 'secular-humanist' today, it should be clear from our discussion in section 1.5 that they also had deep roots in biblical and patristic thought. What we find missing in Ficino's hermetic humanism from the perspective of the creationist tradition is an *equal* emphasis on the harnessing of human creativity for altruistic social ends. Ficino's drive toward individual enlightment, even if interpreted in corporate terms as human domination over nature, could be a dangerous and destructive force in history if not checked by the biblical injunctions to self-sacrifice in the service of others.

Pico of Mirandola amplified the ideas of Ficino by drawing on the mystical literature of the Jewish Cabala. Like hermeticism, cabalism was an offshoot of the ancient creationist tradition that developed independently of Latin Western thought and then helped to revitalize the latter during the late Middle Ages and the early Renaissance. In cabalism, however, the idea of creation is stressed more than it is in hermeticism. The basis of all creation is said to be a set of Hebrew letters or divine names that provide the basic laws for all natural phenomena. This theme can be traced from the Old-Testament and intertestamental idea of the law or word of God in creation, through Jewish apocalyptic and rabbinic literature, to the *Sepher Yetsirah* (Book of Formation) of the third to sixth century AD.

Two further developments in cabalism that influenced Pico and other Renaissance Neoplatonists occurred in the late thirteenth century. First, Moses of Leon compiled a lengthy treatise called the *Zohar* (1275–86) which developed a three-level model of the cosmos similar to that of hermeticism. The cabalist model was more complex, however, in that each level in turn manifested a tenfold structure patterned after the ten ciphers (*sephiroth*) which were based on the names or attributes of God. And, second, Abraham Abulafia (*c* 1240–92) developed what he regard as a higher form of Cabala, which allowed immediate communion with the angelic world and the control of nature by the permutation of the twenty-two letters of the Hebrew alphabet.

Pico's own version of the Cabala was still rather rudimentary compared to that of some later Renaissance cabalists we shall consider shortly. He adopted a simplified three-level model of the cosmos corresponding to the three levels described in Genesis 1:6ff. and identified it as the framework of Ficino's 'natural magic' based on the power of the world soul. The detailed correspondences between the higher and lower levels (as in the *Zohar*) then allowed him to understand this natural magic as a 'marrying' of things in heaven with things on earth. But Pico also developed what he called a 'spiritual magic' (some called it 'demonic') based on the direct invocation of the angels much as Abraham Abulafia had added his higher Cabala to the 'way of the Sephiroth' of the *Zohar*. The resulting possibilities for access to the divine being, and hence for human knowledge and creative power, were even greater than those conceived by Ficino.

Whatever one's sense of the value of these ideas may be, they cannot be ignored as part of the background of the scientific and theological developments of the sixteenth century. In fact, some of the key figures in the immediate background of both the Protestant Reformation and scientific revolution were keenly interested in them as we shall see.

Lefèvre d'Étaples (or Faber Stapulensis, 1455–1536), the leading pre-Reformation thinker in France, published two editions of Ficino's translation of the hermetic corpus, one in 1494 and one in 1505. Though Lefèvre avoided any association with the natural magic espoused by Ficino, hermetic influence can clearly be seen in his *Introduction to Astronomy* (1503). For instance, he compared the human effort to reconstruct (in the imagination) the heavens and their motions with the original creation of the heavens by God. Human science was thus dignified as part of the image of the divine in humanity.

It would be helpful to know whether the more immediate sense of the spiritual world allowed by the hermetic cosmology (in comparison to the Aristotelian cosmology of the Middle Ages) was a factor in Lefèvre's downplaying the significance of works and the sacraments as channels of grace in salvation. Lefèvre's regard for theologians like Augustine and Cusa would have to be considered here as well, but such a major shift in the understanding of salvation and of the sacraments suggests more than just a matter of theological preference. It may well reflect a corresponding shift in cosmology, and hermeticism could have provided this for Lefèvre and others who were rethinking their theology in the late fifteenth and early sixteenth centuries.

A second pre-Reformation thinker with such interests was Johann Reuchlin (1455–1522). As Lefèvre introduced the hermeticism of Ficino into France, Reuchlin introduced the cabalistic ideas championed by Pico into southern Germany. His treatise *On the Wonder-Working Name*, published in the same year as Lefèvre's first edition of the hermetic corpus (1494), was the first thoroughly cabalistic book ever written by a non-Jew. Reuchlin's Christianity showed primarily through his identification of that divine name with the name of Jesus which, as in the New Testament, had taken the place of Yahweh, the Old Testament name for God.

Reuchlin also saw the four Hebrew letters in the name of God (YHWH) as the basis for Pythagoras' numerology based on the number four. Pico had already suggested such an association, but Reuchlin carried it much further and even referred to his own work as that of 'Pythagoras reborn'. Apparently, the Pythagorean connection became quite prominent in the minds of Reuchlin's readers: an anonymous work entitled *Letters of Obscure Men* (1515–17) stated that Reuchlin's treatise on cabalism contained the sayings of the ancient sage Pythagoras, who was known to have practised the unlawful art of necromancy. Significantly, Reuchlin approved of the esoteric science of Pythagorean numerology and championed the Pythagorean counsel of secrecy because such ideas could not be understood by the common people. This was enough to guarantee the disapproval of the leading Protestant Reformers for hermetic and cabalistic ideas in general, as we shall see in section 3.2

Similar ideas appeared in the works of Trithemius of Sponheim (1462–1516) and his student Agrippa of Nettesheim (1486–1535). The latter was particularly important for his emphasis on the basic points of the creationist tradition in his famous treatise *On Occult Philosophy* (published *c* 1531): the creation of all things by number, weight and measure (Wisd. 11:20); the creation of the human soul with a faculty of reason by which it could comprehend the structure of the cosmos; the unity of all nature, both heaven and earth (here due to the universal presence of the world-soul); the infusion of all creation with law-abiding energies; the application of mathematics to the mechanical arts; the mandate of humanity to cooperate in the work of divine creation; and even the directive that this mandate be carried out for the benefit of one's fellow humans. The criterion of social benefit was, admittedly, secondary: the point was made in a preliminary address to the reader in which Agrippa attempted to stave off the charge of heresy. It is a useful reminder, however, of the kind of ethical stance any science would have to assume if it was to win public approval in a Christian society.

The Florentine perspectivists and the hermetic-cabalists represent two very different forms of the creationist tradition, one bordering on secular naturalism and the other on the verge of uncontrolled superstition. Together they indicate the richness and potential for productivity in the creationist tradition of the Renaissance period.

But they also indicate the need for a more balanced approach that could check the extremes of secularism, on the one hand, and superstition, on the other. The attempts of the early Reformers of the sixteenth century to achieve such a balance is best understood against this background; so are the attempts of leading scientists of the sixteenth century like Copernicus and Paracelsus.

Nicholas Copernicus (1473–1543)

Copernicus's treatise *On the Revolutions of the Celestial Spheres*, written in stages between 1512 and 1542 and published in 1543, is one of the most important works in the entire history of science. For the most part it is a technical work with only occasional references to the philosophical and theological ideas we are interested in here. Taken on their own, these comments would be almost impossible to interpret, and scholars have differed widely in their conclusions. Following the approach of Alexandre Korye, we shall interpret Copernicus as 'a man deeply imbued with the entire, rich culture of his period . . . a *humanist* in the best sense of the word'. He was trained in canon law, medicine and philosophy as well as in mathematics and astronomy (the latter two subjects he studied at Bologna under Domenico Maria Novara, himself a humanist influenced deeply by the Neoplatonic ideas we have discussed in the paragraphs above).

For these reasons we assume that Copernicus's occasional remarks about philosophy and theology are to be taken seriously. They are not just concessions to the eclectic tastes of the time but represent the true convictions of the author. And where Copernicus indicates that theological ideals helped motivate him to initiate and pursue his programme of research, we may take these confessions at face value. (Motives involved in his final decision to publish his manuscript will be considered later.)

It is helpful to begin with a brief look at the *Commentariolus*, a short prospectus which Copernicus circulated privately among his friends while the larger work was still in the early stages of preparation. Several features stand out here which help us to understand Copernicus's motivation. The most prominent is Copernicus's insistence that all the planetary orbits (both deferents and epicycles) be perfectly circular and that all motions around these circles be perfectly regular and uniform with respect to their proper centres.

Copernicus's persistence in adhering to strict principles and his clear-headed application of them to the 'very difficult and almost insoluble problem' of planetary motion is truly awesome. In general, it bespeaks a profound conviction in the rationality ('a more reasonable arrangement') of the world and hence in the reality to be ascribed to the mathematical entities one is dealing with theoretically. The specific kind of rationality and reality Copernicus subscribed to was derived from the Aristotelian scholastic tradition. The planets moved as a result of being embedded in an interconnected set of perfect spheres: hence the circular orbits. Copernicus realized, however, as a result of the failure of previous attempts of this kind, like Fracastoro's, that these spheres could not all have the same centre and that epicyclic spheres would have to be allowed.

Still it was not the mere insistence that orbits be circular that differentiated Copernicus's procedure from Ptolemy's: it was the added stipulation that the motions of the planets in their circular orbits be perfectly regular and uniform about their own proper centres. This followed from the aforementioned Aristotelian notion of celestial spheres on the supposition that the motion of the spheres is naturally and invariably a uniform rotation. Here we have the long-term effect of the idea of impetus developed by John Buridan and his school in the fourteenth century, an idea that was still cultivated in the Renaissance scholasticism Copernicus was exposed to at Cracow and elsewhere.

Several other features of the *Commentariolus* reflected the Renaissance Neoplatonism that influenced Copernicus, particularly during his studies at Bologna. First there was the dissatisfaction expressed with Ptolemy's system on the grounds of its lack of simplicity: it was 'neither sufficiently absolute [Aristotelian emphasis] nor sufficiently pleasing to the mind [Neoplatonic]'. This dissatisfaction led him to attempt a solution 'with fewer and much simpler constructions than were formerly used'. In the final version published in 1543, there was actually little or no gain in simplicity over Ptolemy's system as far as geometrical constructions were concerned: at least forty-six different cycles were required to account for all the planetary motions. But in the *Commentariolus* Copernicus had hoped to make his system work with only thirty-four circles. In any case, Copernicus eliminated the equants that were required by Ptolemy's system and provided a semblance of uniform circular motion.

A second 'Neoplatonic' feature reflected the discipline of mathematical perspective developed by Toscanelli and his students in early fifteenth-century Florence. Copernicus repeatedly expressed his satisfaction in explaining a variety of phenomena as they appear from the earth as a result of the earth's motion around the sun. There is a preference for simplicity of explanation here, but also an aptitude for perspective-shift which would not have been likely prior to the work of the Florentine perspectivists.

A third 'Neoplatonic' feature of Copernicus's proposed system was the location of the sun at the centre of the universe. It has been suggested by several historians that this innovation was based on the dynamical centrality of the sun in hermeticism and in late medieval Neoplatonism generally. Such a connection is by no means proven historically, however, and other historians have rejected it.

The motivating ideas of the *Commentariolus*, then, are clearly related to the creationist tradition of the late Middle Ages and the early Renaissance. Still, there are no explicit references to God or to the idea of creation itself. Such comments appear for the first time in the preface and first part he wrote for his treatise, *On the Revolutions*, when preparing it for its publication in 1543. It is difficult to know precisely how to interpret these late references to the idea of creation. On the one hand, they appear to be only concessions to Christian piety: Copernicus was keenly aware of his writing for a larger audience, both mathematicians and theologians, learned and unlearned alike. On the other hand, no one would doubt that Copernicus really believed in the theological points he made.

One of the references to the idea of creation appears in the preface addressed to Pope Paul III. After describing the inadequacies of the Aristotelian and Ptolemaic systems already discussed in the *Commentariolus*, Copernicus says that he went through a prolonged period of uncertainty as to which system was the best. Then, at last, he says, he 'began to chafe that the philosophers could by no means agree on any one certain theory of the mechanism of the universe, wrought for us by a supremely good and orderly Creator . . .' Although the wording here is rather stereotyped, it may accurately reflect Copernicus's mental struggle at a turning point in his personal development. The allusion to the Creator is not gratuitous: it comes precisely at the point of Copernicus's frustration with the inconsistency of the Hellenistic natural philosophers. The sequel, in this case, was not the repudiation of natural philosophy as such but a resolve to read more widely in the works of philosophers, particularly the Pythagoreans. The sense is that somewhere among the ideas of the ancients there must be a clue to a solution that would uphold the regularity, uniformity and symmetry that befitted the work of God. Belief in the ultimate compatibility of biblical faith and Greek science and criticism of the diversity and unverifiability of the views of the secular philosophers – both features of the creationist tradition since the second century AD (section 1.1) – thus sustained Copernicus in his quest for deeper understanding of the cosmos.

Two further references to the idea of creation occur in the first part of *On the Revolutions*. The first of these is made in an attempt to counter the Aristotelian notion of natural place. The earth must be at the centre of the cosmos, according to Aristotle, because it is natural for the heaviest element to gravitate towards the geometric centre. In contrast, Copernicus affirms that there can be many centres of gravitation because 'gravity is but a natural inclination, bestowed on the parts of bodies by the Creator . . .' Here again we have one of the basic ideas of the creationist tradition: the laws of nature are not intrinsic, and cannot be deduced a priori: rather they are imposed or infused by God in such a way that they appear to operate automatically. This idea had been diluted to some extent during the thirteenth century but was reaffirmed in connection with the condemnation of 1277 and was influential in the fourteenth-century antecedents of Copernicus. The relatively conscious adherence of Copernicus to that tradition may be seen by a comparison with the more secular interpretation of Fracastoro described earlier.

The other reference to the idea of creation appears in relation to the idea of the immensity of the cosmos. Copernicus concluded that the dimensions of the universe must be at least two thousand times larger than previously thought. He even suggested the possibility of an infinite universe or, at least, of an infinite void space beyond the stars. The issue could not be resolved on the basis of mathematical astronomy alone, he concluded; it was a matter for the natural philosophers (i.e., physicists) to settle. Yet the immeasurable distance of the fixed stars was consistent with the greatness of 'this divine work of the great and noble Creator'. These speculations are clearly rooted in the ideas of the infinity and omnipotence of God as developed in the late medieval period and continued in various places during the Renaissance.

We assumed at the outset that Copernicus was conversant with the philosophical and theological ideas of his time. The results of our brief study have vindicated this assumption in finding Copernicus to be a faithful son of the creationist tradition. In fact, a review of the different aspects of that tradition as they were reaffirmed in the late medieval period (section 2.3) will show that practically all of the contributions of that period had a part to play in this renaissance man's thought. A similar review of our treatment of the early Renaissance will show that he drew on both the Aristotelian-scholastic and the Neoplatonic-perspectivist traditions. The hermetic-cabalist tradition was probably not a significant factor, however, in spite of the fact that some modern historians have claimed that it was. Copernicus did refer to the Pythagoreans, but only to their views on the motion of the earth, not to their numerology. He also cited the hermetic writings, as Ficino had done, to support the idea of the dynamical centrality of the sun. But in the next breath he also cited Sophocles and Aristotle, so we may infer that all these citations were merely a way of literary illustration. Copernicus was neither as secular in outlook as Alberti and Fracastoro, nor as mystical as Ficino and Pico. He should be located somewhere near the centre of the creationist tradition as it was represented in the context of Renaissance thought.

The Experimental Tradition to Paracelsus

Of all the varied aspects of the medieval creationist tradition, the one that was least developed was the appreciation of the relevance of industrial and technological innovation for the progress of basic science. As a result, nature was conceived as existing in an ideal state of equilibrium rather than as the malleable substance we think of today. Aristotle's mechanics described things as having a natural context outside of which they did not behave normally and towards which they would return if displaced. Similarly, Galen's medicine described the functioning of the body as a balance of humours which had to be maintained in health and restored in the event of disease.

In contrast, the new ideal of scientific knowledge introduced in the Renaissance was that we only know things as artifacts. That is, we only truly know things that we have made ourselves and natural things that we have succeeded in measuring or analyzing into parts and reconstructing. The new ideal of analysis did not entirely displace the old – indeed, many modern epistemologies have attempted to synthesize the two ideals – but there was a major shift in the new direction in the fifteenth and sixteenth centuries: first in the mechanical arts and astronomy, and then in metallurgy and medicine. And along with this shift came a renewed sense of the ethical problems raised by technology and a restatement of the biblical criteria for technology assessment.

Artisans and Astronomers

The interest in measuring instruments itself was not new. It was encouraged by the belief that God had created all things by measure, number and weight (Wisd. 11:20), a belief that was revitalized by the Neoplatonic revival of the fifteenth century. Somehow this motivation had to be combined, however, with the actual use of instruments like mechanical clocks and navigational tools which were being produced with increasing skill and accuracy during the Renaissance.

One of the principal centres of production was Nuremberg in Bavaria. Nicholas of Cusa is said to have purchased three scientific instruments there in 1444. Even if Cusa was not much of an experimentalist himself, his influential vision of the possible benefits of experimentation to science lived on in George Peurbach (1423–61) and his associate John Regiomontanus (1436–76), the pioneers of modern observational astronomy, in Vienna. In 1457 they planned to observe a lunar eclipse and found that the time predicted by the astronomical tables then in use (the Alfonsine Tables of 1252) was in error by eight minutes. Measurement of changes in the apparent size of the moon as it moved around the earth also led the two to criticize Ptolemy's system of planetary motions, and this observation later came to the attention of Copernicus at a time when he was beginning to develop his own system of the heavens.

The production of new instruments and the composition of new tables of data were to be a major factor in the rise of modern science. In 1471 Regiomontanus chose Nuremberg as the site of his own observatory due to the accessibility of instruments there. After his death in 1476 his work was carried on by his associate Bernard Walther who performed the first uninterrupted series of astronomical observations. The data produced were used by Tycho and Kepler a century later.

If there was anything lacking in the experimental philosophy of the Nuremberg school, it was the ideal of investigating and publishing for the benefit of others rather than merely as a self-aggrandizing response to market conditions. There was a great demand for Regiomontanus's improved astronomical tables (*Ephemerides*, 1474) primarily due to their usefulness in navigation and astrology. However, after Regiomontanus's death, Walther refused to circulate most of the more recent astronomical observations that had been made. Copernicus owned a copy of the Regiomontanus-Walther solar tables (1490), but he did not have access to the other data until much later in his work.

In 1945 the historian Edgar Zilsel published an article in which he argued that the understanding of science and technology as a real benefit to humankind was essential to scientific progress in the early modern period and that this perception grew out of the artisan tradition of the late Middle Ages and early Renaissance. Among the examples of the latter he gave are the following: Around 1400 the Florentine painter Cennini composed a handbook on pigments and painting in the reverence of God, the Virgin, and the saints and 'for the use and profit of any one who wanted to enter the craft'. Similar motivations were expressed in a more secular vein by Roriczer (1486), Dürer (1528), Apian (1532–3), and Tartaglia, among others.

Tartaglia's two pioneering books on ballistics (1537, 1546) were prefaced by discussions of the possible dangers and benefits to society resulting from the improved use of artillery. Under normal circumstances, he reasoned, the publication of such information would be 'cruel and deserving of no small punishment by God', but under the circumstances of the threat of Turkish invasion he felt compelled to make his findings public. As it happened, the benefits accruing to both science and society from Tartaglia's insights into the dynamics of falling objects far exceeded the advantage of short-term improvements in aiming cannon derived from his tables of gun elevations. But the fact that early modern scientists saw themselves, and came to be seen by the general public, as contributing to the common good was of utmost importance for the development of strong social support for the relatively new and untried enterprise.

The most impressive instance of the influence of Christian concern for the public good on scientific development took place in conversations between Copernicus and Tiedemann Giese, Bishop of Kulm at the bishop's castle in 1539. According to his young associate, George Joachim Rheticus, Copernicus wanted to publish astronomical tables and rules of calculation based on his new system of the heavens for 'common mathematicians' and to keep the underlying hypotheses and proofs to himself and his personal associates in accordance with the 'Pythagorean principle' of education.

Bishop Giese, on the other hand, had 'mastered with complete devotion the set of virtues and doctrines required of a bishop by Paul' (1 Tim. 3; cf. 1 Cor. 7–16), and he realized 'that it would be of no small importance to the glory of Christ if there existed a proper calendar of events in the Church and a correct theory and explanation of the motions'. He therefore argued with Copernicus that the astronomical tables would be 'an incomplete gift to the world' without the supporting theory. Something of an amateur astronomer himself, Giese complained that the existence of tables without explanations had caused great inconvenience and many errors in the past and that the Pythagorean counsel of secrecy had absolutely no place in mathematical science as practised by Christians.

Such was the pressure under which Copernicus allowed Rheticus to publish a 'first report' on his theory (1540) and finally to copy the entire manuscript of his treatise *On the Revolutions of the Celestial Spheres* for printing (1542–3). The place of publication significantly was Nuremberg where Cusa had bought his instruments nearly a hundred years earlier.

We have treated the theological motives behind the publication of Copernicus's work under an entirely different heading from that of the motives that led him to do his research in the first place. Copernicus's motives for research were derived primarily from the scholastic and Neoplatonic traditions of the late Middle Ages and Renaissance, traditions which were rooted in the creationist ideas of the comprehensibility, unity and relative autonomy of nature (sections 1.2–1.4). Giese's motives in urging him to publish were derived more directly from the biblical ideal of mutual service in the Church of Christ (section 1.5), reinforced by the late medieval and early Renaissance artisan tradition of art and technology in the service of humanity. At this critical juncture of history, at least, these different aspects of the creationist tradition worked in marvellous harmony.

Metallurgy and Medicine

Scientific instruments and tables of data were one way in which the Renaissance contributed to the new view of nature. Advances in the technology of mining and in the medical use of chemicals were another. Here, the Neoplatonic emphasis on mathematics was of little use at the time, but the importance of the Christian idea of creativity through the human arts was as great as that of the artisan tradition itself. There were two prominent figures in this sector, Agricola and Paracelsus, who represented opposite ends of the scale socially and financially.

George Bauer Agricola (1494–1555) worked as a town physician in Bohemia and Saxony and studied the extensive mining operations in his area. On the basis of his medical and mining expertise, Agricola corrected the natural history of the classics at several points. He also achieved considerable wealth and status in society. Yet he took a genuine interest in the welfare of the miners, argued for safer working conditions, and exposed himself and his family to considerable danger while tending the sick during the outbreak of plague in 1552–3.

Agricola's importance for our study lies primarily in his discussion of the propriety of disturbing the earth in order to extract its resources. It may come as a surprise to the modern reader to learn that the industry of mining was under heavy criticism already in the sixteenth century for its destruction of farm land, consumption of wood, extinction of wildlife, pollution of water supplies, and disruption of country life, to say nothing of the use of its products for warfare. In view of the perennial nature of these problems, Agricola's response and its bearing on the creationist tradition should be of particular interest to those engaged in 'technology assessment' today.

There are three points in Agricola's response. First, he argued that the wisdom of God in creating the earth was to be seen in his making a variety of things available for human use. So the location of metals underground was no more a reason for leaving them there than the location of fish in the water or birds in the air was sufficient reason for leaving them there. According to Scripture, the ground was given to humanity to cultivate (Gen. 2:15), and this could be done through mining as well as through agriculture.

To state Agricola's thought in modern terms: what is natural is a matter of social and cultural definition. Hunting, fishing and farming were forms of technology that had been accepted as necessary to society and sustained a social structure favouring the rural land owners. Mining, on the other hand, was a growth industry under the control of the new merchant-bankers like the Fuggers of Augsburg. So the economic and social change of the Renaissance was as much a factor in dislodging the Aristotelian idealization of the 'natural' place of things as was the more theoretical challenge of academic theology and philosophy. Agricola was an heir of the creationist tradition insofar as he saw the work of creation as an ongoing process partly entrusted into the hands of humans and realized that human technology was neither good nor evil in itself but had to be assessed in terms of particular criteria.

Agricola's second point was to specify those criteria and to show how, in his experience, the practice of mining satisfied them. First criterion: any human enterprise should benefit those who are directly engaged in it – here Agricola had to deal with the problems of risk: financial risk for the owners and occupational hazards for the workers. Second, that the enterprise should be beneficial to society as a whole – here Agricola argued that to say the Creator had placed metals in the earth to no social purpose would be to accuse him of wickedness. On the contrary, he pointed out, the use of metals was essential to all the other arts, especially to those like agriculture that were held in such esteem by the critics of mining, and hence metals could be used in the protection of life and the preservation of health, as God had willed.

Agricola's third and concluding point was that all God's gifts were good and that it was the responsibility of humans to use them for the good of others as well as for themselves. To reject good things simply on the basis of their possible misuse would be blasphemy against their Creator.

Agricola may appear to have been merely a 'company man' in modern eyes haunted by the memory of technological abuse. He never really dealt with the problems of the ecological damage and social disruption caused by the growth of mining even in his own time, and he implied that companies should never be held responsible for the harm caused by their products when misused. But these were matters beyond his personal influence, probably even beyond his personal understanding. In the arena that Agricola did influence and understand, the health care and working conditions of the miners, his ideas were quite progressive. For instance, he opposed the kind of exploitation of miners practised in Greco-Roman times. Moreover, he must be credited with having attempted a comprehensive Christian ethic that did justice to the needs of employer, employee and society as a whole. Faulty as modern industrial practices were to be, they could be held accountable, at least, to an ethic whose credibility had been established over a period of two millennia and which is still with us today more than four centuries after the seminal work of Agricola.

Very much more clearly on the side of the poor was Philip Theophrastus Bombast of Hohenheim, better known as Paracelsus (c 1493–1541). Like Agricola, Paracelsus was trained as a physician and worked among miners and peasants, chiefly in Austria and Switzerland. Unlike Agricola, he was a hopeless eccentric and was never able to hold a job for long. He spent most of his life on the brink of poverty as a wandering lay preacher repeatedly attacking the academic medical authorities of his time. His epitaph simply stated that he had devoted his life to the art of healing and wished his goods to be distributed to the poor upon his death. Though he was very nearly heretical from the viewpoints of later scientific and theological orthodoxy, Paracelsus understood at least some of the basic truths of both science and theology as well as anyone in European history.

Paracelsus's two principal contributions to science itself were his doctrine of the 'three basic principles' (*tria prima*) of matter and his view of physiology as governed by relatively autonomous organ systems. Both of these ideas had roots in the alchemical-medical tradition of the Middle Ages and were nourished by the hermetic-cabalist tradition of the Renaissance. Their importance lay in their offering alternatives to the Aristotelian doctrine of the four elements and the Galenic physiology based on four humours. In other words, both contributed to the breakdown of the medieval view that conceived of nature in terms of equilibrium states.

The 'three principles' of matter, according to Paracelsus, were mercury, sulphur and salt. These were not quite the same as the chemicals we know by those names today but rather three kinds of product resulting from a typical chemical reaction: a vapour (smoke), a flame (light), and a solid residue (ash). For Paracelsus these three categories also corresponded to three levels of human existence: spirit, soul and physical body. Since spirit was the highest and most powerful level of being, Paracelsus and his followers stressed the importance of mercury (or mercuric oxide) in the treatment of disease. An unorthodox worldview resulted in unorthodox but powerful medicine. Some people were actually healed by it!

Even though Paracelsus did not completely do away with the Aristotelian conception of the elements (earth, water, air, and fire), his 'three principles' did offer an alternative way of looking at matter. It was really quite revolutionary to think of the world in terms of components that are not normally visible but can only be produced through chemical processes. Previously, the only alternative to Aristotle's system had been the atomic hypothesis of the Epicureans. Atoms, of course, were completely invisible, and their production was far beyond the technology of the sixteenth century. Paracelsus put science on the trail of discovering the basic constituents of matter, however, that eventually did lead to the discovery of atoms and beyond.

Paracelsus's physiology was based on the idea that a human being is a microcosm or miniature version of the cosmos, an idea that we have already mentioned in our discussion of Ficino. One of the implications of the microcosm theory was that there could be detailed correspondence between the organs of the human body and the planetary spheres of the cosmos: for instance, the sun corresponded to the heart; Mercury to the lungs; and Venus to the kidneys. The planets did not affect the human organs directly, but celestial events and human diseases had definite correspondences based on their common dependence on forces at work at the level of the world soul.

As a result, Paracelsus saw diseases like the plague as coming from outside the body by infection and regarded them as affecting particular organs rather than as disturbances in the humoral balance of the body as Galenic medicine had taught. The result was a more analytical approach to the structure and function of the body and a more interventive kind of medicine using chemicals targeted at specific organs.

These contributions encouraged a new, more experimental, kind of science in which humans understood nature in terms of the ways they could influence it rather than what it was in its undisturbed state. Like Ficino, Pico, Reuchlin, and Agrippa, Paracelsus was exhilarated by the new sense of human freedom and power over nature. But more clearly than any of his cabalist predecessors, he also had a deeply Christian sense of his work as a healing ministry ordained by God. It was God who had created herbs and minerals, he said recalling the words of Jesus ben Sirach (Ecclus. 38:1–4), and it was God who gave humans the skill to create medicines out of these raw materials and the wisdom to know how to use them at the appropriate time.

To some extent, according to Paracelsus, this skill could be mastered by any physician who was called by God, regardless of religious persuasion. This follows from the fact that God implanted seminal causes in nature at creation and that these were generally accessible to human understanding and control. All that was required was an attitude of humility combined with a persistence in seeking that would allow nature to reveal itself so that the physician could read it like an open book. Compared to the inspired medicine of the Hebrew prophets and Christian saints, the gentile arts based on the 'light of nature' were just crumbs from the table of the Lord (Mark 7:28), but even the children of God depended on the light of nature and needed to learn from the gentile arts, especially when they had lost their natural ability to use that light.

As a devout Christian, however, Paracelsus believed that deeper levels of wisdom were available to humans than those implanted by nature. Moreover, since spiritual and even divine influences were involved in many forms of illness, deeper levels of wisdom were mandatory. For cases such as these, the invitation of Christ was open: 'Come to me . . . and learn from me, for I am gentle and lowly in heart' (Matt. 11:28f.). From Christ flowed the very foundation of truth.

In what exactly did this divine wisdom consist? Unless the sickness was intended by God to lead to death, there would be a predetermined time at which the issue could be resolved one way or the other (cf. Ecclus. 38:13f.). As this time of 'purgatory' passed, the patient might be healed miraculously if he had faith in God. If faith is lacking, however, 'the physician works nevertheless the miracle which God would have accomplished wonderfully if the patient had had faith'. Apparently, the faith and compassion of the physician made it possible for him to discern the right time and prescribe the correct treatment. At this point the boundary between the natural and the supernatural became a bit fuzzy, but that seems to have been the way Paracelsus wanted it. According to our historical analysis, a strict division between nature and supernature only entered into Western theology in the twelfth century. Paracelsus's inability (or unwillingness) clearly to differentiate the two may simply derive from his desire to circumvent scholasticism and return to a more biblical theology.

From his reading of the Bible, Paracelsus derived two things that he felt distinguished the Christian physician from the unbeliever: an article of faith and a sense of calling. The article of faith was that there was no illness that could not eventually be cured. For us today in an age of the promise of 'miracle drugs', this may sound commonplace, but Paracelsus lived in a time when diseases like epilepsy seemed to be beyond cure and new diseases like the plague were at their height. Along with new diseases, however, would come new techniques and new chemicals, he believed. Why? Because Christ himself had said that 'the sick have need of a physician' (Mark 2:17), and he would not have said this if the requisite skills and medicines could not be developed. In fact the very curse of death had been nullified through the work of Christ in vanquishing the principalities and powers that inflicted death. Thus there was no limit to the possibilities of the healing art when practised by a believer.

Paracelsus described his personal sense of calling as a physician as coming from the commandment of Jesus that we love our neighbour as much as we love ourselves (Mark 12:31). This meant not only that every effort should be expended in seeking a cure for our neighbours' illnesses, but that the physician should serve his fellow humans out of true love and not just for the money. The work of the physician was, therefore, a ministry of God's grace as much as the preaching of the gospel was: after all, the welfare of the soul was bound up with that of the body. So the doctor acted not for himself but for God, and he must never take advantage of his position or use his skill to harm his patients.

Like Copernicus, Paracelsus represented something close to the centre of the creationist tradition. But his emphasis was on the ministry of healing and restoration ordained by Christ rather than on the logic and impetus ordained by God at creation. In Copernicus, the autonomy of nature and the independence of science were nearly absolute and needed to be balanced by the sympathetic pastoral direction of Bishop Tiedemann Giese. In Paracelsus, on the other hand, nature and God, science and theology, were all mixed together. What was required in this case was a reworking of his insights with due respect for the rationality and autonomy of nature. Johann Andreae, Francis Bacon and Robert Boyle were to supply this need in the seventeenth century. All three were deeply influenced by the teachings of the Protestant Reformation and their implications, both positive and critical, for natural science.

2. RENAISSANCE SCIENCE AND REFORMATION THEOLOGY THROUGH KEPLER AND BACON

The Protestant Reformation was a cluster of movements during the first half of the sixteenth century that attempted to restore the teachings and practice of the early Church. Principal continental European reformers were Martin Luther and Philip Melanchthon in Wittenberg; Martin Bucer, Wolfgang Capito and Johann Sturm in Strasbourg; Ulrich Zwingli and Heinrich Bullinger in Zurich; John Oecolampadius in Basel; and Guillaume Farel in Neuchâtel and John Calvin and Theodore Beza in Geneva. This is just a short list of names and places, but it will serve to remind us of the diversity of personalities and contexts.

All of these figures had a broad experience of Renaissance culture, and each one must have reflected on the issues raised by the science of the time. On this subject, however, only the thoughts of Luther (1483–1546), Melanchthon (1497–1560), Zwingli (1484–1531), and Calvin (1509–64) are now sufficiently well known for us to make any meaningful observations, and even for these four there is much that we do not yet fully understand. The reason is that most of the Reformers' efforts were directed towards contemporary ecclesiastical and social issues. Moreover, most of the research of modern historians of the Reformation has been focused in the areas of theology and ethics as distinct from issues of science and technology, thus imposing a present-day compartmentalization on the writings of people who may have responded more holistically to the culture of their time even if they did not often address issues of science and technology directly. There is room for much more original research to be done.

Three general questions will help us to focus attention on the interaction of science and theology in the Reformation period: the question of the continuity of Reformation theology with the historic creationist tradition; the question of the possible influence of the special issues of medieval and Renaissance science on Reformation theology; and the question of the possible influence of the distinctive emphases of Reformation theology, in turn, on the development of the physical sciences down to the time of Kepler and Bacon (the early seventeenth century).

In general, the Reformers reiterated the four basic themes of the creationist tradition as we defined them in chapter one. Such continuity with the historic tradition is just what one would expect in view of the Reformation emphasis on the teachings of Church fathers like Basil and Augustine who were regarded as the foremost exegetes of Scripture.

A complementary source of creationist ideas was the renewed interest in the classics which the Reformers shared with their humanist contemporaries. As in the intertestamental, patristic and medieval periods, there was a complex interplay of biblical and Greco-Roman ideas that often defies historical analysis. Also, as in the earlier periods, there were varying emphases and even differing views on some of the particular problems that the idea of divine creation raised and left unresolved. We shall point out some of these nuances as we review the four themes of historic creationist tradition.

Comprehensibility of the World

In the creationist tradition it was believed that the world could be understood by humans at least to the extent that the limits of human experience allowed. Underlying this belief were the doctrines that God had created the world in accordance with his wisdom or rationality and that he had created humanity in his image. As humans participated in God's rationality, they could in principle understand the plan of creation (section 1.2).

The basic ideas of the creation and comprehensibility of the world were reiterated by the Reformers in continuity with the teaching of the Church of all ages. Luther, for example, regarded reason as 'something divine' which permitted humans to understand matters as recondite as the motions of the stars. Melanchthon taught that humans, created in the image of God, have the ability to observe, calculate and control how one thing follows from another in nature. And Calvin pointed to the arts and sciences as evidence of traces of the image of God even in fallen humanity.

In opposition to supporters of papal authority, the Reformers emphasized the divine ordination of Christian laity in secular matters like civil government and the mechanical arts – this was one of the motivations that lay behind their stress on the secular implications of the doctrine of creation. Various scholars have pointed to the influence of William of Ockham and the late medieval nominalist tradition which was often associated with a healthy respect for the independence of the secular powers in an overall covenantal framework. In this respect, the Reformers were in line with the left wing of the medieval creationist tradition even though they were 'conservative' in many other ways.

The net result was that an important reversal of orientation took place in communities influenced by Reformation thought: a high value on the work of artisans and scientists now became associated with the new orthodoxy whereas in the Middle Ages it had been championed primarily by theological radicals. The Reformation stress on the divine calling of the laity was not a new one, but it received a new, more powerful legitimation.

The claim that the Reformation brought about a re-evaluation of secular activities like scientific research naturally raises the question of whether the sciences progressed more readily in Protestant than in Roman Catholic cultures as a result. Scholars have debated this question rather heatedly with no clear resolution of the issue. Certainly, the re-evaluation of the role of the laity in mainstream Protestantism was not necessarily a greater stimulus to innovation than the preservation of that same valuation in the more radical wing of Roman Catholicism. The researcher must look at specific cases to see how theologically-formulated values actually functioned.

When one considers the consistency with which the idea of the comprehensibility of the world recurred among Protestant scientists, one is inclined to believe that the Reformation emphasis on the idea of creation was indeed a factor in the history of science. The idea was stated variously by a series of Lutheran astronomers and alchemists leading down to Johannes Kepler (1571–1630) and Johann Andreae (1586–1654), all of whom were influenced by the ideas of Luther and Melanchthon. It was also articulated in various ways by a number of scientists in the English Reformation tradition leading down to Francis Bacon (1561–1626), many of whom were influenced by the ideas of Calvin and other Swiss reformers. But the idea occurred as well in the writings of radical Catholic naturalists like Giordano Bruno (c 1550–1600), Tomasso Campanella (1568–1639), and Galileo Galilei (1564–1642). It should also be noted that most of these scientists, both Catholic and Protestant, were influenced to a degree by the ideas of Plato and the Neoplatonic tradition, though such philosophic interests were not necessarily in conflict with the creationist tradition as the two had interacted positively through most of their history.

On the basis of the historical evidence, then, we must affirm that the Reformation emphasis on the creation and comprehensibility of the world was a factor, but not a determinative factor, in the history of science. It was not determinative in that it did not by itself make Protestantism a more suitable environment than Roman Catholicism for innovative science. From an historian's perspective, it is enough to demonstrate that Reformation theologians were cognizant of scientific issues and that late sixteenth-century Protestant scientists approached their work with a revitalized theological perspective that provided inspiration and meaning to their efforts.

The influence of the Reformers' doctrine of creation was not determinative for the history of science in another sense: it did not produce a consensus on some of the major issues in the philosophy of science of the later sixteenth and early seventeenth centuries. Foremost among these was the question of the value of mathematics and of mathematical models, in particular, as a means of understanding the world God had created. Astronomers in the Copernican tradition like Rheticus (1514–74) and Kepler tended to value mathematics more highly than did some physicians like Peter Severinus (c 1540–1602) in the tradition of Paracelsus. Those like John Dee (1527–1608) and Thomas Digges (1546–95) who were influenced by Platonic thought naturally valued it more highly than those like Francis Bacon who reacted against Platonic and Neoplatonic influences.

In other words, there were both speculative and empirical emphases in post-Reformation thought just as there had been in the Middle Ages. On the other hand, the difference in emphasis ought not to be overstressed: even 'empiricists' like Severinus and Bacon valued mathematics as a tool of experimental quantification. Their reaction to speculative mathematics was occasioned by its association with seemingly reactionary forces like Aristotelian logic and Neoplatonic hermeticism.

Not only was there significant disagreement as to the *means* of comprehending the world; there were also differing opinions about the implications of the doctrine of creation for the nature of the cosmos and its interconnections. Foremost among these was the question of the possible infinity of the cosmos, an idea that had already been discussed by late medieval philosophers like John of Ripa and Nicholas of Cusa (section 2.3).

The Reformers themselves held that the cosmos was finite and bounded by an outermost sphere (the *primum mobile*) in the tradition of medieval Aristotelian cosmology. Melanchthon rejected the very possibility of an infinite universe. Calvin at one point ridiculed the idea of an extra-cosmic void. So comprehensibility entailed finitude for the most influential teachers of the Reformation.

In the post-Reformation period, however, Thomas Digges, a radical Protestant and the first true Copernican in England, took the radical step (1576) of treating the realm of the stars as extending endlessly far outwards from the planetary realm. Such an infinite extension made sense theologically, Digges argued, in as much as the realm of the stars was the court of God 'to whose infinite power and majesty such an infinite place . . . only is convenient'. The reason why the attribute of infinity did not make the world incomprehensible to Digges was apparently that there was still a fixed point of reference in the sun which was located at the centre.

An even more radical Copernican position was taken by the Italian philosopher, Giordano Bruno, about a decade later (1584). Originally a Dominican priest, Bruno experimented with Reformation theology at Geneva and Tübingen and was influenced by Protestant thinkers like Thomas Digges in Elizabethan England. He developed the idea that the universe reflects the attributes of God to the point that it bordered on pantheism: not only was the structure of the universe a reflection of God's wisdom, but the universe itself was an expression of his immensity. Since the world was not God himself, but only a multiple image of God's simple immensity, Bruno concluded, there must be an infinite number of worlds, as the Epicureans had taught, and there was no fixed centre to things, not even the sun. Evidently, the prospect of an infinite universe suggested new possibilities of human comprehension to Bruno: it was not necessarily the threat to intelligibility that it had seemed to the ancients and even to the Reformers.

Bruno is a peripheral figure for the historian of the Reformation as well as for the historian of science. The importance of his case stems from two factors: the seeming modernity of Bruno's views – he was the first Western European to picture the universe as an immense plurality of worlds the way we do today – and the fact that he was tried and executed for unorthodox beliefs by the Roman Church (Rome, 1600). Consequently, some historians have portrayed him as a martyr for modern ideas at the hands of a reactionary church.

It is true that one of the charges made against Bruno was that he taught an infinity of different worlds, but this teaching was not disallowed by the Roman Church as a matter of (hypothetical) science so much as on the basis of established doctrine. From a scientific point of view the idea of a plurality of worlds was pure speculation at the time, while theologically it seemed to call into question the uniqueness of the Incarnation. Along the same line, Bruno was condemned for holding that Moses and Jesus performed miracles by magic arts and that the Holy Spirit was the world soul as portrayed in Neoplatonic hermeticism. This is hardly the kind of philosophy most modern critics of the Church would want their martyrs to espouse!

From our perspective Bruno and his accusers represent differing emphases within the creationist tradition – Bruno drew his inspiration from the idea of the immensity of God as Origen had done in the third century and Nicholas of Cusa had done in the fifteenth; his accusers were understandably concerned about the implications of hermeticism and about the danger that the idea of creation would be emptied of any meaning if the universe had no recognizable limits or structure. The idea that a world created by God was intelligible to humans created in his image raised important questions about the possible infinity (and eternity) of that world, but it did not settle them as far as the historian can see. Nor can the intolerance of Bruno's accusers be invoked to discriminate between Protestant and Catholic versions of the creationist tradition. Michael Servetus (c 1511–1553), a Catholic influenced by radical Protestant ideas who speculated on the role of the world soul in human physiology, was condemned and executed (1553) for his unorthodox theological views at the recommendation of John Calvin in Protestant Geneva.

We have cited the examples of Digges and Bruno to illustrate the flexibility of the idea of the comprehensibility of the world even within the sphere of Protestant influence. The issue of the possible infinity of a created, comprehensible world was still unresolved in the early seventeenth century as is shown by the response of Kepler to the speculations of Bruno and the new discoveries of Galileo.

Like Bruno, Kepler understood the cosmos as an image of God. But, in the tradition of Martin Luther and keeping with Protestant orthodoxy which was battling against various groups of anti-trinitarians at the time, he drew his inspiration from the idea of the Trinity rather than the divine attributes of immensity and simplicity. Kepler championed the ideas of Copernicus which he imbibed from a line of Lutheran astronomers through his teacher, Michael Maestlin (1550-c 1633). In fact, he was, after Rheticus, the first true Copernican among Lutheran astronomers.

Unlike Bruno, Kepler regarded the sun as the geometric and dynamical centre of the cosmos: it was thus a suitable image of God the Father who was the origin of the Godhead in trinitarian theology. The outer sphere of the stars, which like the sun was stationary in the Copernican system, was the image of God the Son, and the space enclosed by the stellar sphere (the realm of the earth and planets) was the image of the Holy Spirit. Hence the basic geometry of the universe – a sphere with fixed centre, periphery and space between – could be comprehended as a finite, created image of the infinite, uncreated Trinity.

So Kepler developed the idea of the comprehensibility of the world in a way very different from that of Bruno who focused on the immensity and simplicity of God. Even Digges' idea of a sphere of stars extending outward to infinity would not have fit Kepler's notion of the Trinity. The coequality of Father, Son and Spirit required the cofinitude of the centre, periphery and space of the cosmos. The stellar realm could not be (semi) infinite while the sun and planetary space were not.

Kepler's finitist cosmology was challenged by two astronomical discoveries and the speculation they engendered in the early seventeenth century. The appearance of a nova (a previously unknown star) in 1604 led some to suggest that space had immeasurable depths from which stars could be transported towards the earth periodically on immense cosmic wheels. Then, in 1610 came the first reports of Galileo's new discoveries made with a primitive telescope: a large variety of stars that could not be seen with the naked eye were revealed for the first time. Again it was speculated that the universe had infinite depths and perhaps even an infinite number of planetary systems. Galileo himself entertained such infinitist notions in private correspondence influenced no doubt by the speculations of Cusa and Bruno.

Kepler took these suggestions seriously but consistently rejected them. His reasons were partly scientific. An infinite universe with no boundary could not have a unique centre. But the sun appeared to be located at the centre of an enormous cavity in which there were only planets and beyond which there were only stars. So there was insufficient evidence to convince the astronomer that the universe was indeed infinite; appearances suggested just the contrary. Science aside, the obvious discomfort the suggestion of an infinite universe occasioned Kepler and the ingenuity with which he constructed arguments to refute it betray an underlying assumption about the comprehensibility of the world rooted in the creationist tradition.

In spite of the diversity of interpretation of the comprehensibility of the world, there was continuity and consistency on the basic point. Kepler illustrates the underlying idea magnificently. As he wrote in 1599, near the beginning of his career, he believed that the laws of the universe could be discovered by human science:

Those laws are within the grasp of the human mind; God wanted us to recognize them by creating us after his own image so that we could share in his own thoughts . . . Only fools fear that we make humanity godlike in doing so; for God's counsels are impenetrable [cf. Rom. 11:33], but not his material creation.

This creationist faith motivated Kepler to seek a simple way of describing the planetary orbits in mathematical terms. It sustained him through seemingly endless trials and errors and enabled him at length to discover an harmonious system of the planets which included, among other things, the three laws (1604–1619) that bear his name to this day:

(1) the orbit of each planet is an ellipse with one focus located at the sun;

(2) the angular velocity of any planet at any given time is inversely proportional to the square of its distance from the sun (equivalent to the law of equal areas in equal times); and

(3) the period of revolution of each planet is also related to the size of its orbit by a simple power law.

In accordance with his creationist faith, Kepler joyously gave all the credit for his discoveries to God:

I give you thanks, Creator and God, that you have given me this joy in thy creation, and I rejoice in the works of your hands. See I have now completed the work to which I was called. In it I have used all the talents you have lent to my spirit. I have revealed the majesty of your works to those who will read my words, insofar as my narrow understanding can comprehend their infinite richness.

Kepler's 'three laws' became the basis of modern astronomy and were the starting point from which Isaac Newton derived the inverse-square law of universal gravitation later in the seventeenth century. If there was ever a point in Western history at which the progress of science depended on belief in the doctrine of creation, it was in the work of the Lutheran, Johannes Kepler. The reinforcement of basic Christian doctrine brought about by the Protestant Reformation, particularly in the circle of Philip Melanchthon, must be credited with this much at least.

Unity of Heaven and Earth

The second theme in the creationist tradition as we have presented it was the belief that God created all things with the same basic material (itself created out of nothing) and imposed on them the same basic laws of motion and change. From the beginning of the patristic period (second century AD), this belief was directed primarily against the Aristotelian idea that the heavens were fundamentally different from the earth. Specifically, Aristotle taught that the heavens were more directly subject to the providence of God than the earth was, that they moved circularly rather than up or down like the sublunar elements, that they were immutable in substance unlike the four elements of the sublunar realm, and consequently, that they must be made of a fifth element (the ether) different from the four elements found on earth (section 1.3).

These ideas were challenged in various ways by late medieval natural philosophers like Bradwardine, Buridan, and Cusa who developed their own ideas from their belief in the absolute (as well as the ordained) power of God over *all* things (section 2.3). But the teachings of Aristotle still provided the only comprehensive framework for understanding the varied phenomena of nature, and the alternatives posed by these philosophers were generally regarded as mere speculations or hypotheses. The situation was to change dramatically with the birth of a new physics in the seventeenth century. We wish to know what contribution, if any, Reformation theology may have made in this direction.

The fact of the matter is that the leading Reformers accepted Aristotelian cosmology as part of the established science of the time. Luther himself seems not to have paid much attention to it. He ignored fundamental ideas like that of solid celestial spheres made out of a fifth element unique to the heavens. Luther's view of nature was based on the biblical notion of the all-pervading energies of God and was not troubled by the current problems of cosmology. But Melanchthon and Calvin, both of whom were trained in the humanist tradition, particularly valued Aristotle and other classics as the basis for college and university curricula they were responsible for initiating. Their immediate successors, Caspar Peucer (1525–1602) and Theodore Beza (1519–1605), followed in their footsteps, and converts from Roman Catholicism like Peter Martyr Vermigli (1499–1562) and Girolamo Zanchi (1531–90), who were trained in Thomistic thought, reinforced the establishment of Aristotelian ideas. As a result, the cosmology of Aristotle became deeply ingrained in the more educated and influential strata of Protestant culture.

In view of this Protestant conservatism in matters of science education, we would not expect much by way of a stress on the unity of heaven and earth or a direct challenge to the Aristotelian dichotomy. It is certainly true that Melanchthon and Calvin both accepted Aristotelian science as a valid description of the normal course of nature. On the other hand, they both argued, as did their medieval forebears, that this course was neither necessary nor inviolable from God's point of view (*potentia absoluta*). It was a manifestation of God's ordained laws for nature (*potentia ordinata*).

Calvin, moreover, softened the edges of the heaven-earth duality in several ways. For one thing, he did not follow Aristotle in teaching that the heavenly bodies were made of a unique fifth element but adopted instead the Stoic notion that they were made of fire. For another, he stressed the biblical idea that the earth was as immediately controlled by the providence of God as was the outermost heaven (the *primum mobile*).

In fact, Calvin's doctrine of universal and particular providence had the effect of bringing out the parity between heaven and earth in this respect. God's government of terrestrial affairs by the rotation of the celestial spheres and the influences of their luminaries on the earth was viewed by Calvin as an instance of universal providence. On the other hand, his stabilization of the earth against rotational forces and his restraint of the seas and rains lest they inundate the earth were seen (within an Aristotelian framework) as instances of immediate or particular providence.

Thus Calvin directly challenged the idea that God's immediate control was limited to the outermost heavens, and he did this not by resorting to the idea of God's absolute power (*potentia absoluta*) or by appealing to the possibility of miracles, but rather by finding gaps in the fabric of Aristotelian naturalism that seemed to indicate the supernatural activity of God in the ordinary course of nature (*potentia ordinata*). This was as radical a challenge as could be made without rejecting the basic Aristotelian framework in which the earth was at the centre of the cosmos in a realm of falling bodies and changing substances while the planets and stars moved on celestial spheres with circular motion and unchangeable substance. As a reformer and one who wished to distance himself from every suggestion of being a revolutionary, Calvin was unwilling to take such a bold step.

But even these partial challenges by Calvin had no effect as far as we know on the history of astronomy in the latter part of the sixteenth century. Instead, the gradual undermining of belief in a heaven-earth duality was occasioned by purely scientific developments like the discovery of stars (novas) that changed in magnitude, the determination that comets were celestial rather than atmospheric phenomena, and the growing realization that Copernicus had been right in placing the sun at the centre of the planetary system.

Many of the astronomers who contributed to this revolution were Protestants: e.g., Thomas Digges and William Gilbert (1544–1603) in Elizabethan England and Tycho Brahe (1546–1601), Christoph Rothmann (1550–c 1650), and Johannes Kepler in the continental Lutheran tradition. Apparently only in the case of Kepler was theology a significant factor: Kepler's repeated attempts to find a universal law that would account for the motion of both earth and the planets was inspired in part by his analogy between the created cosmos and the uncreated Trinity as we have seen. One result of this model was that the source of cosmic motion was shifted from the periphery of the universe (the *primum mobile*) to the centre (the sun). But the precise meaning and origin of Kepler's trinitarian speculations are not clear: they probably had as much to do with Neoplatonic and hermetic thought as with Protestant theology.

At most, we could argue that one of the reasons for Kepler's attraction to Neoplatonic and hermetic ideas was a dissatisfaction with the apparent distance of God's normal activity implied by Aristotle's system. If so, he had much in common with fellow Lutherans who were interested in the analogy between macrocosm and microcosm found in mystical alchemy: for example, Valentin Weigel (1533–88), Heinrich Khunrath (1560–1605), and Johann Andreae (with whom Kepler exchanged correspondence). A common source of inspiration in the writings of Luther is a possibility worth considering.

However, radical Catholic natural philosophers like Bernardino Telesio (1509–88), Francesco Patrizi (c 1530–97), and Giordano Bruno also challenged the Aristotelian dichotomy of heaven and earth on purely philosophical grounds, inspired by late medieval critics like Cusa and by the hermetic thought of Ficino. So belief in the unity of the cosmos as the object of God's creation and immediate providence can be accounted for simply in terms of the creationist tradition (including Neoplatonic sympathies in opposition to the hegemony of Aristotelian thought) common to a variety of thinkers in the sixteenth century, both Protestant and Catholic. It is difficult to trace any direct influence of the magisterial Reformers here even in the case of Kepler's undoubtedly religious sense of the unity of the cosmos.

If the sixteenth- and seventeenth-century developments that led to the scientific idea of the unity of heaven and earth were relatively free of theological determinants, that does not mean that such developments were without theological meaning. Though medieval Aristotelianism made the providence of God seem remote, at least it affirmed immediate providence for the outermost heavens. If the

Reformers had had their way, such immediate providence would have been affirmed for the earth as well as for the heavens. Rheticus and Kepler, however, both justified the unification brought about by the Copernican system in terms of the late medieval image of God as a clockmaker. As we saw in the case of Nicholas of Cusa (section 2.2), an equalization of heaven and earth in mechanistic terms could have the effect of making God seem equally remote from all things rather than equally near. This, in fact, was the theological tendency that prevailed in the seventeenth and eighteenth centuries.

Relative Autonomy of Nature

The third feature of the creationist tradition was its profound sense of the relative autonomy of nature. The operations and effects of inanimate bodies were viewed as the result of God's creative word or decree which established a specific law of behaviour for each object created. They were, therefore, regular and yet contingent on the governing word or decree of God. Their autonomy was relative, not absolute.

In the Middle Ages, this subtle interplay of biblical motifs was formalized in the scholastic distinction of *potentia Dei ordinata* and *potentia Dei absoluta*. *Potentia ordinata* was the power of God as expressed in the ordinary course of nature and history. *Potentia absoluta* was the freedom which God exercised in establishing that course and which he retained to alter it on occasion (e.g., in miracles or at the eschaton). Under the successive influences of Neoplatonism and Aristotelian natural philosophy, particularly in the left wing of the creationist tradition, the normal course of nature came to be viewed as a virtually autonomous entity referred to as 'Nature'. The regular operations of Nature were clearly distinguished from the occasional interventions of God. In response to this apparent limitation of the sovereignty of God in his creation, more conservative theologians tended to stress the absolute power of God (*potentia absoluta*) and to limit the prerogatives of reason in natural science (sections 1.4, 2.3).

In general, leading Reformation theologians tended to shift the emphasis back to God's *potentia ordinata* while limiting the efficacy of second causes and the scope of human reason within that sphere. The shift of emphasis had to do primarily with two theological doctrines: those of revelation and salvation. Both doctrines were clearly aimed at the teachings of the Roman Catholic Church, particularly as defined by the medieval scholastics. We must review them briefly before passing on to their counterparts in natural philosophy in order to keep a reminder of the historic Reformation emphasis.

The Roman Church viewed new revelations as a recurring phenomenon of history. God continued to reveal himself in miracles, visions, and occasional refinements of doctrine (based on an original, apostolic deposit) through the auspices of the Church. In contrast, Luther and other Reformers viewed the canonical Scriptures as the locus of all divine revelation (*sola scriptura*). To seek to know God and God's will by any other means – whether by speculative reason, private revelations, or the formulation of apostolic tradition – even under the auspices of the Church – was to spurn God's sufficient self-disclosure in the Bible. The Catholic idea of revelation as a recurring act of God through the Church was replaced by the Protestant one of a fixed body of teaching to which the Church itself was subject. The idea of revelation thus shifted from the sphere of *potentia absoluta* to that of *potentia ordinata*.

The Catholic idea of salvation, on the other hand, was already located within the sphere of *potentia ordinata*. Salvation was effected by God's grace channelled through and conditioned by various second causes: some under the control of the individual like natural reason and good works; and some belonging to the priestly function of the Church like baptism, absolution and the Eucharist. The Reformers had to recognize the validity of such exercises since they were prescribed in Scripture; in fact, they went to great lengths to affirm the value of good works and the sacraments against the teachings of radical Protestants like the Antinomians, Libertines and Anabaptists. But the Reformers denied any casual efficacy to human efforts, whether individual or ecclesiastical. Salvation was a gift of God by grace alone (*sola gratia*) and it was available through faith in Christ alone (*sola fide, sola Christo*).

The result as in the issue of revelation was an affirmation of God's revealed will and a rejection of unauthorized ways of seeking salvation such as the invocation of saints or angels. But, whereas the Roman Church based its claims on the notion that the administration of salvific means had been committed to the priesthood, the Reformers defended the idea that God could act in ordained ways that were not reducible to the operation of second causes.

While the principal concerns of the Reformers had to do with theological doctrines like revelation and salvation, they also had implications for scientific issues of the time. In general, the results were rather paradoxical. The operations of nature and the investigations of science were affirmed as part of the ordinances of creation and reaffirmed as part of God's will for a renewed humanity. On the other hand, they were challenged whenever they appeared to conflict with the express teachings of Scripture, particularly those concerning God's care for and salvation of humans.

In other words, the medieval dialectic of *potentia ordinata* and *potentia absoluta* was largely replaced by a Reformation dialectic of creation and salvation ordinances within the sphere of *potentia ordinata*. Still, it amounted to a differentiation of nature and supernature, or, to be more exact, a clear distinction between God's indirect operation through second causes and his direct operation with or without the cooperation of second causes. The result was a series of conflicts in which the interests of science and theology struggled to establish their respective authorities and leading to a temporary resolution in the work of Francis Bacon that was to guide the progress of science in seventeenth-century England. We shall review these conflicts briefly to assess the effects of Reformation theology.

There were three fairly distinct streams of scientific research in the sixteenth century: scholastic Aristotelian science, a burgeoning Copernican astronomy, and hermetic-cabalistic investigations in mathematics and alchemy (section 3.1). Of the three, Aristotelian science was best known and was received most favourably by the Reformers. We shall consider their treatment of Aristotelian naturalism here, and postpone discussion of their reactions to Copernicanism and hermetic-cabalistic thought until our consideration of the fourth theme of the creationist tradition.

Aristotle's stress on the order of the universe suited the Reformers' interest in God's *potentia ordinata* as it had suited similar interests in the twelfth and thirteenth centuries (section 2.1). On the other hand, Luther, Zwingli and Calvin (not Malanchthon so much) agreed with conservatives of the Middle Ages in rejecting the completeness of natural causation. But they did not appeal to God's *potentia absoluta* as medieval scholastics had done and as Pope Urban VIII was to do in his instructions to Galileo (1624, 1631). Instead, they cited apparent gaps in the web of second causes, gaps which were evidence of the direct action of God even within the sphere of *potentia ordinata*.

There are numerous examples of this attempt to find gaps within the domain of second causes. Luther, for example, concluded (1535) from the etymology of the Hebrew word for sky (*shamayim*) that the heavens were composed of a watery substance (*mayim*). This inference from Scripture was confirmed observationally by the blue colour of the sky and the humidity of the atmosphere. Since the remarkable stability of the heavens and the constancy of their motions could not be accounted for on the basis of the natural properties of water, they could then be taken as a sign of the power of God's sustaining word.

Another example given by Luther and later developed by Calvin (1554) was the gathering of the terrestrial waters into seas (Gen. 1:9). According to Aristotelian principles, the Reformers argued, earth should gravitate as much as possible to the centre of the cosmos and be completely covered by water. The fact that the waters were confined to seas and there was dry ground suitable for habitation was, therefore, a perpetual miracle: it was part of the established order of things, but it could not be accounted for on purely naturalistic principles.

In reaction to the naturalism of Aristotelian philosophers of their time, Luther, Zwingli and Calvin came to view efforts to achieve complete causal explanations as a threat to the sense of God's providence appropriate to Christian piety. Only Zwingli came close to rejecting the operation of second causes as such, but all three disallowed the power of second causes to effect all that happens in nature and history.

In fact, it was in order to secure the immediate, regular operation of God in nature and history that Calvin articulated his doctrine of particular providence, which we discussed earlier. Particular providence was God's continuous, direct intervention within the sphere of *potentia ordinata*, an intervention which assured his continuous control of the strategic forces affecting human life. Instances of particular providence included regular phenomena like the containment of the waters and the stability of the earth against rotational forces. They also included common variations in normal phenomena like the seasons and human heredity. Since 'accidents' like these could not be accounted for entirely by the principles of Aristotelian natural philosophy, or even by those of astrology which were based on Aristotelian naturalism, they too could be taken as indications of God's immediate and continuous providence.

On the other hand, Calvin also taught a doctrine of universal providence, and this provided some justification for the theoretical investigations of natural philosophers, as well as for the more practical skills of physicians and astrologers. As long as scientific endeavour did not contradict the express teachings of Scripture (not just the popular idiom sometimes used by Moses) or infringe on the territory of particular providence, it could serve the glory of God and the benefit of humanity. The art of medicine, for example, was based on knowledge of the natural properties of herbs and the influences of the stars that determined the most propitious times for their use. All such arts and sciences relied on the universal providence of God operating through second causes and were valued as part of the ordinances of creation.

The teaching of the Reformers was, therefore, both restrictive and affirmative with respect to scientific endeavour. Within the Lutheran tradition, these two emphases were embodied in the respective teachings of Luther and Melanchthon. The important school of natural philosophers that looked to Melanchthon as their theological mentor carried on the Aristotelian tradition of seeking the underlying causes of natural phenomena, and this tradition bore much scientific fruit culminating in the work of Johannes Kepler. Even though the geocentric cosmology of Aristotle and Ptolemy was gradually replaced by the heliocentric astronomy of Copernicus, Melanchthon's stress on the relative autonomy of nature based on the ordinances of creation was continued to good effect. Luther's more critical attitude towards Aristotelian naturalism was apparently not a significant obstacle.

Within the Calvinist tradition, on the other hand, both the affirmation and the restriction of science continued side by side and often gave rise to conflicting emphases. This diffraction of the Calvinist synthesis is best seen in Elizabethan England where differing attitudes towards the established Church tended to force the issue. In the mid-sixteenth century, prior to the Elizabethan settlement, Robert Recorde (c 1510–58) exemplified a Protestant approach to science that balanced faith with reason and valued astronomical research as a demonstration of the providence of God in creation. Like the Reformers themselves, Recorde rejected a literalistic interpretation of the Bible in matters of astronomy. Yet he saw no need to reinterpret Scripture to accommodate new ideas like those of Copernicus. Such an unproblematic approach to astronomy could still be followed by Thomas Hood as late as 1588.

The general situation became more polarized, however, after the accession of Mary Tudor (1553) who tried to re-establish Roman Catholicism as the official religion of England. Hundreds of Protestants emigrated to southern Germany and Switzerland. Some developed stronger sympathies with the Calvinist theology and church policy of Geneva, while others followed the more moderate line of Heinrich Bullinger at Zurich. When Elizabeth succeeded Mary in 1558, she established the episcopal form of church government as a 'middle way' and gave ecclesiastical positions to moderate clergy who were willing to support her policies. These moderates tended to emphasize the side of Reformed thought that showed regard for universal providence and the working of God through second causes. A few examples will suffice.

Thomas Cooper (*c* 1517–94) published a volume of sermons in 1580 while serving as Bishop of Lincoln. He followed Calvin in affirming that all seeming chance or fortune is really the result of divine providence. But providence for Cooper was just the operation of God through second causes. Conversely, what we call nature 'is nothing but the very finger of God working in his creatures'. The idea of God working outside the regular channels established at creation must have been as repugnant to Cooper as the practice of Puritan radicals who conducted 'prophesyings' outside the auspices of the established Church.

A better known example is Richard Hooker (*c* 1554–1600), the protégé of John Jewel and John Whitgift, two of the pillars of the Elizabethan church. After his appointment as Master of the London Temple (1585), Hooker debated the merits of the Anglican church order with the eloquent Puritan, Walter Travers, and out of this altercation came his major defence, *Of the Laws of Ecclesiastical Polity* (1593–7). Like Bishop Cooper, Hooker stressed that all God's operations are limited by the laws established at creation and so are not violent or casual, but regular. In fact, there was a direct analogy in his mind between the laws of nature and a 'kingdom rightly ordered'.

Similar views were held by establishment-supported laymen like Walter Bailey, physician to the Queen. In a treatise he wrote on the medicinal properties of the bathing waters of the realm (1587), Bailey stressed that God had ceased from new acts of creation after the sixth day of creation (Gen. 2:3), having given to his creatures 'a nature and power by which they stand and fall'. At present, then, God works mostly by natural means: to say that he acts supernaturally would be to subvert both nature and philosophy.

These Elizabethan moderates were following Calvin in stressing the *potentia Dei ordinata*. They wished to restrict the possibility of new revelations and miracles that might subvert the new order they were trying to establish; in this, too, they were taking a leaf out of Calvin's book. But they tended to reduce Calvin's teaching about *potentia ordinata* to the doctrine of universal providence through second causes, and they gave less attention to his teaching about particular providence which would have made nature more directly dependent on the continuous activity of God and left less scope for the autonomy of nature.

It was the more radical Protestants, particularly the Puritans, who stressed the doctrine of particular providence. The best known example is William Perkins (1558–1602), the leading Puritan theologian of the late sixteenth century. While he adopted a scholastic method of presentation to meet the standards of contemporary scholarship, Perkins differed from Aristotle in stressing the contingency of all natural processes. Even though various qualities and virtues had been implanted in things at creation, he argued, they could not function or even sustain themselves against decay without the quickening providence of God. Normally, it was true, God did act through natural means, but he also worked without means above or even against nature; in miracles, for example.

Perkins was not an extremist by any means. He was loyal to the Church of England and as early as 1588 he denounced the presbyterian and congregationalist schismatics for undermining the authority of the state. It was probably from the schismatic radicals that the most vocal challenge to the idea of natural causation came. Most of our evidence for Puritan strictures on the scientific quest for second causes comes from the early seventeenth century. However, we may surmise that such pious concerns were voiced already in the late sixteenth century because Francis Bacon had to defend his programme for scientific research against such 'a religion that is jealous' as early as 1603.

Bacon saw both the established Aristotelianism of the universities and the hostility to science of the radical Puritans as threats to the progress of science. His instinctive efforts to forge a middle way were thus parallel to Calvin's similar efforts half a century earlier, though Bacon was more extreme than Calvin both in his rejection of Aristotle and in his affirmation of natural causation.

In his criticism of the stranglehold he felt Aristotelian thought had on the universities, Bacon may have been influenced by the strictures of Puritan preachers and lecturers, several of whom had been fellow students at Trinity College, Cambridge. Aristotelian philosophy had brought about a second fall, Bacon contended. Instead of listening to and interpreting nature to discover her laws, Aristotle and his followers had committed the sin of prescribing laws for her. But, rather than seek the causes of phenomena in scholastic manuals of philosophy, scientists should go to the book of nature itself.

Bacon's criticism of the Puritan extreme was no less severe. The doctrine of providence should not be invoked, as was done by the more zealous divines, in such a way as to discourage the scientific quest for natural causes, for 'certain it is that God worketh nothing in nature but by second causes'. Still the contemplation of nature need not detract from our sense of dependence on God. Though the study of physics may at first incline some people to atheism, further progress will bring them back to religion as they find the wisdom and power of God reflected in his creation.

Though not a major contributor to the sciences himself, Francis Bacon provided his age with a vision of the viability of science in a Christian culture. Rather than trying to carve out a place for piety within the framework of Aristotelian natural philosophy, as Calvin and the other Reformers had done, Bacon projected a new view of nature which allowed both the full operation of second causes and the full dependence of all things on God. In this new order there would be no gaps in natural explanation, so God would have to be seen to function immediately in the whole of nature or else not at all. Bacon's hope was that the new science would not displace God's providential activity the way Aristotelian science had done. Unfortunately, this was not to be the case, at least, not in the long run.

Bacon's solution to the sixteenth-century conflict of science and religion was effectively to separate the two antagonists. Nature and grace were two separate kingdoms or departments of the *potentia Dei ordinata*: the kingdom of nature was accessible through the arts and sciences based on human reason and observation; the kingdom of God was accessible through the forgiveness of sins based on the teachings of Scripture. Ultimately the two were united in God: one was based on his works; the other on his word. But the clear separation of the two in this life implied a far greater autonomy of nature and far more individualism in religion than either Scripture or the Reformers had ever intended.

Ministry of Healing and Restoration
The fourth theme in the creationist tradition also related to the power of God, but not the power of God in creation and providence so much as the power God had placed in human hands in order to renew that creation. In the first few centuries after Christ, this power was believed to manifest itself primarily in miraculous healings that demonstrated the outpouring of God's Spirit on the Church. The monastic movement beginning in the fourth century developed the skills of ancient medicine and technology as part of the Christian ministry of renewal though a secularizing process set in as early as the twelfth century. Still important practitioners of medicine like Arnold of Villanova and Paracelsus viewed their work as a ministry of healing in the medieval and Renaissance periods (sections 1.5, 2.3). We wish to know what impact the Reformation had through its revitalization of biblical and patristic teachings, particularly on the idea of the social value of the sciences later popularized by

Johann Andreae and Francis Bacon. We shall trace first the Lutheran tradition down to Andreae, then the Calvinist tradition down to Bacon.

The Lutheran Tradition to Andreae

Luther followed patristic and medieval commentators in viewing the human arts as restoring at least a semblance of Adam's original dominion over nature. In fact, Luther foresaw a new era of scientific and technical progress consequent upon the reformation of religion and the renewal of the image of God in humanity. Physicians and alchemists were viewed as contributors to this restoration due to the wonders they could perform based on their knowledge of the secret powers of nature. Such secular vocations were ordained by God as part of the work of creation, and their practitioners were, therefore, coworkers with God. But, though Luther saw an analogy between human arts and the works of God, he regarded the arts as functions of human nature, not works of the Spirit through human skills. This was a result of his clear distinction between creation and salvation ordinances which we discussed earlier.

Also in keeping with the creationist tradition, Luther and Melanchthon applied the Christian ideal of service to the arts and sciences as well as to other secular activities like politics. Self-exalting ambition like that attributed to various popular charismatic leaders was strongly discouraged. Instead, the arts and sciences were sanctioned in so far as they contributed to social and moral development of the community as a whole.

The danger of this criterion of social benefit was that it could lead to a conservative, or even reactionary, attitude towards new scientific ideas. This is most clearly seen in the case of Luther's and Melanchthon's attitudes towards the new astronomy of Copernicus.

In 1549 the first reports of Copernicus's work filtered back to Wittenberg through the correspondence between Melanchthon and Copernicus's assistant, Rheticus (section 3.1). Luther's only recorded reaction to the new ideas is found in his *Table Talk*. It was rather negative:

So it goes now. Whoever wants to be clever must agree with nothing that others esteem. He must do something of his own. This is what the fellow does who wishes to turn the whole of astronomy upside down. Even in these things that are thrown into disorder I believe the Holy Scriptures, for Joshua commanded the sun to stand still and not the earth [Josh. 10:12].

Clearly the issue for Luther was not a technical question of the merits of heliocentric theory, but one of the seeming ambition of the astronomer and the possibly disruptive effect his teachings might have on a Christian society. The same was true of Melanchthon's initially hostile reaction.

We must remember that Luther and Melanchthon were deeply alarmed by the social upheavals of the 1520s and were sensitive to any criticism of the educational programmes they had instituted particularly at the university level. Melanchthon's insistence on the proper order and subdivision of topics for instruction was particularly vulnerable to ideas as novel as those of Copernicus.

So the criterion of social benefit which was part of the creationist tradition could have a restraining effect on the development of science. But, in the long run, it could also be beneficial. If, as we have argued, the main reason for the failure of Greco-Roman science to sustain long-term growth was its lack of strong social support, then a major advance would require the construction of a new image of the sciences as contributing to recognized goals like the amelioration of the human condition. So the strictures of the Reformers (based on those of the Church fathers in relation to Greek science) could serve the long-term interests of science by forcing it to project a new public image that would help gain the kind of social support it needed.

Melanchthon himself illustrates this tendency to look more favourably on new astronomical ideas once they were seen to serve the interests of the community. As early as 1549 he spoke more positively of Copernicus's work. As he put it a few years later (1552), the inquisitiveness and zeal of astronomers like Copernicus can widen the scope of human knowledge.

> Therefore we must not refrain from investigating the wisdom in the work of God . . . We cannot overlook the fact that the sciences are a gift of God in order to recognize him and thereby to maintain life in a wiser order.

Following the leadership of Melanchthon, a series of Lutheran astronomers studied the work of Copernicus. At first they were only pragmatically interested in the possibility of improved calculations, but gradually they came to accept the underlying hypothesis that the sun was really stationary at the centre of the planetary system. Kepler's early acceptance of heliocentric cosmology (c 1590) led to his pioneering efforts to discover the mathematical laws that describe the motions of the planets around the sun. In accordance with

Christian teaching, Kepler felt himself under obligation to publish his results for the glory of God even though he realized that others might then use them to make advances he might otherwise have reserved for himself.

While Copernican astronomy finally passed the test of social utility, the hermetic and alchemical traditions came increasingly under fire. In fact, the reason that Copernicanism found more favour in Protestant communities than in Catholic circles of the early seventeenth century was that it had been championed by a school of Lutherans who were not associated with the extremes of Renaissance hermeticism and cabalism (section 3.1). In contrast, the case of Giordano Bruno imprinted an association between Copernican ideas and Pythagorean exaltation on the minds of prominent Catholic officials like Cardinal Bellarmine. Bellarmine's experience with Bruno made him suspicious of Galileo's work as early as 1611, even though Galileo had even less sympathy with the occult sciences than Kepler had!

Luther, himself, had rejected the idea of the Renaissance magus popularized by Ficino, Reuchlin and Agrippa. The ideas of individual self-exaltation and Pythagorean secrecy associated with these arts were clearly incompatible with his sense of the solidarity of the Church. None the less, a series of Lutheran scholars and physicians did cultivate occult sciences like alchemy: for example, Andreas Osiander (1498–1552), Valentin Weigel (1533–88), Heinrich Khunrath (1560–1605), Michael Maier (1568–1622), and Johann Andreae (1586–1654). Their inspiration may well have come from Luther's sense of the energies of God diffused through all creation as well as from the direct influence of Reuchlin and Paracelsus (section 3.1).

The principal critic of the occult sciences in the Lutheran tradition was Andreas Libau (or Libavius; c 1560–1616). In the tradition of Melanchthon, Libau stressed the importance of corporate accountability for the sciences in contrast to the individual enthusiasm of alchemists like Paracelsus and his followers. Libau studied at Basel (1588) where, through the earlier teaching of Theodore Zwinger and Thomas Erastus, the name of Paracelsus had become synonymous with disrespect for the ancients and an exaltation of human powers over nature. In the early seventeenth century Libau wrote vehemently against the Paracelsians (particularly, Oswald Croll whom we shall consider later) for being socially irresponsible and for using their supposed knowledge for personal gain.

However unfair these criticisms may have been to Paracelsus, who was an eccentric at worst, they were salutary for the image of the alchemical tradition as a whole. The danger was that they might also encourage an attitude of resignation in the face of the recalcitrant structures and awesome powers of nature. In this respect, the optimism of the hermeticists and alchemists was a helpful counterbalance. The two sides of the creationist tradition, the charismatic and the socially responsible, thus complemented each other as was later pointed out by Andreae. Responding to the criticisms of Libau, Andreae wrote a description of the ideal Christian society (*Christianopolis*, 1619) as one in which alchemical research was done for the benefit of medicine and technology. Thus the strictures of Lutheran orthodoxy helped to purge alchemy of the pride and arrogance associated with the image of the Renaissance magus and paved the way for a more fruitful science of chemistry in the seventeenth century.

The Calvinist Tradition to Bacon

A similar development occurred in the Reformed tradition of southern Germany and Switzerland. Calvin followed Luther quite closely in his estimate of the arts and sciences. Like Luther, he saw in secular disciplines like medicine a God-given skill based on knowledge of the hidden correspondences of nature. Like Luther also, Calvin viewed such skills as based on the gifts of God in nature and clearly differentiated them from the more important work of God in salvation, but he regarded them as part of the work of the Spirit, none the less. In fact, Calvin's distinctive insistence that miracles of healing had ceased after apostolic times led him to view the arts as God's ordained means of ministering to the body in the present age.

So Calvin had a fair sense of the biblical ministry of healing if not a millenarian anticipation of the restoration of all things through science and technology. He advocated the idea of social utility as a check to unbridled enthusiasm. In this respect, Calvin was influenced by the humanist socio-political ideal of the common good (as was his elder colleague Martin Bucer, the leading reformer at Strasbourg). But Calvin's sense of Christian vocation immeasurably deepened the social aspect of his teaching. Since the arts and sciences were gifts of God's Spirit, they were to be used for the common good of humanity. They were good in themselves, but, if used for personal ambition or greed, they became evil. Taking the gifts of God in vain was just as much a violation of the third commandment as taking the name of God in vain (Exod. 20:7).

Calvin combined the dialectic of individual human skill and social responsibility with the differentiation of creation and salvation ordinances we discussed earlier. While the arts and sciences were based on nature as created by God, the love of neighbour, needed to direct their use, was a supernatural gift that had been lost at the Fall and was restored through the grace of regeneration, which alone can 'erase from our minds the yearning to possess, the desire for power, and the favour of men'.

It will come as no surprise, then, that Calvin spoke harshly of the hermetic and cabalistic strains of Renaissance philosophy. Agrippa of Nettesheim was singled out for particular censure, but Calvin undoubtedly had the entire tradition of Ficino, Pico and Reuchlin in mind. Their ideas were criticized on both counts mentioned above: they used the name and mysteries of God for personal ambition (thus transgressing the commandment of love), and they sought access to God and knowledge of his decrees through the hierarchy of angels, a practice that was forbidden in Scripture on penalty of death (Exod. 22:18; Lev. 20:6, 27; Deut. 18:10). Calvin specifically rejected the hermetic notion that Moses and Jesus performed miracles by magic arts, one of the teachings for which Bruno was condemned and executed in 1600.

The continental Calvinist tradition did not produce a school of occult natural philosophy comparable to that of the Lutheran tradition. But there were isolated figures like Oswald Croll (c 1560–1609) whose medical training was at Heidelberg, Strasbourg and Geneva. One recent historian, Owen Hannaway, has claimed that Calvin's ideas stimulated Croll's adaptation of Paracelsian teachings to the mainstream of Reformation theology. Actually, Croll was far closer to Ficino and Paracelsus than to Calvin in his spiritualistic interpretation of the physician's craft. Whereas Calvin made regeneration the prerequisite for the attitude of humility and self-sacrifice needed by arts like medicine, Croll made it prerequisite to the skill of healing itself. Croll thus combined the spheres of nature and grace in the work of the physician in a way that Calvin would have rejected as a 'mingling of heaven and earth'.

On the other hand, Croll could claim to pass the basic double-criterion posed by Calvin. He challenged the aspiring physician to seek new medicines for the benefit of humanity, and he made it clear that the practice of alchemy was a form of Christian discipleship in his view, not a means to salvation. It may be that the strictures of Calvin did exert some influence on Croll in spite of significant differences between the two. If so, the long-term effects of these strictures can only be judged to have been beneficial for science: Croll's reformulation of the ideas of Paracelsus have been credited with gaining academic recognition for the medical value of many chemicals that otherwise would not have been used.

Finally, we must trace the lines of the debate in Elizabethan and early Stuart England culminating in the reform programme of Francis Bacon. Both the idea of the creative powers of humanity and the criterion of social benefit were already present on the English scene, at least in humanist circles, as parts of the general Renaissance worldview. Differing emphases developed, however, between Neoplatonists and the stricter Protestant clergy in the later sixteenth century. Bacon had to straddle the two positions, just as he had to straddle the Aristotelian and Puritan positions with respect to the relative autonomy of nature, in order to commend the scientific enterprise to English society as a whole.

The major representatives of the Neoplatonist tradition in English science were John Dee, William Gilbert (1544–1603), Sir Walter Raleigh (1552–1618), Thomas Harriot (1560–1621), and Robert Fludd (1574–1637). All were influenced by the hermetic-cabalist ideas of Ficino, Pico, and Agrippa. Accordingly, they espoused the Renaissance magus image of the potential of humanity, according to which initiates could perform miracles by exploiting the hidden energies of nature.

The ideal of social service was commonplace in Renaissance England, but it was the Protestant clergy (both Anglican and Puritan) who popularized the ideal among the middle classes (the merchants and the gentry) and who took the Neoplatonists to task on this score. A few examples will suffice.

There was already a strong emphasis on social reform in the preaching of early English Reformers like Thomas Starkey (d. 1538), Hugh Latimer (d. 1555), Nicholas Ridley (d. 1555), and John Hooper (d. 1555) who were influential during the reigns of Henry VIII (d. 1547) and Edward VI (d. 1553). At this stage the principal continental influences were Luther, Melanchthon, Bucer, Zwingli, Oecolampadius, and Bullinger, all of whom had stressed the obligation to fulfil the Christian commandment of love.

Latimer and his pupil, Thomas Becon (d. 1567), were particularly vociferous in calling attention to the needs of the poor: they championed the practice of true religion as care for orphans and widows (Jas. 1:27) in contrast to the hypocrisy they associated with Catholic monasticism. Hooper interpreted the third commandment as forbidding the use of God's name for personal glory or profit, especially in the occult arts and sciences. He specifically criticized the printing of the hermetic writings of Trithemius and Agrippa due to their advocacy of conjuring spirits and their Pythagorean secrecy. In so far as the arts and sciences could be dissociated from magic and astrology, however, Hooper valued them as gifts from God for the maintenance of life and the restoration of health (Jas. 1:17). His views thus followed those of Calvin almost exactly.

The impact of early Reformation social teaching on science can be seen in the case of the leading English naturalist of the mid-sixteenth century, William Turner (d. 1568). Turner combined the two callings of medicine and the priesthood throughout most of his career. A close friend of Latimer and Ridley during his student days at Cambridge, he was ordained by Ridley in 1552 and was an ardent advocate of religious reform all his life. He was one of those who went into exile for his beliefs during the reign of the Catholic, Queen Mary. Turner wrote a number of controversial theological works and published an English translation of the Heidelberg Catechism in 1572.

During his travels on the Continent, Turner became interested in the work of Paracelsus on the healing properties of mineral waters. In fact, the earliest reference to Paracelsus we have in the English language is in a tract on mineral waters which he wrote in Basel in 1557. In his travels in Switzerland and Germany, Turner probably also heard criticisms of Paracelsus for his supposed arrogance and greed. Later, back in England, he stressed the moral obligation of scientists to work for the benefit of humanity in his treatise on the medicinal properties of wines (1568).

Another example of Protestant social conscience in the practice of medicine is the work of William Bullein (d. 1576) and his brother Richard (d. 1563). Having taken Holy Orders about the same time as Turner (1550), William resigned them in order to practice medicine at Durham soon after the accession of Queen Mary (1553).

Bullein castigated the irreligion and unscrupulous practice of some contemporary physicians in his portrayal of Dr. Tocrub the Nullafidian ('unbeliever') in his *Dialogue Against the Fever Pestilence* (1565). By way of contrast, he described his brother Richard as the ideal Christian physician, 'a zealous lover in Physicke, more for the consolacion and help of th'afflicted sicke people beyng poore, than for the lucre and gaine of the money of the welthie and riche'. A Latin inscription over the two brothers' tomb in London states that William devoted his own medical services to rich and poor without distinction as well.

The preaching and practice of Christian charity thus continued unabated in the Elizabethan period even though the focus of theological controversy shifted to matters of church polity. One further example of interest is that of the Puritan Robert Johnson (1540–1625) who served for a while (c 1570) as chaplain to Sir Nicholas Bacon, the father of Francis Bacon. Johnson continued the Reformed tradition of clerical social service by founding schools and re-endowing hospices during his tenure as rector in Rutland (1584).

Late sixteenth-century Puritans were critical of the same two features of the occult arts and sciences that John Hooper had singled out: the lack of Christian humility associated with the invocation of angels and the Pythagorean tradition of secrecy. It is at this point that Calvin's influence is probably the most noticeable: in 1561 there appeared an English edition of his *Warning Against Judicial Astrology*, in which he criticized hermeticism, cabalism and alchemy, as well as astrology. The typically Calvinist contention that the power to alter the substance of nature belongs only to God, not to alchemists, is found, for instance, in the works of William Perkins around the turn of the century.

Such were the diverging currents of the creationist tradition in the late sixteenth century when Francis Bacon formulated his programme for the advancement of the sciences. Recent historians have pointed out that Bacon derived much of his inspiration from the hermeticism of Ficino, Telesio, and Bruno and from the alchemical tradition of Paracelsus. In the mechanical arts and natural sciences he saw the promise of a restoration of Adam's original dominion over nature – a vision common to the hermeticists, but shared only by Luther among the Reformers. He also adopted the Paracelsian view of the plasticity of nature: the substance of things could be altered by humans to bring out the virtue of properties hidden since creation. Thus, in addition to the restoration of lost innocence through Jesus' words of forgiveness, Bacon saw a restoration of human dominion foreshadowed in Jesus' deeds, particularly his healing diseases and subduing the forces of nature.

But Bacon was a political realist, not an enthusiast. He realized that the arts and sciences could not command the social support they needed as long as they were associated with personal ambition and the quest for individual power. Accordingly, he revised the hermetic vision in a number of ways to answer the criticisms raised by the clergy.

First of all, Bacon stressed the fact that the arts and sciences were dependent on the grace of God even though their aim was only temporal. A 'great instauration' or restoration of human dominion had been promised by God to Adam and again to Daniel (Gen. 1:28; Dan. 12:4). Prayer was thus an important part of any effort towards the advancement of science. The student of science was encouraged to pray specifically for a revival of learning following Bacon's own example.

To God the Father, God the Word, God the Spirit, we pour forth most humble and hearty supplications; that he, remembering the calamities of mankind and the pilgrimage of this our life, in which we wear out days few and evil, would please to open to us new refreshments out of the fountain of his goodness, for the alleviating of our miseries.

Thus it was to God's grace, not to human ingenuity alone, that the sciences were to look for help.

Secondly, Bacon made a clear distinction between the wonders to be accomplished through science and the original creative acts of God by referring back to the hexaemeral tradition of the Church fathers. God took six days to create things by supernatural means, and then he rested from his creative work. With the exception of the partial curse placed on nature following the fall of the first human pair (Gen. 3:14–19), the laws of nature had remained unchanged from that day to the present, and they would continue unchanged until the eschaton when there would be a new creation. In the meantime God was not idle. God preserved creation by a universal providence and did many works of healing and restoration. Thus God was the 'Creator, Preserver and Restorer of the universe'. But, whereas the works of creation and preservation (and salvation of the soul) belonged to God alone, the opportunity to serve as the agents of healing and restoration was open to all. As Bacon put in a prayer to be used by writers:

We humbly beg that this mind may be steadfastly in us, and that thou, by our hands and also by the hands of others on whom thou shalt bestow the same spirit, wilt please to convey a largesse of new alms to thy family of mankind.

In both of these points, the attribution of all constructive human activity to the grace of God and the restriction of the arts and sciences to the bounds of nature established by God, Bacon was following the line of Calvin. We do not know just how much of Calvin's writings he had read, but there can be little doubt of Calvin's influence, whether direct or indirect. Such influence is clearly suggested by the way Bacon dealt with the double-criterion Calvin had established for assessing the arts and sciences: the criterion of social benefit and the strict separation of creation and salvation ordinances.

First, Bacon stated that all human knowledge should be used, not for personal gain, but for the benefit of humanity. A passage from the essay *Of the Interpretation of Nature* (1603) illustrates the way in which the Reformation's teaching on the 'law of love' helped to shape this social awareness:

> But yet evermore it must be remembered that the least part of knowledge passed to man by this so large charter from God must be subject to that use for which God has granted it, which is the benefit and relief of the state and society of man; for otherwise all manner of knowledge becometh malign and serpentine . . . ; as the Scripture saith excellently, *knowledge bloweth up, but love buildeth up* [1 Cor. 8:1].

As Bacon put it in his essay *Of the Advancement of Learning* (1605), science should not be a shop for profit or sale, but a storehouse for both the glory of the Creator and the relief of the human estate. In the ideal scientific community (the 'House of Solomon' in the New Atlantis), workers daily sang hymns of praise to God and prayed to him 'for the illumination of our labours and the turning them into good and holy uses'. Those, like the monks (and even some presbyterian Puritans, according to Bacon), who concentrated on the praise of God to the exclusion of caring for their neighbours were guilty of neglecting the second table of the Law and hypocritically violating the teachings of the New Testament (Jas. 1:27; 1 John 4:20). Their self-discipline and communal rule could be emulated, but they would be put to better use by the new order of God's servants, the research scientists.

Following the example of earlier Protestant critiques, Bacon criticized Renaissance hermeticism and Paracelsian alchemy as being motivated by personal ambition and for restricting the benefits of knowledge to an elite. Instead, he envisioned an international network of research facilities exchanging information with one another in a common effort to benefit all nations. However, Bacon did not rule out ambition; he tried to harness and prioritize it. Ambition to increase one's own power over others (like that associated with hermeticism and alchemy) was the most vulgar and violent form; ambition for one's country was more noble than personal ambition, yet still basically covetous and disruptive; only ambition to increase the shared power of all humanity over the universe was sufficiently altruistic and peaceful to be an appropriate sign of the Kingdom of God (1 Kgs. 19:12; Luke 17:20).

The second indication of Calvin's influence is Bacon's differentiation of creation- and salvation- ordinances in his critique of the excesses of Renaissance hermeticism. Bacon rejected the notion (found in hermetic texts like the *Asclepius*) that the perfection of alchemy and ceremonial magic would lead to spiritual rebirth. He also eliminated the idea of a system of correspondences between the heavens and the human body based on the presence of the world soul in order to differentiate more clearly between the Spirit of God and the forces of nature. With ethical and theological safeguards like these, Bacon hoped, the sciences would embark on an era of unprecedented growth and all humans would benefit as a result.

Conclusion

We have now reviewed Reformation theology and its impact under the four headings of the creationist tradition inherited from the early Church. What, on balance, can we say the effect of the Reformation was on the development of the sciences through the early seventeenth century?

Positively, we may say the following: the teachings of the Reformers gave the secular arts and sciences unprecedented legitimacy as evidences of the image of God in humanity, as witnesses to universal providence, and as aspects of the Christian ministry of healing and restoration. They also popularized the fundamental criterion of public benefit without which a socially acceptable programme for the advancement of the sciences such as Bacon's would not have been possible.

On the more negative side, the Reformers were conservative in ways that occasioned later conflicts. Most of them adhered to Aristotelian cosmology as the best science available for pedagogical and apologetic purposes. As a result, they were not open to new ideas like the heliocentric system of Copernicus and the possibility of an infinite universe. Some tried to eliminate the Aristotelian dualism of heaven and earth and place all things under the direct sovereignty of God, but they failed to alter the late medieval tendency to view the cosmos as a unity in increasingly mechanical terms.

Moreover, the Reformers introduced a new dichotomy into the sphere of God's ordinances (*potentia Dei ordinata*): the clear differentiation between creation and salvation ordinances. Calvin tried to bridge the two with his doctrine of particular providence, but in order to give concrete examples he had to find gaps in the order of natural causation so as to make room for the direct action of God in everyday life. As belief in the existence of such gaps declined in the seventeenth and eighteenth centuries, the locus of God's immediate influence was gradually to become restricted to inward experience.

Finally, in their concern for communal solidarity and social justice, the Reformers made insufficient allowance for individual genius, and they took an unduly negative stance towards the occult arts and sciences that had contributed so much to the creativity of the Renaissance. The long-term effect of their strictures may have aided the shift of interest to more exact sciences like chemistry. But the increasingly mechanistic science of the seventeenth century and the Romantic revival of the late eighteenth must also be seen as partial consequences of their strictures against hermetic and cabalistic thought.

For all that, the Reformation provided scientists of northern Europe with a worldview that encouraged the development of alternatives to both Aristotelian naturalism and Neoplatonic hermeticism. Whereas late medieval philosophers had only Aristotle to work with, and Renaissance philosophers had to choose between Aristotle and Plato, Francis Bacon had three dialogue partners: Aristotelian naturalism, Neoplatonic hermeticism and the Protestant critique of both. The progress of the sciences in the seventeenth century benefited from all three of these components in a way that it could not have done if there had been no Reformation in the sixteenth century.

3. THE SEVENTEENTH CENTURY: SPIRITUALIST, MECHANIST AND PLATONIC TRADITIONS THROUGH LEIBNIZ, BOYLE AND NEWTON

The seventeenth century was ushered in by the generation of Galileo, Kepler and Bacon; it culminated in the work of Boyle, Newton and Leibniz. By the beginning of the eighteenth century the fundamentals of modern physics had been established, and the 'scientific revolution' was well on its way.

Several general characteristics of the seventeenth-century development should be noted. A major feature of the period was the shift of the focus of activity in the sciences to the northwestern part of Europe, particularly France, Germany, the Low Countries (Belgium and the Netherlands), and England. In religion there was a gradual shift of emphasis after the Thirty Years War (1618–48) from confessional differences (between Catholic, Lutheran and Reformed) to a common quest for tolerance and political stability. This was particularly true in England where much of our story takes place. Christians saw themselves either as loyal to the established church of their nation or as Nonconformists rather than along the explicitly confessional lines laid down in the sixteenth century. Their chief concerns were to avoid the extremes of fanatical enthusiasm, on the one hand, and atheistic materialism, on the other. In so far as various scientific ideas were associated with either of these extremes, common theological beliefs were activated that helped articulate and legitimate alternative scientific ideas.

In terms of the major themes of the creationist tradition, the theology of the seventeenth century was continuous with that of the late medieval and Reformation periods. There was very little that was new. It is the ways in which the motifs of the creationist tradition were utilized that will be the focus of our study in this section. Many of the fundamental ideas of modern science evolved out of concepts that had formerly been largely theological or metaphysical.

However, the ways in which various scientists utilized creationist themes differed dramatically. Historically it is no longer possible to treat the creationist tradition as a unified whole: it must be subdivided into derivative, more specialized traditions that define themselves over and against each other as much as in terms of traditional themes. Accordingly, we shall group the major contributors to the period into three broad traditions – the spiritualist, the mechanist, and the Platonic – and treat them separately while pointing out ways in which they influenced and reacted against each other.

Aristotelian natural philosophy continued to command some respect in the seventeenth century, but it gradually fell out of favour. We have discussed the reasons for rival ideas of Copernicus and Paracelsus and their growing popularity in the previous two sections. Consequently, we shall not give separate consideration to Aristotelian ideas here. Many of them were absorbed into the three traditions we shall consider.

The place of Aristotelianism as the dominant paradigm of science was taken over by the mechanical philosophy, associated primarily with the names of Descartes, Gassendi and Boyle. In competition with the mechanical philosophy, as with Aristotelian tradition before it, was the spiritualist approach to nature based on the ancient tradition of hermeticism and the work of Paracelsus and Andreae. In the seventeenth-century the spiritualist tradition was associated primarily with the name of Van Helmont, but it merged with an ongoing quest for encyclopedic or unified science known as 'pansophism'; we shall treat the two together as one continuous tradition. The roots of pansophism went back as far as the encyclopedic art of Raymond Lull in the late thirteenth and early fourteenth centuries. In the early modern period, it was particularly associated with the names of Comenius, Hartlib and Leibniz, all of whom had ties with seventeenth-century spiritualism.

Finally, steering a middle course between the mechanical and spiritualist traditions in British natural philosophy was a Platonist tradition that flourished at the University of Cambridge and culminated in the work of Isaac Newton. In the eighteenth century, Newtonianism was to become the dominant paradigm of physical science, supplanting and partly assimilating the mechanist tradition as the mechanist tradition had supplanted the Aristotelian tradition before it.

The differences between these three traditions can best be seen by considering one of the major concerns of the seventeenth century – whether theology and science should be regarded as separate disciplines or whether they should be integrated to some extent into a comprehensive wisdom. Put in another way, should the immediate action of spiritual agents (human or divine) be categorized as separate from the action of matter, or should the two be integrated in some way? The three traditions we shall examine were divided on this issue, with the mechanists generally opting for a clear separation, the spiritualist-pansophists preferring a degree of integration, and the English Platonist tradition trying to steer a middle course.

The choice made regarding the relation of matter and spirit had clear implications for one's view of matter and hence for science itself. Mechanical philosophers like Descartes and Boyle regarded matter as entirely passive, whereas spiritualists regarded matter as inherently active due to the immanence of individual spirits or energies. The English Platonists and Newtonians saw matter as passive in itself, but activated by spiritual or supra-mechanical principles which governed groups of bodies.

As the protagonists perceived these issues, there were real dangers on either side. A clear separation of matter and spirit could lead to a view of matter as seemingly autonomous and make the spiritual redundant as far as science was concerned. On the other hand, any inclusion of spirit in natural philosophy could lead to a naturalistic explanation of the spiritual and encourage pantheism or even outright atheism. Or, in an attempt to avoid the implication of atheism, either side could produce an appeal to a 'God of the gaps', that is, a concentration of God's activity in those phenomena for which naturalistic explanations were lacking.

While there was little that was new theologically in the seventeenth century, there was ample concern for the viability of the inherited themes of the creationist tradition. In so far as pious Christian natural philosophers were unable to resolve these issues, many eighteenth-century philosophers abandoned the creationist tradition as an interpretive scheme for their life and work.

Consequently, the examination of the controversies of the seventeenth century is more than an academic exercise. One cannot help but be impressed with the degree to which theology was a vital factor in scientific development throughout this phase of the scientific revolution. One must also ask why the theological tradition that inspired such accomplishments had become so shaky that it rapidly lost its credibility in the following century.

The Spiritualist Tradition from Helmont to Leibniz

Helmont

The most important figure in the development of early seventeenth-century chemistry was the Fleming, Joan Baptista van Helmont (1579–1644). Helmont was a Paracelsian. Though he had earned a medical degree from the University of Louvain in 1599, he rejected the standard Galenic medicine of the time and found new direction in the unorthodox writings of the sixteenth-century alchemist Paracelsus. But he avoided some of the more speculative notions of Paracelsian alchemy like the treatment of human nature as a microcosm with detailed correspondences to the structure of the stellar realm. Helmont's positive contributions to chemistry include the discovery of carbon dioxide, the development of the idea of specific 'gas' corresponding to each chemical substance, and an early formulation of the law of the conservation of matter.

Many of Helmont's major contributions were motivated by theological ideas embedded in the creationist tradition. One of these ideas was the ancient notion of seminal principles or 'ferments' implanted by God in the primordial waters of creation. Augustine had used this idea, and Paracelsus had developed it into the notion of an *archeus* or formative spirit in each organic entity (animal, vegetable, or, in alchemical thought, even mineral). The *archeus* was present in the seed of each organism, ruled its growth, and survived its death in a gaseous discharge.

Helmont developed the idea of seminal principles in empirical terms by postulating a 'spirit' or 'gas' as the smoke given off when a chemical is burned. Each chemical substance had its own distinctive 'gas' that could be produced and identified; e.g., *gas carbonum* (what we call carbon monoxide) and *gas sylvester* (carbon dioxide and nitrous oxide). The original substance could be reconstituted experimentally, according to Helmont, if its gas were recombined with water. Water vapour was not a 'gas', however, since water was the raw material utilized by the Spirit in forming the creation (Gen. 1:2). The value of this philosophy was its recognition of an irreducibly unique character in each chemical substance and each organism. Its weakness was its inability to show that all material beings, even living ones, have some fundamental constituents (later called chemical elements) in common.

The remarkable continuity of the creationist tradition to this point is illustrated by Helmont's famous willow-tree experiment, designed to show the primacy of water as the substratum of all living things. Helmont's experimental procedure was basically the same as that discussed by Nicholas of Cusa in the fifteenth century and described in the Pseudo-Clementine *Recognitions* as far back as the fourth century (section 1.4).

In addition to such minor motifs, the major themes of the creationist tradition also appear clearly in the work of Helmont. Underlying the idea of seminal principles, for instance, is the theme that God determined the properties and laws of all things through the same decree by which he created them, constituting what we have termed the 'relative autonomy' of nature (section 1.4). What we call 'nature' is just the effect of that decree. As Helmont confessed in his *Oriatrike or Physicke Refined*:

I believe that Nature is the command of God, whereby a thing is that which it is, and doth that which it is commanded to do or act. This is a Christian definition [as opposed to an Aristotelian one] taken out of the Holy Scripture.

On the basis of God's creative decree all beings have the power to operate in accordance with their own properties and laws.

For that most glorious Mover [God's Spirit] hath given powers to things, whereby they of themselves and by an absolute force may move themselves or other things.

A characteristic feature of the spiritualist tradition from Helmont to Leibniz was a correspondence between the decree of God and the relatively autonomous work of creatures.

On the more practical side of the creationist tradition, Helmont was strongly motivated by the ideal of the Christian physician who received his calling and wisdom directly from God (Ecclus. 38) and dispensed medicines without charge to the poor (Matt. 10:8) – what we have termed the 'ministry of healing and restoration' (section 1.5). The image of God, he argued, was found not in human reason (as the scholastics held), but in charity and humility. This theme of science as a form of charity will appear again in Comenius and Hartlib.

As an advocate of the Christian ideal of charity, Helmont clearly distinguished between Aristotelian 'reason' and empathetic understanding. Reason, according to Helmont, attempts to dominate the thing known and discerns only multiplicity. It originated with the fall of Adam and tends towards death as Helmont's experience of scholasticism amply demonstrated. Understanding, on the other hand, attends to the unique nature of a thing and discerns its vital principle and unity. Understanding is a gift from God tending towards life and depends continually on divine grace. Characteristically, Helmont saw the physician, not the priest, as the one called by God to exercise this healing ministry. Through a reform of the medical profession, the effects of the fall could be reversed, and the original perfection of things could be restored. This Utopian theme is also characteristic of the spiritualist tradition in the seventeenth century.

The wide influence of Helmont is due largely to the efforts of his son. Francis Mercury van Helmont (1614–99) was responsible for the publication of his father's works after the latter's death in 1644, and he disseminated his father's ideas through his contacts and travels in England and Germany. As a close friend of two of the major figures of the pansophist tradition, Hartlib and Leibniz, he encouraged various programmes aimed at the construction of a unified science and the reunion of the Protestant churches.

The eventual decline of Helmontian and Paracelsian ideas in England towards the end of the century was bound up with the political associations of spiritualist ideas that began during the Civil War (1642–49) and the Interregnum (between Charles I and Charles II, 1649–60). The ideas of the German spiritualist, Jacob Boehme (1575–1624), were championed by various Seekers, Familists and Quakers. John Webster, an Independent who attacked the universities of Oxford and Cambridge for neglecting the ideas of Paracelsus, Helmont and Boehme (1654), was suspected of Familist and Leveller sympathies. Francis Mercury van Helmont, himself, was briefly associated with the dreaded Quakers during his visit to England in 1670–78.

These Nonconformists valued the spiritualist tradition for its universalist and democratic implications for church and state. In the mind of the moderate Puritan and Anglican public, on the other hand, the sectarian groups were associated with anarchy and materialistic pantheism. Richard Baxter, for instance, attributed the willingness of some sectaries to shed blood to the disruptive influence of Paracelsian ideas. One should not associate spiritualism exclusively with the English sects, however. Prominent Helmontians like Nicholas Le Fèvre and Thomas Shirley served as personal physicians to Charles II after the Restoration of 1660. Elias Ashmole, another alchemist sympathetic to the ideas of Helmont, was a founding member of the Royal Society of London (1660).

Comenius and the Hartlib Circle

However, a more socially acceptable form of spiritualism, commonly referred to as 'pansophism', was introduced into England by Comenius and Hartlib. Johann Amos Comenius (1592–1670) was a member of the Bohemian Brethren and served in his later years as the last bishop the Brethren had as an independent church. He studied at the Reformed University at Herborn, where he was influenced by the encyclopedic science of Johann Heinrich Alsted, and at Heidelberg where he was impressed by the efforts of David Paraeus towards reunion between the Lutheran and Reformed churches. Through his reading, he also imbibed the Utopian visions of Johann Andreae and Francis Bacon, discussed in the previous section.

One of Comenius's most famous works, *The Labyrinth of the World* (written in 1623, published in Czech in 1631), looked forward to a 'reformation of the whole world' based on the restoration of human science to its pristine, prelapsarian state. Though Comenius concluded this work on a pessimistic note, reflecting the reverses suffered by his people during the Thirty Years War, his proposals for a universal Christian science or 'pansophy' were well received and published by Samuel Hartlib in London in 1637–42. With the approval of the Long Parliament, Comenius was invited to visit to England to help Hartlib found a research institute, modelled on Bacon's projected 'House of Solomon'. During his stay in London (1641–42), Comenius wrote his classic, *The Way of Light* (not published until 1668), a pansophist manifesto in which he anticipated an era of unprecedented progress in the sciences and in their beneficial impact on society.

Throughout Comenius's work there is an emphasis on programmes for public education and international cooperation that would involve the populations of all nations in the labours and fruits of the scientific enterprise. One recent biographer has aptly summarized Comenius's programme as 'a prescription for salvation through knowledge raised to the level of universal wisdom, or pansophy, supported by a corresponding programme of education'.

Samuel Hartlib (c 1600–1662) was an expatriate from Polish Prussia who settled in London (1628) after his homeland was occupied by imperial armies during the Thirty Years War. Like Comenius, he was inspired by the Utopian visions of Andreae and Bacon; he had two of Andreae's works translated into English and published. As we have seen, he was responsible for the publication of Comenius's pansophic manifesto in 1637 and for the latter's visit to London in 1641. He also published the Utopian work of his colleague Gabriel Plattes, *A Description of the Famous Kingdome of Macaria* (1641). The latter was addressed as an appeal to the Long Parliament for the promotion of scientific research, universal education, and socialized medicine which would 'lay the corner stone of the world's happiness'.

Though Hartlib received no financial support from Parliament, he used what private funding he had to subsidize the work of promising alchemical adepts like Thomas Vaughan, George Starkey, Frederick Clodius, and Robert Boyle. Starkey is noteworthy for his defence of the medical techniques of Paracelsus and Helmont against the criticisms of the Galenic College of Physicians and for his refusal to desert the poor of London during the plague of 1665.

Like Comenius, Hartlib stressed the need for communication and cooperation in scientific research. Through his 'Office of Address' for the exchange of letters, he promoted the communication of useful discoveries among scientists of Europe and America for the benefit of the general public. An important result was the requirement that alchemical ideas be discussed in a common language that was comprehensible to all. In the context of the late seventeenth-century reaction to spiritualist groups in general, this discipline imposed on alchemical work was necessary for the viability of the emerging science of chemistry.

The criterion of communicability and social utility was deeply embedded in the creationist tradition and had been applied to alchemical studies in both Lutheran and Reformed traditions in the late sixteenth century. One of Hartlib's closest associates, John Drury, updated the traditional theme in an apology for the 'Office of Address' in terms of the Christian duty to share all knowledge, both religious and scientific. Robert Boyle (c 1647) also called for the open communication of medical knowledge which God intended 'for the good of all Mankind'. Like Drury he appealed to the Christian duty of charity citing 'our Saviour's prescription . . . *Freely ye have received, freely give*' (Matt. 10:8 AV). To a degree this humanitarian ideal lived on in the writings of Henry Oldenberg (c. 1618–77), who served as corresponding secretary for the Royal Society of London after 1662.

Hartlib's Utopian and pansophist associations did not prevent him from valuing the developing mechanical philosophy. In fact he was responsible for introducing Robert Boyle to Gassendi's atomism in the 1640s. As we shall see later, Boyle's natural philosophy developed along more mechanist lines in the 1650s, and he did not remain in the spiritualist or pansophist tradition.

Leibniz

Gottfried Wilhelm Leibniz (1646–1716) is one of the most profound and difficult philosophers of Western history. Like other major thinkers, he does not fit neatly into any tradition; he defines a tradition or philosophy of his own. Leibniz was influenced by the work of Boyle, whom he met in London in 1673, as well as that of other mechanical philosophers like Descartes, Gassendi, and Huyghens. As pointed out earlier, the three traditions we are considering are not separate entities, but overlapping, interacting aspects of one continuous stream of development. After a brief interest in the mechanical philosophy in the early 1670s, however, Leibniz rejected its dualism of matter and spirit and developed his own distinctive views. Several features of his thought make sense only when viewed in the context of the spiritualism of Helmont and the pansophism of Comenius. We shall consider these here.

Whereas many Nonconformists and political radicals valued the spiritualist tradition for its levelling implications for society, Leibniz valued it for the sense of order and harmony it brought to a world of turmoil and fragmentation. In particular, he stressed the value of reason against the claims of enthusiasts to new revelations and repudiated the followers of Jacob Boehme as fanatics. Some historians have concluded that Leibniz betrayed his spiritualist roots in trying to make the truths of faith palatable to human reason. As we shall see, this is only partly true.

Leibniz was a close friend of Helmont's son, Francis Mercury, whom he met in Mainz in the year 1671: the two had common interests in alchemy, cabalistic number theory, the development of a universal science, the integration of faith and knowledge, and the reunion of the Protestants in a universal church. Though precise lines of influence are difficult to trace, there are enough points of contact between the two Helmonts and Leibniz to suggest that Leibniz's peculiar notion of active principles in nature was rooted in the Helmontian idea of vital principles implanted in matter by God.

In his mature philosophy, Leibniz called these active principles 'monads', and he developed a highly original metaphysic based on the orchestration of the monads through a harmony pre-established by God. Of more immediate significance for the history of physical science was the earlier version of Leibniz's active principles, his notion of *vis viva*, which was a vital (or motive) force that inheres in a moving body. In the case of a falling body it is the product of the weight and the height through which the body has fallen. In modern terms it is the kinetic energy of the moving body. Leibniz's *vis viva* is similar to the late medieval notion of 'impetus' and conveys the same sense of a vitality intrinsic to the nature of an object as created and set in motion by God. Leibniz stressed the idea of vitality in contrast to the notion of mere inertia that had developed through the work of Descartes and Newton.

One of the most important issues of natural philosophy in the seventeenth and eighteenth centuries was what happened to the quantity of motion in the event of a collision between two bodies. John Wallis (1668) showed that the sum of the products of the mass and velocity (i.e., the momenta) of the bodies, in any given direction, was conserved. Christiaan Huyghens (1669) showed that the sum of the products of the mass and the square of the velocity was conserved in elastic collisions. But what happened to the latter sum (equivalent to Leibniz's *vis viva*) in inelastic collisions, e.g., when the bodies stuck together? Clearly it was not conserved in any outwardly visible way.

On the basis of his belief in the inherently active character of matter and without experimental evidence, Leibniz postulated that the quantity of *vis viva* was in fact conserved, even in inelastic collisions. Somehow it was absorbed into the dynamics of the constituent particles of the colliding bodies. Later, in the nineteenth century, it was discovered that the lost mechanical energy was converted into heat, by then understood as another form of energy. Thus Leibniz anticipated the law of the conservation of energy, one of the basic conservation principles in classical modern physics.

The inherently dynamic nature of matter in Leibniz's natural philosophy was an important consideration in his dispute with the Newtonians in the early eighteenth century. Both Newton and Leibniz were concerned to see nature as the product of the activity of God, but in differing ways. Whereas Newton and his disciples saw the activity of God in his use of supra-mechanical principles and repeated intervention in the activity of matter, Leibniz found it in the operation of the original divine decree by which matter was invested with an energy that would continue indefinitely and undiminished in quantity. As he wrote in 1715:

. . . the same force and vigour remains always in the world, and only passes from one part of matter to another, agreeably to the laws of nature, and the beautiful pre-established order . . . Whoever thinks otherwise, must needs have a very mean notion of the wisdom and power of God.

Implicit in Leibniz's account was the supposition that even inanimate creatures exhibit a degree of intelligence. All creatures are the subjects of God, not just in the passive sense of receiving commands, but also in the active sense of executing them flawlessly in concert with one another. God, according to Leibniz, is like a king who not only provides laws, but also educates his subjects and endows them with the capacity to fulfill them. Moreover, the coordinated fulfilment of such decrees was inherently teleological and could not be accounted for in strictly mechanistic terms.

We noted earlier that participation in the spiritualist tradition was not incompatible with an interest in the mechanical philosophy. In some respects, Leibniz's concept of nature was more like the mechanical philosophy than the spiritualist one. For instance, he rejected Newton's use of supra-mechanical forces as an illegitimate appeal to occult qualities. And, whereas the Helmontian idea of the *archeus* was a supra-mechanical force that governed the behaviour of material substance, Leibniz's *vis viva* was conceived as entirely mechanical in the sense that it was a function of matter in motion, though neither passive like inertia nor a merely linear measure of motion like momentum.

In the terms of the creationist tradition, Leibniz thus stressed the relative autonomy of nature almost to the point of suggesting complete independence from its Creator. Even miracles were not fresh interventions by God for Leibniz, but rather instances of laws of reasons of a higher order than those presently known to us, but ordained by God from the beginning. The effects of substances which seem to contradict their normal properties must be viewed as resulting from their original God-given essence.

It is important to note, however, that for Leibniz the 'essence' of a thing included its 'union with God himself' as its Creator as well as its obedience to the laws of mechanics; it was not autonomous in the sense of being separate from God. As Leibniz put it in his correspondence with the pietist leader, Philip Jacob Spener:

Thus I hold that, even if individual effects in nature can be explained mechanically, nevertheless, even mechanical principles and their effects, all order and all physical rules in general, arise *not* from purely material determinations, but from the contemplation [*consideratio*] of indivisible substances, and especially of God. Thus I think I am able to satisfy those prudent and pious thinkers who rightly fear that the philosophy of certain men among the moderns [i.e., the mechanical philosophers] is too material, and that it prejudices against religion.

In the final analysis, Leibniz remained faithful to the spiritualist vision of all things existing in God.

The spiritualist tradition was a vital force of its own in seventeenth-century science. Based on the creationist idea of the relative autonomy of nature, it contributed in significant ways to the development of both chemistry and physics, particularly through the work of van Helmont and Leibniz. It also contributed through the work of Comenius and Hartlib to the formation of social and moral values of the emerging scientific community, based on the creationist ideal of the ministry of healing and restoration. The great strength of the spiritualist tradition was its ability to generate powerful organizing principles like gas, matter and force (energy) and to give them empirical meaning in quantifiable form. The major weakness of the tradition was its inability to press beyond the uniqueness and independence of natural entities to probe their common constituents and determine their laws of interaction.

The Mechanist Tradition from Descartes to Boyle

The principal figure in the early development of the mechanical philosophy was René Descartes (1596–1650). Descartes is so well known as the founder of modern philosophy in general and of the rationalist school in particular that it is easy to lose sight of his roots in scholastic theology. He was trained in the classical liberal arts curriculum at the Jesuit College of La Flèche. One of the standard texts used in the Jesuit schools (as well as in many Protestant universities) of the seventeenth century was the *Metaphysical Disputations* (1597) of Francesco Suarez. Since Suarez was an important formative influence on Descartes, we shall take a brief look at his thought.

The Scholastic Background: Suarez

After the Council of Trent (1545–63) declared the modified Aristotelianism of Thomas Aquinas normative for all Catholics, a new movement of scholastic theology developed in the Roman Catholic church. Francesco Suarez, who taught at the University of Salamanca in Spain, was one of the most important representatives of this neo-scholasticism.

We recall that one of the principal issues in scholastic theology was the relationship between *potentia absoluta* and *potentia ordinata*, the absolute and ordained powers of God. It was generally agreed that the laws of nature were ordained by God as the normal pattern of natural events. The problem was that the idea of *potentia ordinata* could lead to the suggestion that the laws of nature were somehow self-operating or automatic, once established. Late medieval theologians had countered this tendency by stressing *potentia absoluta*, the absolute power of God to choose, suspend, and even alter the laws of nature.

The contribution of Suarez was an interpretation of the laws of nature designed to avoid this dilemma. The laws of nature, he held, were not rules God imposed on nature, but rules God imposed on himself. In contrast to the spiritualist tradition, Suarez viewed inanimate creatures as incapable of either understanding or obeying God's laws. So the laws of nature had to be executed by God himself operating on a material substance that was completely passive. These two themes, an all-active God and a passive matter are the characteristic theological ideas we find (in differing contexts) in mechanical philosophers like Descartes and Boyle. It is important to see that they were developed as a way of stressing nature's *dependence* on God, even though they were sometimes later taken to imply an *autonomous* view of nature.

French Mechanical Philosophy: Descartes, Mersenne and Gassendi

The context in which Descartes developed his ideas was entirely different from that of Suarez. The scholastics had worked within an Aristotelian frame of reference even though many of them had been critical of various particulars of Aristotle's philosophy. In Aristotle's worldview the earth stood still, the universe was finite, and the planetary spheres were moved by their desire to match the eternity of God. With the adoption of Copernicus's model of the universe, however, the consistent structure of the scholastic framework crumbled, and in its place there emerged a paradox: all things were now in motion, even the earth, but there was no general mechanism for generating this motion comparable to the role of the *primum mobile* (the outermost celestial sphere) in Aristotle. The entire question of the relation of God to matter and motion had to be rethought.

Descartes was the first to offer a consistent system of natural philosophy to replace that of Aristotle. He developed the idea of the passivity of matter in such a way as to stress the immutability as well as the omnipotence of God. Matter was incapable not only of behaving in accord with God's laws, but even of continuing in existence without the continual creative action of God. In other words, there was no real difference for Descartes between the work of God in sustaining the world, and his original act of creation; each instant of time was a new creation. In philosophical terminology, Descartes' position is often described as a form of 'occasionalism'.

Since matter was entirely passive for Descartes, like the unformed matter of Aristotle it had no innate qualities, no character of its own. Positively this meant that matter was entirely receptive to the mathematical laws imposed on it by God. Hence, Descartes concluded – as Aquinas had done in the thirteenth century (section 2.2) – that matter must be quantifiable. It must have geometric extension. But Descartes went further than Aquinas in making geometric extension the very essence of matter and concluding that it must be made up of corpuscles (not necessarily indivisible atoms) with definite sizes, shapes and speeds. Matter was, therefore, completely different from mind, the latter being unextended and indivisible. This Cartesian dualism of mind and matter was perfectly consistent with the traditional view of the soul as a simple, immaterial substance. But it ran directly counter to the Catholic doctrine of transubstantiation: if the substance of a body could not be distinguished from its geometric extension as Descartes held, the flesh and blood of Christ could not possibly be the true substance of the eucharistic hosts offered in churches around the world.

Negatively, since matter was entirely passive, Descartes would not allow it any innate qualities (other than geometric size and shape) or capacities for influencing other bodies. There was no such thing as weight or gravity or magnetism for Descartes, and there were no causal relationships among events. There was only a continuum of material bodies in relative motion sustained by the continual re-creation of God. In fact, the only element of contingency in Descartes' system was due to the presence of human minds: through free choice, minds could influence the direction (though not the speed) of motion of some of the corpuscles in their bodies and thereby have a role in the determination of history.

Since the existence and behaviour of matter depended entirely on God, the laws of physics were a direct expression of the attributes of God. For Descartes the most important attributes of God were his eternity and immutability. Not only was God immutable in his nature, but he was also immutable in his action. In other words, God was entirely consistent in the way he acted, always producing the same effects under the same circumstances.

As a result of the immutability of God's being and acts, two things could be concluded. For one thing, the laws governing physical nature could never change or be violated in any way. The laws of physics, therefore, were eternal and immutable like God. After all, they were simply the rules God had imposed upon himself, and, since God always acted in accordance with the same rules or laws, he always produced the same kinds of effects. Thus there could be no miracles in the sense of violations of the laws of physics. Once God had decreed the laws governing events, in Descartes' universe, there were no exceptions. On the other hand, all events were new creations of God: they were not produced automatically with previous events as causes. Paradoxically, the role of God in nature was ubiquitous and yet highly constrained (by God's own nature) at the same time. Providence was so universal that it could not be recognized in any particular instance.

Secondly, the immutability of God implied for Descartes the conservation of the amount of matter and the amount of motion in the universe. The amount of motion was the sum of the products of the quantity of matter (i.e., extension or bulk) and the speed of motion (in whatever direction) of all the bodies in the universe. Descartes expressed this principle of conservation in three laws:

(1) each body continues in its given state of rest or motion unless it collides with another body;

(2) each body will move in a straight line unless constrained to move otherwise;

(3) when one body collides with another there is a transfer of motion from the stronger to the less strong in accordance with seven special rules of impact.

According to Descartes, all the phenomena of nature could be explained in terms of these laws, even the seemingly 'occult' phenomena of gravitation, magnetism and light.

As Edgar Zilsel pointed out in 1942, Descartes established the modern concept of 'laws of nature' by joining the theological idea of God's ordaining laws for all creatures with the new empirical laws of post-Aristotelian science. The idea of laws of nature was popularized later in the seventeenth and eighteenth centuries and eventually became quite secular in meaning. The eventual elimination of any reference to God led to the notion that the laws were possessed by nature rather than prescribed for nature by God.

For Descartes, then, the continued existence and behaviour of matter was predictable because it was based on the eternity and immutability of God. It was so predictable, in fact, that Descartes could speculate about possible ways in which the present universe could have evolved in accordance with the laws of nature from an original chaos of material particles. A primordial (hypothetical) assemblage of matter in motion would evolve into the universe as we know it through the mutual collisions of the particles in accordance with the laws of motion. There was no need to appeal to the miraculous or to occult qualities of any kind. Even plants and animals could be viewed as machines with what appear to be natural movements determined by the motions of hidden strings and fluids.

Without denying that the world was in fact formed miraculously, i.e., by God's *potentia absoluta*, as taught by Scripture and the Church, Descartes imagined a hypothetical cosmos coming to look just like the present one solely by God's *potentia ordinata*, as understood by unaided human reason. Paradoxically, the assimilation of divine providence to the idea of creation (occasionalism) could thus be turned around into an assimilation of divine creation into universal providence (naturalism). The creationist tradition thus led Descartes to the idea of the possible eternity of the world, as it had led the medieval scholastics before him (section 2.2). Conversely, just as the stress on *potentia ordinata* in the Middle Ages produced a reaction in the late thirteenth century, Cartesian philosophy produced various reactions both within the mechanist tradition and beyond it in the late seventeenth century, as we shall see.

The story of the reception of Descartes' mechanical philosophy in the seventeenth century is very similar to that of the initial resistance, gradual assimilation, and subsequent reaction to the natural philosophy of Aristotle in the thirteenth century (chap. 2). Ironically, it was primarily the continued adherence to Aristotle in the churches and universities of the seventeenth century that provided the initial resistance to Cartesian ideas. During the 1640s the (Reformed) universities of Utrecht and Leiden ruled against the teaching of anti-Aristotelian ideas in Descartes. In 1662 the arts faculty of the (Catholic) University of Louvain issued a similar ruling. In 1650 the Ninth General Congregation of the Jesuits condemned fifteen propositions related to the teachings of Descartes. In 1663, at the instigation of the Jesuits, Descartes' philosophical writings were placed on the Index of Prohibited Books until such time that they were suitably corrected. In 1671 the Court of the University of Paris commanded its theologians to enforce a royal edict prohibiting any philosophy but Aristotle's. The universities of Angers and Caen became officially anti-Cartesian later in the 1670s.

Much of this initial reaction was due to the inherent conservatism of the overseers and professors of the institutions involved and should not be taken as reflecting the ecclesiastical or academic communities as a whole. As early as 1628, Descartes was encouraged by Cardinal de Berulle, founder of the French Oratorians, to apply his method to the problems of medicine and mechanics – 'the one would contribute to the restoration and conservation of health, and other to some diminution and relief in the labours of mankind'.

The primary concerns of conservative theologians seem to have been Descartes' methodological scepticism, his separation of natural philosophy from positive theology, and, for Catholics, the implications of his equation of matter with geometric extension for the doctrine of transubstantiation. Many moderate theologians felt that the essentials of Christian faith were not threatened.

As early as 1645 the city council of Utrecht forbade anyone to write either for *or against* Descartes. At Leiden, the Cartesian methodology was ably defended by Christoph Wittich in the 1670s and was generally supported by theological followers of John Cocceius (1603–69) who sought a purely scriptural basis of theology that complemented Descartes' procedure of separating natural philosophy from theology. In Calvinist Geneva, François Turretin (1623–87) took a positive interest in Descartes' natural philosophy and only objected to the application of his methodical doubt to theological issues. Catholic theologians, particularly some of the Jesuits, charged that Descartes' equation of material substance with geometric extension would undermine the dogma of transubstantiation. On the other hand, there would have been no need for the widespread efforts to discourage interest in Descartes' teachings if the latter had not also achieved a degree of popularity in the colleges and universities under ecclesiastical control.

By the mid-eighteenth century even the strongholds of conservatism had altered their earlier opposition. In 1704, Jean-Alphonse Turretin, the son of François praised Descartes' *Discourse on Method* as containing the best precepts for the pursuit of knowledge. Through the efforts of the Oratorian, Nicholas Malebranche (1674–5), and the Jansenist, Antoine Arnauld (1671–81), both strong Augustinians, aspects of Descartes' philosophy came to be regarded by many French Catholics as supportive of official Church dogma. Some Jesuit schools also adopted Cartesian principles in the eighteenth century, partly as a means of counteracting the traditional Augustinianism of the Jansenists. In 1706 the Fifteenth General Congregation of the Jesuits allowed the defence of the Cartesian system as an hypothesis and praised it for its overall completeness and consistency, if not for its correctness. Descartes' ideas were officially recognized even at the University of Paris in 1720. As in the case of the reception of Aristotle in the thirteenth century, the remarkable thing about the creationist tradition is not so much its initial resistance to new scientific ideas as its ability to assimilate them.

The two principal French churchmen to develop the mechanical philosophy of Descartes in the early seventeenth century were Marin Mersenne (1588–1648) and Pierre Gassendi (1592–1655). A primary objective for both men was to protect the mathematical sciences from association with the hermetic numerology of Ficino, Pico, Bruno, Fludd, and the so-called Rosicrucian Brotherhood.

Mersenne was concerned about what he saw as a confusion of matter and spirit, the natural and the supernatural, and a limitation of the power of God in the hermetic appeal to natural magic. In particular, he opposed some of Robert Fludd's ideas about spiritual sympathies between bodies: e.g., between a weapon and the body it had wounded. By way of contrast, Mersenne championed Descartes' idea of treating living systems as machines, though he was not as confident as Descartes of the human mind's ability to determine the inner mechanisms of bodies – the omnipotence of God meant for him that one could never know for sure how God had designed things. Curiously, Mersenne's anxiety about the dangers of hermeticism and, indirectly, his support for the mechanical philosophy were partly inspired by the Jesuit campaign against Rosicrucianism in the early 1620s – a point worth noting in order to show that a conservative religious movement can have 'progressive' as well as reactionary effects with respect to a new philosophy.

Mersenne advocated the disciplining of alchemy by the elimination of mysticism and secrecy, the use of clear terminology, and the foundation of public alchemical academies for the improvement of human health. Thus he played a role in French science comparable to that of Hartlib in England, though Mersenne was less supportive of alchemical studies than Hartlib. Both men were as concerned to organize and encourage the work of others as to develop their own scientific ideas.

Pierre Gassendi gave a distinctively new direction to the mechanical philosophy in three ways. First he treated continued existence and the power of causal influence as inherent properties of material bodies, even allowing for weight and internal energy as well as mere bulk. Thus he shifted the course of the mechanical philosophy away from the occasionalism of Descartes towards naturalism.

Secondly, Gassendi incorporated the atomism of Epicurus and Lucretius into the mechanical philosophy. He claimed that all physical phenomena could be explained in terms of the motions of indivisible corpuscles or atoms of varying weight, size and shape. He was not the first to do so: Galileo, Hariot and Beeckman had already advocated the idea of atoms in their early versions of the mechanical philosophy. Gassendi's two major Epicurean treatises, published in 1649, made the ideas of classical atomism more widely available. Moreover, by limiting the amount of matter in the universe to a finite quantity and by crediting God with the original endowment of atoms with motion, he made atomistic ideas more palatable to Christian minds.

Third, Gassendi advocated the idea of an infinite void space that was later utilized by Newton. In part, this idea was a by-product of Gassendi's interest in atomism, which postulated an infinite void as the framework for the activity of the corpuscles of matter. It also reflected the influence of the Italian naturalists, Patrizzi and Campanella, and earlier medieval speculations about the possibility of an extra-cosmic void (section 2.3).

English Mechanical Philosophers: Digby to Boyle

The progress of the mechanical philosophy after Descartes, Mersenne and Gassendi has largely to do with its reception and subsequent development in England. The main theological and social stimulus towards the reception of the mechanical philosophy was a growing tendency to associate spiritualism with pantheism and anarchy and the consequent need to find a viable alternative conducive to ecclesiastical peace and political stability. There were four principal figures involved: Kenelm Digby (1603–65), Thomas Hobbes (1588–1679), Walter Charleton (1620–1707), and Robert Boyle (1627–91). We shall touch on Digby, Hobbes and Charleton briefly before discussing the culmination of the seventeenth-century mechanical tradition in the work of Robert Boyle.

Digby and Hobbes represent two opposing ways of interpreting the mechanical philosophy: Digby stressing the immateriality of the soul and Hobbes reducing it to a manifestation of matter in motion.

Sir Kenelm Digby was a devout Catholic and a moderate Aristotelian in philosophy. As a sincere Christian and a Royalist, loyal to Charles I during the English Civil War (1642–49), he was deeply disturbed by the proliferation of radical Protestant sects at that time. In particular, he wished to refute the millenarians' doctrine of mortalism – the teaching that the soul ceases to exist at death and awaits the final resurrection for its regeneration. As an exile in Paris (1643–54), Digby met Descartes and other members of Mersenne's circle. He saw in the mechanical philosophy and its matter-spirit dualism a powerful weapon against the radical doctrines of materialism and mortalism. Accordingly, he followed Descartes in viewing plants and animals as machine-like though, like Gassendi, he held that matter consisted of atoms endowed with efficient causality.

Whereas the mechanical philosophy of Digby was intended to bolster belief in the spiritual, the mechanical philosophy of Hobbes was a form of materialism. Even mental and spiritual phenomena, according to Hobbes, had to be extended, if they were real at all, and hence were manifestations of matter in motion. There was no such thing as an immaterial soul or free will. At one point, Hobbes even referred to God as a 'simple corporeal spirit' with magnitude and extension.

Leviathan, Hobbes' famous political treatise, was written during his exile (as a Royalist) in Paris and published in 1651. Hobbes not only advocated the absolute power of kings but questioned the authenticity of biblical narratives about the activity of spirits and the occurrence of miracles. Common as such outright scepticism is today, it was nearly unheard of in the mid-seventeenth century, at least in print.

Hobbes made no significant contribution to science as such, but he had a tremendous impact on the development of the mechanical philosophy. His writings were taken by many as evidence of an anti-Christian bias in the mechanical philosophy as a whole. During his years in Paris (the 1630s and '40s) he was known to have frequented the circle of Mersenne and as a close friend of Gassendi. Some of Gassendi's distinctive ideas on atoms and the void were included in Hobbes' treatise *On Bodies*, published in 1655.

We have seen how the development of science can be influenced by theological ideas providing targets for reaction as well as positive influences. Much of seventeenth-century mechanical philosophy was a reaction to the perceived dangers of the hermetic and spiritualist traditions. Much of late seventeenth-century English thought was also a reaction to Hobbes' materialism and the perceived dangers of the mechanical philosophy. The Platonist tradition we shall discuss later departed radically from the mechanical model in its attempt to restore a proper sense of the direct involvement of God in natural events. There were also those who continued to work within the mechanical philosophy while modifying it and interpreting it within a Christian context. We shall discuss two of these 'loyalists': Walter Charleton and Robert Boyle.

The fascinating thing about Charleton and Boyle is that they were both adherents of the spiritualist views of Helmont in the late 1640s and early '50s and then converted to the mechanical philosophy in the mid 1650s. In fact, Charleton's *A Ternary of Paradoxes*, published soon after the execution of Charles I (1649), was the first translation of any of Helmont's works into English. Charleton had served as a physician to Charles I since 1643. According to the preface to his translation (1650), he originally found Helmont's elevation of understanding over scholastic reason attractive as an aid to peace in a time of civil and ecclesiastical strife.

By 1652 Charleton was shifting towards the mechanical philosophy of Descartes and Hobbes, and in 1654 he published a translation and commentary on one of Gassendi's Epicurean treatises under the title, *The Epicurean-Gassendian-Charletonian Physiology* ('physiology' meaning the physics of all material substances). Reversing his former preference, Charleton now rejected the spiritualist idea of a world soul responsible for correspondences and sympathies between spatially separate bodies. Undoubtedly, he was influenced in this by the attack on Robert Fludd's hermeticism launched by Mersenne and Gassendi. Moreover, spiritualist ideas had by this time become closely associated with sectarian religion and anarchy in England. In place of the spiritualist world of correspondences, Charleton now advocated Gassendi's mechanical world of atoms moving in an infinite void.

In the wake of the publication of *Leviathan* (1651), Charleton had to be careful to dissociate Gassendi's version of Epicureanism from the mechanistic materialism of Hobbes as well as the spiritualism of Fludd and Helmont. Thus he stressed, as Gassendi had, the idea that the atoms were originally created and endowed with motion by God. But he went a step further than Gassendi in order to avoid any suggestion of naturalism: even though the atoms moved in accordance with laws dictated by God, they moved blindly and were incapable of either producing or maintaining an ordered cosmos without God's continued providence.

So, according to Charleton, atomism actually provided a proof for the existence and continual providence of God. Without God there would be nothing; or, if there were anything, it would only be a chaos. Moreover, unlike the French philosophers, Charleton held that living beings could not be explained in mechanical terms: the organization of plants and animals also required the special providence of God. The mechanistic account of the world had gaps, in effect, and required God to fill them. This was one of the first modern instances of what is known as 'natural theology', the attempt to demonstrate the existence and activity of God from the phenomena of nature.

Robert Boyle experienced a conversion from spiritualist to mechanist leanings similar to Charleton's, though it seems to have taken a longer period of time. The historical reconstruction of the evolution of Boyle's thought is complicated by the fact that many of his writings contain sections written years prior to their publication. We shall offer a plausible account of Boyle's conversion, the reasons for it, and the impact it had on his natural philosophy.

In the 1640s and early '50s, Boyle was closely associated with the Utopian projects and alchemical research of Samuel Hartlib, as we have noted. During this period he first examined the atomist ideas of Descartes, Gassendi and Digby, but he remained uneasy about their acceptability at late as 1653 and specified that his papers on the subject were to be burnt. In the early sections of *Some Considerations touching the Usefulness of Experimental Natural Philosophy* (written in the late 1640s), when he first discussed the new atomical philosophy, Boyle retained many elements of the Helmontian outlook. By the late 1650s, however, when Boyle wrote the later sections of *Usefulness* and *The Sceptical Chymist*, he had repudiated what he then saw as Helmont's confusion of the natural and the supernatural. In particular, Boyle criticized the reliance of Helmontians on direct revelations of chemical secrets from God (possibly referring to Thomas Vaughan of the Hartlib circle).

Various reasons have been suggested for Boyle's change of mind. In the background was the rising sectarian activity associated by many with spiritualist views. Historians like James R. Jacob have pointed out that the anarchistic movements of 1646–48 were particularly alarming to Boyle at a time when he and his brother Broghill were trying to secure their inheritance to family property in Ireland. Apparently, Boyle left behind his earlier ethic of virtue for virtue's sake, in dependence on the unmerited grace of God, due to its association with the antinomianism of radical Puritans and sectarians like the Familists. In its place, he developed a new ethic of self-reliance in which God helped those who helped themselves. This should not be taken as a sign of mere temporizing on Boyle's part: as his circumstances changed, his assessment of the relative merits of Utopian and establishmentarian strategies for improving society naturally changed too. As an educated person and, potentially at least, a man of property, Boyle began to see the value of utilizing the resources at his disposal 'as means to do hansom things with'.

The final steps in Boyle's conversion to the mechanical philosophy took place in the late 1650s. An important factor here was his move to Oxford where, in 1656, he joined a group of scientists who met in the lodgings of the moderate Puritan divine, John Wilkins, at Wadham College. This 'Oxford group' included William Petty, Christopher Wren, John Wallis, and Seth Ward, the nucleus of the later Royal Society of London. Since the group included both Puritans and Anglicans, supporters of the Commonwealth and Royalists, the principles on which it operated were latitudinarian in religion and pragmatic in politics. Its two great fears were enthusiasm and anarchism.

In addition to these social and theological factors in Boyle's development, there were important advances in technology and experimental science to be considered. In the mid 1650s, Otto von Guericke (1602–86) had publicly demonstrated the power of a vacuum in a cavity using a suction pump he had designed. Boyle immediately saw the potential of such experiments as a means of demonstrating the mechanical concept of air pressure. Using a pump built by his assistant Robert Hooke, he performed a variety of experiments and concluded that the apparent power of the vacuum was due to the difference in air pressure between the evacuated cavity and the surrounding atmosphere. There was no longer any need, according to Boyle, to appeal to final causes like nature's abhorrence of a vacuum.

Boyle also investigated the compression of pockets of gas under varying pressures and concluded that the volume of a gas decreased in proportion to the mechanical pressure exerted on it. In other words, the pressure of the gas was inversely proportional to the volume it occupied – a quantitative relation known to all students of physics and chemistry as 'Boyle's law'. Moreover, Boyle concluded that gases were composed of discrete particles moving in a vacuum. Compression merely crowded the particles together; conversely, rarefaction stretched them apart. All this could be explained by mechanical principles.

From this new perspective, the mechanical philosophy gradually took on greater plausibility in Boyle's mind. He saw the immense importance of moral self-determination in life. He noted, as Digby had already, that the sectarians who were threatening the social order also tended to be mortalists: they did not accept the Church's teaching of the immortality of the human soul. Like Digby, Boyle viewed the mortalist heresy as a threat to the uniqueness of human nature and to belief in moral freedom. In order to counter the mortalist threat, Boyle opted for the matter-spirit duality of the mechanical philosophy which stressed the incapability of inanimate matter to follow God's laws in the way humans were expected to do.

Boyle thus adopted Descartes' notion of matter as completely passive. He did not regard each instant as a new creation, and he did not treat plants and animals as machines, without a teleology, as Descartes did. But he viewed the ability of the atoms to behave in lawful ways as entirely due to the power of God's original creation and continuing concourse. This view is best expressed in a classic passage of *The Usefulness of Experimental Natural Philosophy* (published in 1663):

> . . . methinks we may, without absurdity, conceive that God . . . did divide . . . the matter, which he had provided, into an innumerable multitude of very variously figured corpuscles, and both connected those particles into such textures or particular bodies, and placed them in such situations, and put them into such motions, that by the assistance of his ordinary preserving concourse, the phaenomena which he intended should appear in the universe must as orderly follow, and be exhibited by the bodies necessarily acting according to those impressions or laws, though they understand them not at all, as if each of those creatures had a design of self-preservation, and were furnished with knowledge and industry to prosecute it . . .

In other words, the lawful behaviour of the atoms was not due to any intelligence on their own part and did not detract from the uniqueness of humanity in possessing the capacity for real self-preservation and industry.

Like Charleton, Boyle had to face a second threat – that of Hobbes' materialism. Consequently, he followed Charleton in arguing that mere matter, even with the laws God had granted it, could not be expected to produce the kind of organization one observes in living beings. In these cases, seminal principles must be involved (as the spiritualists held), and these in turn pointed to the design and activity of God. Thus Boyle was critical of Descartes' version of the mechanical philosophy for not providing any evidence of the operation of God in the physical world. For similar reasons he was not satisfied with Gassendi's Epicurean atomism, in which God merely endowed the atoms with motion and then retired from the scene. Moreover, he rejected Gassendi's idea of absolute space and time as an infringement on the free creative power of God.

Thus Boyle tried to steer a middle course between the spiritualism associated with the sectaries and the mechanistic materialism associated with Hobbes. The result was a stratified view of matter in which the lowest level of mere atoms operated along completely mechanical lines and the higher levels of living beings were clearly supra-mechanical. Intermediate levels, like those of crystals and metals were subject to question. In his earlier writings, Boyle viewed the growth of crystals and gems as exhibiting seminal principles and special providence just as the growth of living creatures did. But in later writings he treated the structure of gems as reducible to the underlying geometry of the arrangements of atoms. In effect, like Charleton, Boyle was appealing to gaps in the mechanical account as evidence of the design and immediate providence of God. If crystals could be explained in terms of atomic structures, why couldn't living creatures? Once having made a clear separation between the current activity of God and the mechanisms invested in matter, Boyle was bound to reduce the scope of evidence for divine providence through his own scientific investigations.

The mechanical philosophy, as we have seen, had its roots in late medieval scholasticism and the idea of God's *potentia ordinata*, the ordinary exercise of God's providence. It gave an account of the origins and maintenance of motion that replaced the outdated Aristotelian world view. The source of the world's dynamism was no longer the *primum mobile* at the outer boundary of the cosmos, but the creation and energizing of numerous atoms or corpuscles of matter. The new mechanics could be cited as evidence of the existence and activity of God just as well as the medieval version could. Only now God was viewed as the Designer and Lawgiver, whereas before he was the Prime Mover and Desire of all things.

The mechanical philosophy was not the only candidate to replace Aristotle as the dominant paradigm in the seventeenth century. Its principal competitor was the spiritualist tradition. In the second half of the century, a decision in favour of the mechanical philosophy was made by leading English scientists and clergy. Their reasons were partly theological (opposition to sectarian millenarianism and mortalism) and partly social (fear of anarchy), as well as strictly experimental (quantitative treatment of air pressure).

The effects of this decision were enormous. The mechanical philosophy was to become the dominant paradigm of Western science for the next two centuries and an integral feature of Western technology and industrial manufacture to this day. Though challenged by the Platonic and Newtonian philosophies we shall discuss next, it incorporated the scientific content of the latter in the eighteenth century and maintained its hegemony in Western thought through most of the nineteenth century. The benefit of the decision for mechanism was a viable programme for understanding and controlling nature at its most fundamental, material level. The weakness was an isolation of the material, mechanical aspects of nature from the aesthetic, moral, and religious dimensions.

This separation of material and spiritual was not an accident. It was programmed into modern science and culture in reaction to the perceived dangers of the more holistic science and culture of the spiritualists. The mechanical philosophy that emerged in late seventeenth-century England was not just a scientific programme for investigating the mechanical aspects of nature. After all, spiritualists like Hartlib and Leibniz were also interested in mechanical problems. The new paradigm for physical science was intentionally designed as a means of establishing a clear antithesis between the material and the spiritual.

In hindsight, we may say that there was no available alternative consistent with the progress of science and human welfare. Given the theological inheritance of the Middle Ages, in which God's direct action and the normal causal connections of nature were mutually exclusive, the only way to isolate the mechanical aspects of nature was to bracket out the spiritual. The decision in favour of the mechanical philosophy was not made until the mid-seventeenth century, but the theology that required it had been worked out as early as the twelfth (section 1.4).

The Platonist Tradition to Isaac Newton

The third seventeenth-century tradition we shall examine was centred at the University of Cambridge. In a sense it is a much narrower movement than the international spiritualist and mechanist traditions we have studied. Its importance stems from the fact that it culminated in the development of a new mathematical physics by Isaac Newton. Newton's ability to conceptualize principles like universal gravitation that transcended the mechanical philosophy of the seventeenth century was facilitated by the ideas of a group of Cambridge Platonists led by John Smith and Henry More, partly mediated through the teachings of the mathematician Isaac Barrow. First, we shall look at the Cambridge Platonists in order to discern the theological roots of Newton's physics. Then we shall look at the Cambridge mathematicians, Isaac Barrow and Isaac Newton.

The Cambridge Platonists: Smith and More

The Cambridge Platonists were a group of academicians who developed a rationalized form of Neoplatonism as an alternative to the mechanical philosophy of Gassendi and Hobbes. At first they were sympathetic to the rationalism of Descartes, but during the 1650s and early '60s they turned against mechanical philosophers like Descartes and Boyle.

The alarm against mechanist ideas was first sounded in the 1640s by John Smith (1618–52). Smith had been a pupil of the Cambridge Puritan Benjamin Whichcote, sometimes regarded as the founder of the Cambridge Platonist school, though he himself was not a philosopher. Smith's views best represent the philosophical stance of the school in the 1640s. In reaction to the heated doctrinal controversies of Protestant scholasticism, he had turned to mystical philosophy of the third-century Neoplatonist, Plotinus. Smith saw significant points of contact between the Platonic psychology of Plotinus and the introspective rationalism and matter-spirit dualism of Descartes. Indeed, his directive to 'seek for God within thine own soul' had a striking similarity to Descartes' retreat within to establish his own existence and the existence of God. On the other hand, Smith rejected the Epicurean atomism of Gassendi as a masked form of atheism. In particular, he objected to the idea that motion was inherent in matter as militating against the idea of divine creation and providence.

Henry More (1614–87) became the principal advocate of Cartesian ideas in England after the premature death of Smith. He also took over Smith's role as defender of the faith against Epicureanism, materialism and atheism. To Smith's critique of the Epicureanism of Gassendi, More added his own campaign against the materialism of Hobbes in his *Antidote against Atheism* (1653). At this stage, More found Descartes' idea of the sheer passivity of matter useful since it provided evidence for the independent existence of spiritual beings like God and human souls. He even found evidence of the original version of atomism in Genesis 1 – an irrefutable proof to 'atheistical wits' and 'mere naturalists' that Moses was a 'Master of Natural Philosophy'.

Gradually More came to see the ideas of Descartes as unsuited for his campaign against materialism. His disaffection with Descartes' mechanical philosophy began in the late 1640s and led to a final repudiation of Descartes in the mid 1660s. The first clear statement of his new views was made in *The Immortality of the Soul* (1659), a work that had a formative influence on Newton during his undergraduate years at Cambridge. Interestingly, it was written at the same time that Boyle underwent the final stage of his conversion from spiritualism to the mechanical philosophy. In fact, More's final rejection of Descartes' philosophy was partly the result of his antipathy to Boyle's new explanation of the power of a vacuum (1660).

For Boyle, the power of a vacuum could be explained in terms of purely mechanical concepts like atmospheric pressure. More was not convinced. If the pressure or weight of the atmosphere was so great, he asked, why doesn't it flatten a lump of soft butter? Unlike the Aristotelians and Cartesians, More accepted the existence of a vacuum, but he reasoned that its properties could best be explained on the basis of an active spirit that was present even in the absence of matter. Beginning in 1662, More argued his point with Boyle for twenty years. As we saw in our discussion of Boyle, scientific theories in the seventeenth century were governed by theological (and social) views as much as by information about the properties of material substances.

The major problem with Descartes' philosophy for More was its identification of extension with matter and the consequent denial of extension to spirit. If so, More concluded, the spiritual would be incapable of having contact with matter and might as well be ignored, as Hobbes had concluded. In order to prove the materialists wrong, therefore, it would be necessary to show that spiritual substance was extended so as to permeate and influence matter. In other words, More revived the ancient Stoic and Neoplatonic idea of the world soul. He called it the 'Spirit of Nature' or 'hylarchic (matter-ruling) principle'. To demonstrate the need of such a spirit, More appealed to the many phenomena which could not easily be accounted for in terms of mechanical concepts: e.g., the sympathetic vibrations of strings, magnetism, gravity, and the generation of plants and animals. The Spirit of Nature was unconscious and impersonal, but it engineered these supra-mechanical phenomena by directing the motion of the particles of matter in accordance with the designs of God.

More's mature Platonism can be contrasted with Boyle's version of the mechanical philosophy at this point. Boyle, too, recognized that some phenomena, particularly biological ones, could not be explained in purely mechanical terms. However, for Boyle, such supra-mechanical phenomena were the exception, not the rule. For More, on the other hand, there was 'no purely Mechanicall Phaenomenon in the whole Universe'.

In opposition to Descartes' identification of extension with matter, More concluded that matter and spirit were both extended in space. What distinguished them was that spirit was active and subtle while matter was passive, gross and impenetrable. Against Descartes, More concluded that space could exist even without matter and that matter was located *in* space. Space was thus independent of matter – infinite, absolute, and uncreated. According to More, space was a representation or 'shadow' of the divine essence in nature. In effect, More substituted a hierarchical view of reality for the radical dualism of the mechanical philosophy. Between God and matter, in descending order, were absolute space (a direct manifestation of God) and the Spirit of Nature (a separate subordinate entity).

As Max Jammer pointed out in 1954, More's concept of absolute space had roots in the Jewish and Christian cabalist traditions, which viewed God as the *maqom*, or place of the world (section 3.1). As early as 1653 More had studied cabalistic writings with the help of his friend and patroness, Lady Anne Conway, and he was deeply influenced by them. But More was not a cabalist himself. In fact, he found cabalism to be inconsistent at points with Christian doctrine. The cabalistic notion of a series of ten emanations of God giving rise to the phenomenal world, for instance, contradicted the doctrines of the Trinity and creation *ex nihilo*.

Similarly, More's concept of the 'Spirit of Nature' or 'hylarchic principle' may have been inspired by the Paracelsian-Helmontian idea of an 'archeus' ruling over each organic entity. Yet More was not a spiritualist either. Though he gradually parted company with the mechanical philosophy in the 1650s, he retained much of the rationalism of Descartes in his philosophy. In fact, More criticized Paracelsus, Boehme, Francis Mercury van Helmont, and Thomas Vaughan for relying on divine illumination, rather than human reason, in their scientific work. In addition, More lacked the pragmatic interests of the spiritualists and pansophists in experimental research and social reform.

The Cambridge Mathematicians: Barrow and Newton

Barrow and Newton were not primarily philosophers like the Cambridge Platonists: they were mathematicians and biblical scholars. In 1663 Barrow became the first Lucasian Professor of Mathematics at Cambridge. In 1669 he gave up the Lucasian Chair in order to devote himself to the ministry of the Word and sacraments, and Newton was appointed to succeed him.

Though Barrow as not a Platonist in the proper sense, he was deeply influenced by the Platonic ideas of Henry More, and he developed a more precise version of these in his mathematical lectures. As early as 1652, Barrow was utilizing Descartes' idea of the passivity of matter to argue for the existence of spirit. Like More, he criticized Descartes for separating spirit so surgically from matter, thus making nature 'blockish and inanimate'. The mechanical laws of nature, he concluded, could not account for such phenomena as magnetism and the growth of living beings.

In 1665, Barrow gave a lecture 'Of Space and Impenetrability', which provided the young Newton with the starting point for his own natural philosophy. Barrow criticized Descartes' teachings for implying that matter was infinite and eternal (though Descartes did not draw these implications himself). Since a God who creates could increase or decrease the amount of matter in the universe, one could not regard matter as sharing his attributes without running the risk of denying creation. Space, on the other hand, could neither be augmented nor diminished. Hence it was immutable as More had taught. Space must also be infinite, or else God would be bounded. Similarly it must be eternal, or else God would once have been nowhere. Barrow concluded, therefore, that space and time were a mathematical representation of the divine omnipresence and eternity.

Newton's new physics was essentially a mathematical version of the mechanist idea of matter supplemented by the ideas of absolute space and the operation of supra-mechanical principles like gravity to mediate between bodies. All of these ingredients were provided by the mechanist and Platonic traditions as we have seen: the passivity of matter, by Descartes, Boyle and More; absolute space, by Gassendi, Charleton, More, and Barrow; the idea of universal active principles, by More and Barrow. But it required the mathematical skill and the ascetic discipline of Newton to combine these ingredients into a workable mathematical physics.

Newton first developed his ideas on God and nature in a paper, 'On the Gravity and Equilibrium of Fluids' (written in the late 1660s). The characteristic features of this early work that place Newton squarely in the tradition of More and Barrow are the rejection of Descartes' identification of extension with matter as leading to atheism and the postulation of absolute space and time as 'emanent effects' of God and 'dispositions of all being'. Following More and Barrow, Newton viewed the attribution to God of extension and duration as the only way to preserve the biblical doctrines of monotheism and creation *ex nihilo*:

> If we say with Descartes that extension is body, do we not manifestly offer a path to Atheism, both because extension is not created but has existed eternally, and because we have an absolute idea of it without any relationship to God, . . . Moreover, if the distinction [made by Descartes] of substances between *thinking* and *extended* is legitimate and complete, God does not eminently contain extension within himself and therefore cannot create it; but God and extension will be two substances separately complete, absolute, and having the same significance.

In order to maintain a clear distinction between the created and uncreated, Newton felt, it was necessary to separate space (and time) from the realm of matter and place it on the side of the divine.

So the basic principles of Newton's natural philosophy were rooted in the creationist tradition as mediated by Henry More's critique of the mechanical philosophy of Descartes.

The development of Newton's theological interpretation of space and matter can be traced in the mature physics of his *Principia Mathematica* ('Mathematical Principles of Natural Philosophy': first edition, 1687) and *Opticks* (first edition, 1704). Newton's thinking on specific issues changed over the years, and some historians have developed complex accounts of the ebb and flow of the differing emphases. There was a period around 1675, for instance, when Newton tried to account for phenomena like gravity and the diffraction of light in mechanical terms. He postulated an etherial fluid of tiny particles that transmitted forces by streaming from one body to another in a manner reminiscent of Descartes' mechanistic explanations. By 1680, however, Newton had abandoned the attempt to find a mechanical explanation for gravity. Though he continued to speculate on the existence of a variety of ethers, he never embraced the mechanical model again. Here, for simplicity, we shall treat Newton's basic principles as firm and unchanging after the late 1660s.

As Newton later explained to Richard Bentley (1692), he wrote the *Principia Mathematica* with 'an eye upon such principles as might work with considering men, for the belief of a Deity'. In the context of his concern to refute atheism, Newton followed More's strategy of postulating supra-mechanical forces like gravity to account for the interactions between isolated bodies of matter. Since such forces were not explicable as properties of matter, the latter being passive, and could not be accounted for in terms of mechanical contact between bodies, they were evidence of God's imposition and maintenance of control on the stuff of the universe. In effect, Newton's active forces were a mathematical version of More's concept of a Spirit of Nature, similarly adopted in an effort to refute atheism. In place of More's hierarchical model of God, space, the Spirit of Nature, and passive matter, Newton substituted his own hierarchy of God, space, active principles (like gravitation), and passive matter.

A comparison with the spiritualist and mechanist traditions will clarify the distinctive place of these ideas. Newton agreed with the spiritualists that God had prescribed laws for nature, but he did not view these as immanent in matter and specific to individual creatures as the spiritualists did. The principle of gravitation was imposed on matter and universal in scope, like More's Spirit of Nature. On the other hand, Newton agreed with mechanists like Descartes and

Boyle that matter by itself was entirely passive, but he did not view the inertial motion and collisions of material bodies as an adequate explanation of inanimate phenomena like gravitation, the diffraction of light, and cohesion. The principles involved in phenomena like these were active and supra-mechanical.

Newton's supra-mechanical principles accounted for the origin of motion, not just its transmission from one body to another. Thus they played a role analogous to that of the *primum mobile* in Aristotle's cosmology. On one hand, they were directly subject to divine influence; on the other, they operated in accordance with regular natural laws. Like the *primum mobile*, therefore, they provided a link between the natural and the supernatural worlds.

So, even though they depended directly on God, Newton's supramechanical principles were not 'miraculous' or supernatural in the sense of being unpredictable, and they in no way interfered with the ability of scientists to explain phenomena in terms of second causes. Gravity, for instance, operated according to a precise mathematical law: its strength was proportional to the product of the masses of, and inversely proportional to the square of the distance between, the bodies between which it operated. Even comets, traditionally thought to be direct acts of God, obeyed this universal law and were periodic phenomena according to Newton. The value of gravitation as evidence of God's activity was due to the fact that it could not be derived from intrinsic (primordial) properties of matter such as mass and extension: hence, it required the imposition of a supra-mechanical law on matter. An important consequence was that laws like that of universal gravitation could not be deduced from first principles by pure reason as mechanical philosophers like Descartes had hoped. They could only be inferred from an empirical study of the phenomena themselves.

As we have seen, the concept of a law of nature was derived from the ancient Near Eastern belief that God ordained laws for all his subjects, even inanimate ones. This idea was transmitted to modern western Europe by the medieval scholastics. It was developed in the late sixteenth century by Suarez and in the early seventeenth by Descartes, whose writings influenced the early members of the Royal Society and Newton. Thus there is a clear line of transmission in the context of the creationist tradition through the seventeenth century before the idea of laws of nature was secularized in the eighteenth century.

Newton did not entirely eliminate the need for the extraordinary exercise of God's power, however. There were at least two points, as he saw it, where the laws of nature were inadequate. One, of course, was the creation of the world system itself. This was not just a matter of faith: it was a direct implication of Newton's physics. One of the basic laws of mechanics (Newton's third law of motion) was that for every action there was an equal and opposite reaction. Clearly this law did not apply to the moment of creation, however. God set all things in motion, but he was not set in motion himself. Therefore, as Newton put it, the First Cause of all things was certainly not mechanical. Furthermore, the detailed structure of the solar system could not be explained in mechanical terms either, according to Newton. For example, the co-rotation of the planets and co-planarity of their orbits could only be accounted for by the deliberate design and direct action of God in creation.

Once the bodies of the universe were set in motion and the supra-mechanical laws of nature were imposed, the world could 'continue by those laws for many ages', as Newton put it in the 1706 (Latin) edition of his *Opticks*. It would only require the willing concurrence, or general providence, of God for its continuance. However, at least two problems would eventually arise in such a way as to require divine intervention. For one thing, irregularities would appear in the orbits of the planets due to the gravitational interaction with passing comets as well as with each other. At some point these irregularities would become so great that the planetary system would require a re-formation.

Secondly, the amount of motion (i.e. velocity) in the universe would gradually decrease through friction and inelastic collisions, and periodic reformations would be required to restore it. Newton was never quite sure just how God would accomplish such a refor-mation. He made an exhaustive study of biblical prophesies like 2 Peter 3:7–13 to find answers. But at some time, in some way, a supernatural intervention by God would be necessary. Indeed God was capable of intervening at any time, since the very framework of space and time was his emenant effect. Thus, God was . . .

. . . a powerful ever-living Agent, who being in all places, is more able by his will to move the bodies within his boundless uniform sensorium [space], and thereby to form and reform the parts of the Universe, than we are by our will to move the parts of our own bodies.

The problem of the dissipation of motion in Newton's cosmology was due to the underlying dualism of active principles and passive matter. Active principles like gravitation were superimposed on a recalcitrant matter in the form of fundamental particles. The particles were infinitely hard, immutable and inert. Though created by God in the beginning, they did not manifest his continued presence as space did or his immediate activity as active principles did.

It was at this point that Leibniz took issue with Newton. A brief comparison between the two is instructive for the differing ways in which the theological ideas of the creationist tradition could be developed. There were two fundamental issues: the autonomy of nature and the relationship of God to space.

Leibniz, as we have seen, held that God had endowed brute matter with the ability to execute his laws perpetually. It was partly his belief in the indefatigability of creaturely motion that led him to postulate a *vis viva* (equivalent to the later idea of energy) that was conserved even in inelastic collisions. According to Leibniz, the *vis viva* was absorbed into the internal dynamics of the constituent particles of the bodies even when the latter ceased to move visibly. Newton, on the other hand, refused to allow a reduction of the inner dynamics of bodies to mechanical terms due to his own concern to preserve the role of God in the cosmos. As a result, God was required to restore the amount of motion supernaturally at various intervals. To Newton, a lack of complete autonomy in nature was consistent with the omnipotence of God. For Leibniz, on the other hand, it was a denial of the perfection of the original creation and, hence, inconsistent with the omnipotence of God.

Similarly, Leibniz could only see Newton's postulation of absolute space as the elevation of a creature to quasi-divine status. Corresponding to Leibniz's view of nature as nearly autonomous, was a view of God as highly transcendent, beyond all space and time. Consequently, Leibniz advocated a concept of relational space which had similarities to the post-Newtonian view of space-time developed by Albert Einstein. Newton, on the other hand, viewed space as God's means of controlling all nature. Absolute space, for him, like the decaying amount of motion in the universe, was required by the notion of an omnipotent God, whereas just the opposite conclusions were reached by Leibniz.

In his theology, Newton was an Arian. His views were not widely known during his lifetime and did not influence the teaching of the Church of England in any way. However, they were influential for an important group of his disciples, including Samuel Clarke and William Whiston, whom we shall discuss in the next chapter.

Indeed there was an organic (if not necessary) relation between Newton's natural philosophy and his Arianism. This can be seen by looking again at his concept of the relationship between God, space and time. For Newton, God was not outside space and time.

God's infinity was an infinite extension or spatial infinity, and his eternity was a limitless duration or unending time. God's extension and duration constituted space and time as we know them. When challenged on this point by Berkeley and Leibniz, Newton added a note to the second (1713) edition of the *Principia* which differentiated his view from a pantheistic identification of God with space and time but did not alter his essential position:

> He is not eternity and infinity, but eternal and infinite; he is not duration or space, but he endures and is present. He endures forever, and is everywhere present; and by existing always and everywhere, he constitutes duration and space . . . he is omnipresent not *virtually* only, but also *substantially*. . . .

This correlation of God's eternity with unending time meant that all of God's acts, internal and external, could be placed on a time line. Newton saw God as 'He that was and is and is to come' (Rev. 1:4,8, altered to suggest a temporal sequence of past, present and future for God), rather than the mysteriously transcendent God of scholasticism for whom all time was a single point (*totum simul*). Therefore, Newton could not differentiate between God's internal operations (*opera ad intra*), like the generation of the Son and the procession of the Spirit, and his external operations (*opera ad extra*) by appealing to a qualitative difference between eternity and time. Christ was, for Newton, the pre-existent Son of God, begotten before all worlds, but his generation was an event on the same time line as the creation of the world. The only difference between the generation of the Son and the creation of the world was that the former was invisible and temporally prior to the latter. Before the creation of this visible world, God exercised his omnipotence by creating an invisible world, as Origen and Basil had held (section 1.2). But, for Newton, this invisible creation included the Son of God as well as the angels. The Son was, therefore, a perfect creature, the first and greatest of all God's creatures, but neither co-eternal nor consubstantial with the Father. Thus the notion of God's eternity as limitless duration or unending time made Arianism a plausible Christology for Newton.

The overall consistency of Newton's Arian Christology with his natural philosophy can also be seen from his view of space as an 'emanent effect' of God. Space played the role, in Newton's mind, of the eternal Son of God in traditional theology. It was eternal; it was an image of God's substance; it was the primary mediator between God and his creation; it was that without which God would not be the God of Scripture. However, space was entirely impersonal and could not be regarded as a second hypostasis or personal companion of God. Newton's God was, therefore, alone in infinite space and endless time, having only a finite creature to share with (after creation) for a limited time. Again his natural philosophy made the Arian view of God and Christ quite plausible.

In order to assess Newton's contribution to our understanding of God and nature, one must recall the situation in theology and science as he found it. The dominant paradigm of natural philosophy was the mechanist tradition which was predicated on a dualism of spirit and matter, God and nature. Newton rightly sensed that such a dualism was unbiblical, and would lead to deism, or even atheism, if allowed to persist unchallenged. Positively, then, we may view Newton as a champion of biblical theism, a view in which God is active in nature, and nature is only relatively autonomous. The affirmation of a First Cause was, for Newton, a legitimate part of natural philosophy, not an import from some other mode of knowledge that transcends science.

On the negative side, however, one must recognize that Newton's doctrine of God was far from biblical. In order to defend the faith, he rightly insisted that it be 'as agreeable to reason as possible'. Unfortunately, for many, orthodox Christianity appeared far from reasonable in Newton's day. As Newton saw it, the traditional idea of divine transcendence, that of the 'Athanasian Creed', for instance, made God appear static and uninvolved in history, effectively leading to atheism. The doctrine of the Trinity appeared to him as an illogical mystery, without biblical foundation and tantamount to polytheism. Consequently, Newton turned his back on some of the most important truths of biblical theism in order not to 'render it suspect, and exclude it from the nature of things'.

One must also be concerned about the way in which Newton made room for God in his physics. Newton's intent was clearly to formulate a natural philosophy that would vindicate his faith and refute atheism. The need for supra-mechanical, active principles and for periodic supernatural interventions were his two principal ways of securing God's participation in nature. But supra-mechanical principles could be regarded as perfectly natural and even 'mechanical' in a more generalized sense of the term. This was how Newton's physics was to be interpreted by materialists and mechanists in the later eighteenth century. In effect, belief in the regular activity of God (*potentia ordinata*) was to be swallowed up by the idea of the autonomy of nature in the eighteenth century as it had in the twelfth. And, paradoxically, as Richard Westfall has pointed out, Newton himself could regard his work as the perfection of the mechanical philosophy rather than its denial.

Moreover, Newton's physics was better than he realized. Once mathematical physicists of the eighteenth century accepted his 'supra-mechanical' principles, they were able to show that the decay of motion in the solar system was negligible and that there was no need for periodic reformations of the planetary orbits. This left God without much to do as far as the physical world was concerned except concur with the laws of mathematical physics. Nature finally became viewed as entirely autonomous.

ADDITIONAL READING

Debus, A. G., *Man and Nature in the Renaissance* (Cambridge, 1978).

Dillenberger, J., *Protestant Thought and Natural Science* (Garden City, New York, 1960; London and Nashville, 1961) chaps. 1–4.

Dobbs, B. J. T., *The Foundations of Newton's Alchemy* (Cambridge, 1975).

Farrington, B., *Francis Bacon: Philosopher of Industrial Science* (New York, 1949).

Goodman, D. C., ed., *Science and Religious Belief, 1600–1900: A Selection of Primary Sources* (Dorchester, 1973), chaps. 1–12.

Hall, A. R., *The Scientific Revolution, 1500–1800* (London, revised ed., 1983).

Hall, M. B., *The Scientific Renaissance, 1450–1630* (New York, 1962).

Hannaway, O., *The Chemists and the Word* (Baltimore, 1975).

Jacob, J. R., *Robert Boyle and the English Revolution* (New York, 1977).

Jacobi, J., ed., *Paracelsus: Selected Writings* (2nd ed., Princeton, 1958).

Jammer, M., *Concepts of Space* (2nd ed., Cambridge, Mass., 1969).

Kaiser, C. B., 'Calvin's Understanding of Aristotelian Natural Philosophy', *Calviniana*, ed. R. V. Schnucker, *Sixteenth Century Essays and Studies* 10 (1980), pp. 77–92.

Kearney, H., *Science and Change, 1500–1700* (New York, 1971).

Klaaren, E. M., *Religious Origins of Modern Science* (Grand Rapids, 1977).

Kocher, P. H., *Science and Religion in Elizabethan England* (San Marino, 1953).

Koryé, A., *From the Closed World to the Infinite Universe* (Baltimore, 1957).

Langford, J. J., *Galileo, Science and the Church* (revised ed., Ann Arbor, 1971).

Lindberg, D. C., and Numbers, R. L., eds., *God and Nature: Historical Essays on the Encounter Between Christianity and Science* (Berkeley, 1986), chaps. 3–8.

McGuire, J. E., 'Force, Active Principles and Newton's Invisible Realm', *Ambix* 15 (1968), pp. 154–208.

Munitz, M. K., ed., *Theories of the Universe* (New York, 1957), pp. 149–219.

Pagel, W., *Paracelsus: Introduction to Philosophical Medicine in the Renaissance* (revised ed., Basel, 1982).

idem, *Joan Baptista Van Helmont* (Cambridge, 1982).

Randall, J. H., Jr., *The Career of Philosophy, Vol. I: From the Middle Ages to the Enlightenment* (New York, 1962).

Rattansi, P. M., 'The Social Interpretation of Science in the Seventeenth Century', *Science and Society, 1600–1900*, ed. P. Mathias (Cambridge, 1972), pp. 1–32.

Rosen, E., trans., *Three Copernican Treatises* (3rd ed., New York, 1971).

Thomas, K., *Religion and the Decline of Magic* (New York, 1971).

Webster, C., *The Great Instauration: Science, Medicine and Reform, 1626–1660* (London, 1975; New York, 1976).

Westfall, R. S., *Science and Religion in Seventeenth-Century England* (New Haven, 1958; Ann Arbor, 1973).

idem, *The Construction of Modern Science* (New York, 1971; Cambridge, 1977).

idem, *Never At Rest: A Biography of Isaac Newton* (Cambridge, 1975).

Yates, F. A., *Giordano Bruno and the Hermetic Tradition* (Chicago, 1964).

idem, *The Rosicrucian Enlightenment* (London, 1972).

Zilsel, E., 'The Genesis of the Concept of Physical Law', *Philosophical Review* 3 (1942), pp. 245–79.

idem, 'The Genesis of the Concept of Scientific Progress', *Journal of the History of Ideas* 6 (1945), pp. 325–49.

4

THE HERITAGE OF ISAAC NEWTON: FROM NATURAL THEOLOGY TO NATURALISM
(the eighteenth century)

1. THE NEWTONIAN TRADITION FROM NEWTON TO HUTTON

The eighteenth century or Enlightenment period is often viewed as a radically new departure in Western thought. It can be portrayed, for instance, as a cultural transition from faith to reason, or from the hegemony of theology to the dominance of natural science. It should be apparent from the material covered in earlier chapters, however, that such transitions had been alternately proffered and resisted many times since the eleventh century. In the eighteenth century the names were different, but the issues were fundamentally the same as in earlier periods. Newton's natural philosophy could be interpreted in such a way as to stress either the natural or the supernatural side just as the Aristotelian natural philosophy could in the late Middle Ages or the hermetic could in the Renaissance. If there was a significant shift in the eighteenth century, it came from the fact that science and technology had placed Western Europeans in a position of dominance over the peoples they colonized and over nature itself.

Theological beliefs continued to play an important role in the development of the natural sciences throughout the eighteenth, and well into the nineteenth century. The main difference from earlier periods was that there was less orthodoxy and more variety – ranging from orthodox trinitarianism to monistic materialism – in the theological stances assumed. The fact that unanimity in theology seemed more remote, or even impossible, undoubtedly contributed to the later (nineteenth and twentieth-century) tendency to suppress personal convictions in science – scientists no longer needed theological legitimation for their work anyway – but this trend was only dimly evident in the eighteenth century itself.

If there is any unity to the eighteenth century, as far as science and theology are concerned, that unity stems from the person and work of Isaac Newton. Newton had a very distinctive view of the relationship between God and nature, and his ideas were quite well known and understood in the eighteenth century. Still they may seem strange to those of us today who are accustomed to associate his name with nineteenth-century mechanistic and reductionist ideas.

For Newton, laws of nature like universal gravitation depended on God's immediate presence and activity as much as the breathing of an organism depends on the life-principle within. Like breathing, the operations of nature were regular and natural. Yet there was no possibility, in Newton's view, of taking them to be self-explanatory. Like breathing, they gave no indication as to how the present system originated or how its laws were sustained. Moreover, like breathing, they were subject to modification (e.g., suspension or acceleration) by the free self-determination of the life within. God and nature were thus in a symbiotic relationship, according to Newton, each pointing to the reality and reliability of the other.

Newton's position provided the standard against which all others in the eighteenth century measured and adjusted their own views of God and nature. For pedagogical purposes, we may categorize the varied thinkers of the period in terms of four basic responses to Newton:

(1) the Newtonians themselves who followed the master in affirming a basically stable, steady-state symbiosis of God and nature, and, within nature, of matter and spirit;

(2) monists and materialists who went beyond Newton by granting energy, life, and even thought to matter itself (not just to nature) and thus affirmed a deeper unity of matter and spirit;

(3) anti-Newtonians and anti-materialists motivated by the desire to reaffirm a more traditional theology (some more dualist and others more monistic than Newton's view);

(4) proponents of analytical mechanics (and chemistry) who went beyond the master by attempting to account for the very origin and stability of the present system of nature in strictly mechanical terms without reference to divine presence or activity.

Theologically minded readers with a homiletical bent might refer to these four responses as: God required–natural theology (1); God reduced–hylozoic monism (2); God reaffirmed–conservative anti-Newtonianism (3); and God retired–neo-mechanism (4). The purpose of the categorization is to ensure as much as possible the comparison of like thinkers with like. However, the lines are not sharply drawn and, as in any taxonomy, there are many intermediate cases and cross-influences.

So Newton's views provide unity to the eighteenth century only as a point of reference for agreement and disagreement. In fact, Newton's God-world symbiosis was satisfactory to few other than his most loyal followers. His assimilation of divine providence to cosmic functions like upholding gravitation and replenishing motion suggested a trend towards deism or materialism to the anti-Newtonians, many of whom were also concerned about the anti-trinitarian theologies of Newtonians like Clarke and Whiston. On the other hand, Newton's refusal to speculate concerning the origins of the cosmic system raised a red flag for the more bullish and mathematically inclined of his followers, the neo-mechanists. And his appeal to divine providence as the source of continued motion was regarded by monistic naturalists as detracting from the integrity and self-determination of nature. None of these emphases were entirely new: in fact, *all* of them can be seen as truncated forms of the historic creationist tradition. But the coherence of that tradition had gradually been lost and with it the possibility of providing a theological and ethical framework for scientific endeavour as a whole in the Western world.

The characteristic idea of the Newtonians was a symbiosis of God and nature, and of theology and science. A God-nature symbiosis meant, in this instance, a somewhat simplified doctrine of God, tending in some cases to unitarianism and deism. In the case of strict Newtonians, it also meant a low view of matter as absolutely inert and passive. The inertness of matter was used as evidence for the all-encompassing activity of God, and the omnipotence of God was cited in support of the stability of the present order of nature. In some cases, God's control of nature through active principles was also taken to legitimate a particular political order (based on a strong monarchy). This latter, political form of Newtonianism is particularly evident in writers like Samuel Clarke in England and Voltaire in France.

Even though the Newtonian tradition was just one of several streams of thought in the eighteenth century, it was far from homogeneous in itself. In this section we shall review a variety of options within that tradition. For one thing, we must allow for regional variation among the Newtonians of England, America, continental Europe, and Scotland. In England and America, it is useful to differentiate further between three groups of Newtonians: the anti-trinitarian Anglicans, Samuel Clarke and William Whiston; English matter theorists and astronomers like John Keill and Roger Cotes; and English and American Independents (Congregationalists) like Isaac Watts and Cotton Mather. Even within these subgroupings, we shall find considerable variation of thought, with most Newtonians leaning either to the side of hylozoic materialism or to that of neo-mechanism.

Anti-Trinitarian Anglicans: Samuel Clarke and William Whiston

The two most prominent Newtonians in the early eighteenth century were Samuel Clarke and William Whiston. We consider them first as the standard-bearers for the Newtonian tradition before we glance at a variety of lesser lights who modified Newton's ideas in significant ways.

Samuel Clarke

Samuel Clarke (1675–1729), an ordained Anglican clergyman, was noted among other things for his Boyle Lectures on Newtonian physics and natural theology (1704–5), his scepticism about the doctrine of the Trinity (1705, 1712), and his epistolary debate with Leibniz concerning the relationship of God and nature (1715–16). In all three endeavours, he was the chief spokesman for Newton in science and theology.

Like Newton, Clarke held that the important principles of physics like gravitation were active and supra-mechanical; that is, they could not be accounted for by the motion of passive material corpuscles. The opponents he had in mind here were twofold: the mechanical philosophy of Descartes and the hylozoic monism of Hobbes, Spinoza, Toland, and Collins.

According to the mechanical philosophy, all nature could be explained in terms of matter in motion and God was required only at a metaphysical level as the presupposition of science. The strongest scientific argument against consistent mechanism, according to Clarke, was the existence of supra-mechanical principles like gravitation that were functions of the total mass of the bodies involved, not of the surface areas (or cross-sections) in proportion to which some impulse might be impressed by the surrounding medium. Hence active principles could be taken as indications of the immediate presence and activity of God – albeit under the constraint of God's self-imposed laws – in the same way that miracles were used as evidence by other theologians. But active principles were regular and predictable; they were not themselves 'miracles' in the sense of being unique or unrepeatable.

According to hylozoic monists, on the other hand, matter was invested with life and movement (*conatus*) of its own. Hylozoic monists effectively absorbed God into nature, and spirit into matter. The strongest scientific argument against the monists, according to Clarke, was that there was nothing in Newton's laws themselves to determine the direction in which a supposed inherent motion should occur: the directionality had to be imposed by an externally applied force. Accordingly, without a supra-mechanical First Cause to set things in motion with a particular initial direction (in an absolute space), all things would have remained eternally at rest.

Like a good theologian, Clarke made a point of affirming the activity of God in all events, whether natural (occurring through the agency of active principles) or miraculous. The only difference between the two was that miracles were unusual, whereas active principles (like mutual gravitation) were not. From God's point of view, in fact, the natural and the miraculous were effectively the same. Clearly Clarke's intention, like that of pious Christians as far back as Augustine, was to avoid the suggestion that the 'natural' was in any sense independent of God. The suggestion of independence was a conclusion that many had drawn from the underlying dialectic of God's ordinary and absolute powers. But, intentions aside, Clarke stressed the natural (although not just the material or mechanical) and tried to refute Leibniz's charge (1710) that Newtonians appealed to miracles in their science.

In response to Leibniz, Clarke argued that, even though they depended directly and continuously on the action of God, forces like gravitation and cohesion were not 'perpetual miracles'. Clarke was right to make this distinction for active principles were universal in scope and hence played a fundamentally different role in Newtonian cosmology from that of the instances of particular providence cited earlier by Luther and Calvin (in the context of an Aristotelian cosmology). In other words, the naturalistic tendency in the Newtonians was not just the result of an increasingly comprehensive natural science – there were gaps in Newton's cosmology as great as those in Aristotle's. The tendency to naturalism was a philosophical or theological bent with a history of its own, going back at least as far as the twelfth century.

Part of the apologetic value of affirming the dependence of active principles on providence for Clarke was that the origins of the system of the world were not then amenable to naturalistic accounts. Conversely, if God were not needed to account for the maintenance of the world (by supra-mechanical active principles), Clarke reasoned, he would not be needed to account for its formation either. In that case, everything could be accounted for by natural reason, and belief in a creator God would become as redundant as it appeared (to Newtonians) to be in Descartes' cosmology. On Newton's accounting, however, the world could be seen to be the purposeful result of God's free choice and design.

In all this, Clarke was merely the mouthpiece of Newton. Newton too had affirmed the irreducible role of God in both the formation and the maintenance of the cosmos. But he also invoked divine providence to account for the periodic adjustments needed to provide the solar system with a stability that he could not see resulting from the laws of gravitation and motion alone. Here, under pressure from Leibniz (and possibly with Newton's approval), Clarke was willing to retreat a step. Leibniz required that there be a 'sufficient reason' for every phenomenon, that is, a reason good enough to account for its occurrence at one given place and time rather than another. Otherwise God would appear to be capricious. Clarke responded by grounding the periodic adjustments required to preserve the stability of the planetary system in the eternal decrees of God. In other words, even the occasional suspensions and amendments of the laws of nature were not capricious or random; they were just as much a part of God's ordained will (*potentia ordinata*) as the laws of nature themselves.

Here again (as in the case of Descartes), we have the paradoxical result that an emphasis on the omni-activity of God can lead in the direction of consistent (though not monistic) naturalism. There were six commonly cited ways in which God's actions could play a role in nature:

(1) the creation of matter and setting it in motion in accordance with certain prescribed laws;

(2) the formation of the present world system;

(3) its continued operation;

(4) its occasional reformation;

(5) occasional spiritual intrusions in human affairs through the agency of natural phenomena (e.g., comets and epidemics);

(6) miracles.

Three of these ways – primary creation, spirit intrusions and miracles – were not major issues prior to the philosophical critique of David Hume (mid-eighteenth century): they belonged to the realm of *potentia Dei absoluta*, which no one could positively deny (though the Deists openly questioned biblical miracles, Priestley still believed in them in the late-eighteenth century) but everyone could conveniently ignore for the purpose of natural science. Newton himself accepted all three, but he stressed the role of God in the three other ways we have noted: the formation of the solar system, its continued operation by active principles, and its occasional re-formation. In Clarke's writing, here really an extension of Newton's, it became clear that operation and even reformation were completely lawful and subject to scientific investigation. Only the formation of the solar system remained, for the time being, entirely beyond the province of human science. The programme of the neo-mechanists would later reduce the original formation as well as the occasional reformations to the laws of mechanics thus making God appear entirely redundant.

In theology, Clarke did more than any other scientifically-oriented figure to legitimate and reinforce three tendencies among latitudinarian (low-church) Anglicans and Nonconformists or Dissenters. First there was the tendency we have already noted to limit the present-day actions of God to the (self-imposed) laws of nature.

The second tendency Clarke reinforced was a movement towards equating Christian dogma with the conclusions of 'right reason'. In theory, this move was intended to commend Christian doctrine to scientists and other intellectuals. In fact, the God-givenness of human reason was a venerable idea with roots in the creationist tradition. In practice, however, it often meant limiting religious faith to those doctrines that could command the assent of all reasonable people.

The third tendency reinforced by Clarke is a case in point: a growing scepticism concerning the doctrine of the Trinity. For one thing, Clarke wrote, the idea of three co-equal persons in one individual substance is a logical self-contradiction. By reason, Clarke argued, there must exist one single being who is immaterial, simple (without parts), and self-existent. However, Scripture describes Christ as the 'Son of God' and as 'begotten' by God. Terms like these clearly imply dependence on the will of the Father who alone is self-existent or unoriginate and hence 'God' in the proper sense. In fact, since the eternity of God is infinite duration or everlastingness (after Newton), rather than the transcendence of time, the 'begetting' of the Son must be a temporal act of God like the creation of the world, only indefinitely earlier in time.

As in the case of Newton (section 3.3), one can see here a strong correlation between the notion of absolute space (and time) as an emanent effect of God, the interpretation of God's eternity as everlasting time, and the implausibility of the tri-unity of God – a cluster of ideas that made possible a complete reinterpretation of Christian doctrine in progressive circles of the eighteenth century.

Clarke's importance for English theology stems from the fact that he backed the new liberalism with the authority of Newtonian science. He personally omitted recitation of the 'Athanasian Creed' (the *Quicunque vult* – third and most distinctively Western of the 'ecumenical creeds') and advocated severe qualification of subscription to the Thirty-Nine Articles of the Church of England. His early questions (1705) about the authority of the 'Athanasian Creed' encouraged William Whiston to do his pioneering study (1707ff.) of the doctrine of the Trinity in the early church. Clarke's own full-length critical study of the biblical basis of the Trinity (1712) made such an impact on several Anglican clergymen that they ceased to read the Athanasian Creed in church services. And his proposal to revise subscription to the Thirty-Nine Articles was revived twice in the eighteenth century though it was never carried. But Clarke's influence was, along with that of Whiston, greatest among the dissenting denominations as we shall see momentarily.

William Whiston
William Whiston (1667–1752) was a professional mathematician who succeeded Newton as the Lucasian Professor at Cambridge in 1701. In 1710 he was dismissed on the grounds of his published disagreement with orthodox Christology. Whiston was widely regarded as an Arian (one who views Christ as a primordial angelic creature). Actually, he was more of an Origenist or Eusebian than an Arian in the strict sense: he held that Christ was a 'second god' in the Neoplatonic sense, divine yet subordinate to the supreme God.

Origenist, Eusebian and Arian leanings were all tolerated in the Church of England under Latitudinarian (Whig) policies so long as the advocates of such unorthodox views did not speak out against subscription to the Thirty Nine Articles. Newton himself was an Arian though he only divulged his heterodox views to a small circle of friends and they were not widely known at the time. However, Whiston argued his case publicly and paid the price of dismissal from the chair Newton had once held uncontested. Later in his life (1747), he joined the General Baptists who had officially broadened their standards to embrace a greater variety of theological views. Significantly, Whiston's father had been one of those ministers of Presbyterian-Puritan background who had elected to conform to the standards of the Church of England at the Restoration of the monarchy in 1660. This three-generation slide from Calvinism to latitudinarianism and unitarianism was characteristic of many Christians in the late eighteenth century. We shall see one of its many fruits in the monistic materialism of Joseph Priestley.

Whiston's criticisms of the orthodox doctrine of the Trinity were similar to those of Newton and Clarke, but even more influential.

The two main points that counted against the doctrine in Whiston's view were first that it implied the existence of three coequal gods (if Christ were granted self-existence like that of the Father) and second that the notion of a plurality of divine hypostases came from pagan thought rather than from the simple teachings of Jesus.

Although he was shunned by the Anglican establishment, Whiston's theological views, along with Clarke's, were influential among English Presbyterians like James Pierce and Joseph Hallett who precipitated the 'Non-Subscription Controversy' at the Salters' Hall Conference of Dissenters in 1719. Not only did the failure to enforce subscription to the doctrine of the Trinity bring about the demise of the fledgling union of London Presbyterians, Independents (Congregationalists) and Baptists, but it established the respectability of Arian and Unitarian views within Dissenting Academies for the duration of the century. One such academy was Daventry where Joseph Priestley received early training.

Like Newton and Clarke, Whiston treated matter as entirely passive and dependent on the continued exercise of divine power for its behaviour in accordance with the laws of nature. Whiston pressed this aspect of Newtonianism to its logical conclusion, however: the normal operation of God was consistent and universal, 'acting by fixed and constant rules'. Therefore, whenever possible events should be accounted for in terms of those rules and not ascribed to miracles unless there was sufficient reason to do so.

The desire to explain as much as possible in naturalistic terms had been, as we have seen, a persistent theme in Western thought at least since the twelfth century (Adelard of Bath, Thierry of Chartres, William of Conches). Whiston stood firmly within this tradition in spite of his invocation of divine providence to sustain the processes of nature. In fact, now that comets were understood to be lawful, periodic phenomena, they too could be pressed into service as the natural causes of extraordinary events. For example, Whiston appealed to an ancient appearance of the comet of 1680 to account for the Great Flood (enabling him to date it to 2349 BC), the rotation of the earth about its axis, and the twenty-three degree inclination of the earth's equator to the ecliptic plane. So even idiosyncracies of the present structure of the solar system could be accounted for in naturalistic terms. By treating significant aspects of the system of nature as in process in historical (albeit biblical) time, Whiston thus opened the way for later speculations concerning the origin of the cosmic system as a whole.

On the other hand, Whiston was still a great believer in the supernatural, that is, the presence and power of immaterial agencies.

He occasionally experienced prophetic trances, and, like most of his contemporaries, he could see the hand of Satan and his demons in untoward events like mental disturbance, pestilence and famine. But even the Devil operated through the medium of second causes like meteors which could be investigated scientifically. The Newtonianism of Whiston, like that of Clarke, portrayed God as functioning in mechanically predictable ways. The 'God' later neo-mechanists like Laplace were explicitly to exclude from natural science was fast becoming as monotonous as he was redundant.

English Newtonian Matter Theorists from Keill to Knight

We consider here a group of minor, yet significant, Newtonians who were primarily matter theorists. That is, they speculated about the properties of matter as functions of the underlying corpuscular structure and the active principles of Newton. It was characteristic of Newtonian matter theorists that they regarded the manifest properties of matter as epiphenomena or secondary qualities compared with the primary qualities and forces of the unmeasurably minute atoms.

The Newtonians at hand were primarily scientists, but they were also theologically informed and religiously motivated. Some like Derham and Cotes were ordained as priests. Paradoxically, as we shall see, it was Derham and Cotes who most toned down Newton's emphasis on the omniactivity of God.

Here we shall consider three slightly different directions in which matter theory developed within the Newtonian tradition:

(1) the matter minimalism of Oxford matter theorists like Keill, Freind, and Desaguliers;

(2) the tendency towards matter maximalism of Derham and Cotes;

(3) the two matter types of Gowin Knight.

Oxford Matter Minimalists: Keill and Freind

John Keill (1671–1721) was lecturer in natural philosophy (1694) and professor of astronomy (1712) at Oxford. He was the first to formulate the so-called 'nutshell theory' of matter (1708) and was thus partly responsible for instigating the later Leibniz-Clarke debate (1715–16) concerning the relation of God and nature. Prior to that he had coined the term 'momentum' (1700), one of the most important concepts in modern physics, thus instigating the so-called *vis viva* debate between Newtonians and Leibnizians. Although they were distinct issues, the nutshell theory and opposition to *vis viva* were coordinated thrusts of an anti-Leibnizian campaign. All three elements – the nutshell matter theory, opposition to *vis viva*, and criticism of Leibniz's view of matter as self-active – were clearly stated in the 'authorized' popularization of Newton's ideas, Henry Pemberton's *View of Sir Isaac Newton's Philosophy* (1728).

As Keill defined it, the momentum of a moving object was the product of its mass and its velocity. Like velocity, it is a vector quantity; that is, it has direction in space. The momentum of a body is the impulse that it would communicate to another body at rest. Thus it could be taken as a measure of the force exerted by a falling body on the earth where it impacts. Leibniz (a matter maximalist, if you will) argued that the proper measure of such force should be the product of the mass and the *square* of the velocity (section 3.3), and a philosophical-scientific-theological debate ensued which was never quite resolved. Eventually, second-generation Newtonians like Desaguliers and Boscovich came to the conclusion that both mv and mv^2 were legitimate measures of force.

The *vis viva* debate is interesting for the way in which theological and apologetic (and even political) concerns interacted with experimental physics. The importance for Newtonians of the vectorial nature of force, lay, as we have seen, in the inferred necessity for a prime mover to start things out with a particular initial direction in absolute space. In contrast, scalar quantities, which could be defined without reference to direction, were preferred by Leibnizians partly because they saw motion as inherent in matter by virtue of God's creation and providence. The ostensibly scientific argument about *vis viva* thus involved two totally different philosophies and theologies of nature. Each side feared (or at least claimed) that the other would lead to atheism.

This attempt by Newtonians to empty matter of inherent qualities like motion was paralleled by a reduction of matter to a nutshell in volume and the consequent emphasis on the role of impressed forces in physics and chemistry. The nutshell theory developed one of the most astounding thoughts of Isaac Newton – the notion, first adumbrated in the early editions of his *Opticks* (1704, 1706), that all the atoms in a solid would, if packed tightly together, fit neatly inside a much smaller volume. The scientific rationale for this paradox was that light (consisting of fine material particles for Newton) could pass unhindered through great quantities of transparent substances like glass and water. In other words, matter was highly porous and what appeared to be a solid to human senses was really mostly empty space between indefinitely small atoms. The responsibility for maintaining the apparently stable structure of the macroscopic world thus lay with supra-mechanical forces (and hence with God) rather than with matter itself.

The philosophical effect of Newton's idea was to undermine the very foundation of mechanism and materialism, the notion of the primacy of matter in physics. In fact, the context in which Keill first made the nutshell theory explicit was a series of attacks on the matter theory of Leibniz in 1708, 1714 and 1715. As Keill put it in his 1715 textbook, the proportion between the space occupied by the constituent atoms of a solid and the total volume of that solid is comparable to that of a grain of sand to the whole earth.

Since the amount of matter in a substance was so insignificant, it made sense to describe its macroscopic (chemical) properties in terms of forces acting at a distance between the microscopic atoms. Keill himself attempted (1708) to develop an analogue to Newton's law of gravitational attraction for the attractive forces between the atoms of a chemical compound. John Freind (1675–1728), who studied under Keill at Oxford, described (1709) the matter-minimalist programme as one in which 'almost all the Operations of Chymistry are reduced to their true [i.e., Newtonian] Principles, and the Laws of Nature'. Thus the minimalization of matter did not put natural processes beyond the reach of mathematical science. To the contrary, a subordination of matter to immaterial principles went together with a high degree of mathematical formalism as had often been the case earlier in the Neoplatonic tradition of the Middle Ages and the Renaissance.

Newtonian Matter Maximalists: Derham and Cotes

If the tendency of Newtonian followers of Keill was to minimize the extent and power of matter, that of Derham and Cotes was in a very different direction.

William Derham (1657–1735) is best known for the 'Physico-theology' of his Boyle Lectures (1711–12), which set a standard for the natural theology tradition that culminated in the turn-of-the-century writings of William Paley (1795, 1802).

Derham continued the patristic and Reformed tradition of valuing secular skills as divine gifts. The basic idea is now familiar from figures like Basil, Hugh of St Victor, Paracelsus, Luther, and Calvin. Derham went beyond his forebears, however, in including non-productive, entrepreneurial skills like commerce and management among divine gifts along with more traditionally valued trades like craftsmanship and medicine. He also concluded that Africans and American Indians were, by God's design, less gifted as entrepreneurs than Europeans and that the latter were thereby entitled to 'ransack the whole globe'. At this point in history, western Europeans were clearly achieving a degree of power that made their science and technology as oppressive to nations they colonized as foreign technologies had been to the Israelites in the Old and inter-testamental periods (section 1.5).

Just as God implanted spiritual inclinations in all humans (albeit unequally) at birth, he also impressed active principles like gravitation on all matter at creation. The positive qualities of matter were, for Derham, not intrinsic to matter, but implanted, just like those of gifted people. There was thus a direct analogy here between the socio-political and the natural worlds.

The analogy was powerful, but it came at a price. Just as gifts and inclinations once implanted within humans become part of their nature, so active principles like gravitation and cohesion once impressed on material bodies become properties of their nature. This was a significant departure from Newton's view that active principles represented the continued immediate, though lawful, activity of God.

In fact, Derham was shying away from the suggestion that God could be viewed as a world-soul like Henry More's Spirit of Nature. That such a notion could be inferred from Newton's symbiotic model of God and nature had already been argued by Leibniz in support of his charge that Newton's ideas would lead in the direction of pantheistic materialism. Derham was thus pulled away from the matter-minimalism of Newton and Keill in the direction of another sun, the matter-maximalism of Leibniz. He was also following a variant of the mechanical philosophy developed by Robert Boyle and John Ray according to which the best evidence of the work of God was to be found in the structure and function of living organisms, particularly the instincts imprinted in animals. Whether by the anti-Newtonian pull of Leibniz or the pre-Newtonian push of Boyle and Ray, Derham was inclined to deviate from the strictly Newtonian line.

Another follower of Newton who deviated from the strict Newtonian line was Roger Cotes (1682–1716), first Plumian professor of natural philosophy at Cambridge. A trusted collaborator of both Newton and Whiston, Cotes was given the responsibility of editing and writing a preface for the second edition of Newton's *Principia* (1713). The new preface read like a counter-attack against the arguments Leibniz had mounted against Newton's hypothesis of forces acting at a distance without material mediation. In order to defend Newton, Cotes made two moves that were to have an impact on subsequent matter theory. First, he stated that Leibniz's requirement for a material substratum of all forces would lead to the conclusion that the world was driven to its present state of order by qualities inherent in its material nature rather than by the sheer will of God. In fact, any matter imbued with such qualities must always have existed thus ruling out the notion of an original creation as well as the formation of matter. In this respect, Cotes spoke prophetically of much of later eighteenth-century natural philosophy.

Cotes' second move against Leibniz was to forestall the charge that active principles were occult phenomena beyond the scope of rigorous science. In order to do so, however, he was forced to classify gravitation 'among the primary qualities of all bodies'. Prior to this, Newton had specified the primary qualities of matter to be those like spatial extension, impenetrability, mobility, and inertia which could not be denied as attributes of a portion of matter without denying its very existence. The status of gravitation as a manifestation of God's regular activity in nature seemed to place it on an entirely different footing from the primary qualities even though the law governing it was perfectly mathematical. Newton himself had tried to parry Leibniz's blow by arguing that gravitation was 'seated in the frame of nature' just like the primordial qualities of matter (c 1712) and by grounding the active principles in a subtle material ether (1717). But Cotes' solution was far more radical and ran directly counter to Newton's earlier denial (1692–3) of the notion that gravitation was in any sense a property of matter.

With or without his consent, Newton's foremost mental offspring, the immaterial and supra-mechanical principle of gravitation, had thus been wedded to brute matter, or so Cotes' new preface could be read. And so it was read, particularly among post-Newtonians of the mid-eighteenth century who tended towards pantheistic materialism and neo-mechanism. Cotes thus contributed to a fulfilment of his own dire prediction about the possibility of a purely naturalistic science without God.

Two Matter Types of Gowin Knight

Gowin Knight (1713–72) was born the same year Cotes published the new edition of the *Principia*. Knight is important primarily for his generalization of active principles to account for repulsive as well as attractive forces. Interestingly, it was Cotes who first drew the attention of Newtonians to the role of repulsive forces, in his account of the elasticity of air. Knight, however, went further and attempted 'to demonstrate that all the Phenomena in Nature may be explained by two simple active Principles, Attraction and Repulsion'

(1754). Part of the reason for his appreciation for the duality of forces was Knight's early production of and experimentation with artificial magnets, which, of course, exhibit clear polarity.

For Knight, as for all Newtonians, nature depended directly on the presence and activity of God. But Knight took this principle to its logical conclusion. Even the immutability of the primary qualities of matter merely expressed the immutability of God. And the irresistibility and inexorability of natural causation expressed the immutability of his will (as for Descartes). It appears that Cotes' wedding of active principles to matter had had the effect of eliminating Newton's duality of matter and force for Knight as for others. But rather than force being reduced to a property of matter, as it was for the materialists, matter for Knight was reduced to a function of force and divine power. A similar challenge to the notion of primary qualities was developed by Jonathan Edwards, whom we consider below, as a counter to materialistic monism.

The reduction of matter to a function of force had the effect of requiring two distinct types of matter for Knight, who prefigured in this respect the later work of James Hutton. Unlike gravitation which was universally attractive, electric and magnetic forces could be either attractive or repulsive. Therefore, there must be two types of primary particle, Knight reasoned. Clearly one type of matter consisted of particles that attracted all other particles indiscriminately – this was ordinary Newtonian gravitational matter. In addition, Knight hypothesized another type of matter consisting of particles that attracted gravitational matter but repelled other particles of their own kind. This new, repellant matter accounted for the phenomena of light, heat, electricity, and magnetism. The significant feature of Knight's speculations was the rejection of the homogeneity of matter assumed by the mechanical philosophy and affirmed in most of Newton's writings. Aristotle's five types of matter had been reduced to one by the mechanical philosophers, but that one had now increased back to two, even within the Newtonian tradition.

In a sense Knight's division of the kingdom of matter complemented his elimination of Newton's duality of passive matter and active force. Both moves had the effect of weakening the primacy of matter as an irreducible given in physics, and thus paralleled the notion of the porosity of matter with the 'nutshell' matter theorists. However, Knight's differentiation of two types of primary particle also had the effect of making mutual attraction and mutual repulsion intrinsic properties of those types of matter over and above the mechanical primary qualities common to all particles. As we shall see again in the case of Boscovich and Priestley, the reduction of matter to force could lead to a higher view of matter itself.

English and American Independents: Isaac Watts and Cotton Mather
Newtonian ideas were particularly popular among moderate Independents (Congregationalists) in England and America who were sympathetic to Whig policies of toleration for Nonconformists. Here we shall briefly consider two representative figures: Isaac Watts and Cotton Mather.

Isaac Watts
Isaac Watts (1674–1748) typifies the concurrence in many early eighteenth-century Christians of warm-hearted piety with hard-headed natural philosophy, and of liberal churchmanship with speculative theology. The common denominator to these seemingly contradictory tendencies was the currently popular attempt to differentiate between unambiguous data upon which all reasonable persons should agree and individual speculation consistent with the data. Watts was sparing in his listing of data and, at the same time, expansive in his personal theology.

Though opposed to the excesses of antinomian 'enthusiasm' and ambivalent towards the Great Awakening in America, Watts was concerned to bring a degree of warmth to Calvinist worship through his sermons and hymns. The words and music of hymns like 'O God, our help in ages past', 'When I survey the wondrous cross', and 'Joy to the world' were enough to move even the strictest Calvinists and most hardened agnostics to genuine religious experience. But deep Christian piety did not prevent Watts from affirming that nature was entirely mechanical: so mechanical, in fact, that, once God had imposed the laws of motion (i.e., Newton's laws) on matter at creation, the subsequent formation and history of all things, including living organisms, took place strictly as a consequence of those laws.

Of course, Watts did not deny the complete freedom of God in choosing the laws of nature in the first place, or the complete dependence of both matter and motion on continued divine preservation: this much was in accordance with Newton. However, all the active powers arising from divinely imposed laws could, according to Watts, be included within the 'Mechanical Motions and Powers of Matter' by definition. Here, as with Samuel Clarke and William Derham, Newton's divinely imposed active principles were absorbed into the very mechanical philosophy which they had been designed by Newton to refute.

As to churchmanship and theology: according to Watts, only the clear statements of Scripture should be taken as binding on Christian consciences. One ought not, therefore, to require subscription to human doctrines, not even venerable doctrines like the view of the Trinity enshrined in the 'Athanasian Creed'. Watts, therefore, supported the majority of his dissenting colleagues in opposing the motion to require subscription to 'Athanasian' trinitarian standards at the Salters' Hall conference of dissenting ministers in 1719. One sees here again the impact on dissenting groups of current Latitudinarianism and Newtonian natural theology as mediated by Clarke and Whiston. One can also begin to see the reason behind later efforts on the part of nineteenth-century Presbyterian theologians like Charles Hodge to ground basic Christian doctrines in scriptural data through a quasi-scientific inductive method.

On the other hand, Watts was by no means a minimalist in his personal theology. He did not reject the Trinity or the deity of Christ himself, but rather sought to reconcile those leaning towards Arianism and Unitarianism. Accordingly, he attempted (1722–5) to reformulate the traditional doctrine in order 'to vindicate the true and proper deity of Christ and the Holy Spirit' against the charge that it implied 'three distinct conscious minds' in the godhead. For example, he developed a speculative notion, going back to the seventeenth-century independent, Thomas Goodwin, that Christ had possessed a human soul or conscious mind since the beginning of time. On the basis of this theory Watts could argue that the coexistence with God of a second (divine-human) person did not necessarily imply a plurality of conscious minds in the Godhead itself and thus avoid both Arianism and tritheism. Note that the pre-existence of the human soul in the case of Jesus also had the effect of reinforcing the notion of a strict separability of matter and spirit that was advocated by many British moderates.

Watts' Christology was more than just a curious vagary in the history of Christian doctrine. When Joseph Priestley later decided against the traditional doctrines of the Trinity and matter-spirit dualism on the grounds that they were pagan intrusions into biblical faith, he had in mind teachings then current in dissenting academies influenced by Watts that associated the deity of Christ and the duality of matter and spirit with the idea of the pre-existence of the human soul as found in Plato and Origen. On the other hand, Watts' own speculations were grounded in the incipient rationalism, naturalism and Arianism of the Newtonian philosophy itself. Thus, a dissenting minister known today primarily for his moving hymns could play a vital, if minor, role in the development of eighteenth-century natural philosophy towards materialism and neo-mechanism.

Cotton Mather

Cotton Mather (1663–1728), a leading churchman of colonial New England, was a far more complex figure even than Watts. His modern biographers invariably find outright contradictions: e.g. between his angel-mysticism and his mechanistic worldview; between his empirical medicine and his belief in the existence of a Nishmath-Chajim that governs all bodily functions; and between his concern for rules of evidence and his gullibility concerning the confessions used as evidence in the Salem witchcraft trials. Clearly Mather reflected the confluence of a variety of intellectual and spiritual themes, but, if more eclectic, he was no more inconsistent that many of his contemporaries. Consistency is a distinctively modern ideal and was probably unknown before the nineteenth century. Like most supposed traits of human nature, it is a construct that is meaningful for certain eras and contexts, but not for others.

Our concern here is with the degree and nature of Mather's response to the new science and particularly to Newtonianism. Though more conservative theologically than their English colleagues, the American Puritans had most of the latest books and were current with continental science. Cotton was familiar with the writings of mechanical philosophers like Descartes, Gassendi and Boyle, declaring in 1689 that corpuscularianism was the only right philosophy. Like Charleton and Boyle, he argued (1702) that the atomistic concept of matter required the impression of order by an external agent and thus furnished convincing proof of the existence of God.

Cotton's father, Increase Mather, had been inspired by the appearance of the comet of 1680 – and by the naturalistic *Pensées* of Pierre Bayle whose publication (1682) had been occasioned by the comet – to read up on the latest European astronomical studies. His *Kometographia* (1683) recognized that comets, like planets, move in elliptical orbits. In spite of the fact that he did not fully understand the periodicity of cometary motion and that he still took comets to be direct signs of judgment from God (*pace* Bayle), Increase suggested that their appearance could be predicted scientifically from conjunctions of the superior planets.

Cotton Mather also observed the comet of 1680 and published a technical description of it in 1683. The deep impression made on his mind by this new messenger from the heavens can be sensed from a statement he made in one of his sermons that year: '*Every*

Wheel in this *huge clock* moves just according to the *Rule* which the *All-wise Artist* gave it at the first'. The cosmos thus appeared to be as mechanical in the late seventeenth century on one side of the Atlantic as on the other. Even thunder and lightning, according to Mather (1694), were caused by the mechanical clashing of clouds containing explosive vapours from decaying vegetable matter.

Cotton's mechanistic view of thunder did not exclude the active role of evil spirits, however. According to an older cosmology surviving in passages of Scripture, the Devil was the 'Prince of the power of the air' (Eph. 2:2). In accordance with God's prior design and permission, Satan could use his power to set the cosmic wheels in motion and thus wreak havoc and cause plagues on earth. In context, there was no real 'inconsistency' here. Most early modern machines were operated by humans; wind and water power were ancient but imperfectly harnessed; steam engines and automation came later. Correspondingly, the course of nature was thought to be governed by mathematical laws and mechanisms but also subject to alteration – all the more so as the millennium approached and Satan stepped up his attacks.

Mediating between intelligences like demons and inert matter was a 'Plastic Spirit' which, though lacking intelligence and will, permeated the world and governed the dynamics of matter in accordance with mathematical laws. In individual bodies, the spirit took the form of the Helmontian *archeus* – Mather called it the 'Nishmath-Chajim' – which presided over the metabolism and reproduction of each organism. Mather found clear scientific evidence for the existence of such a spirit in the ability of plants to regenerate themselves from mere cuttings. As with the Platonists, this subtle material substance perfectly expressed Mather's ambivalence regarding the relation of nature to God; it was both natural and spiritual, both autonomous and dependent on God, at the same time. And, like the Cambridge Platonists, Mather saw in the Plastic Spirit evidence that there was something more than mechanics in the operations of nature. The operation of Plastic Spirit was no more unintelligible or 'occultic' than a strictly mechanical account would be.

The impression made by the idea of mechanism was a lasting one, but the idea took on a different meaning in Mather's later work as the result of the newer Newtonian science. The mechanical ideal was reinforced by his reading of John Ray and William Derham and was clearly stated in his influential *Christian Philosopher* (1721), the first textbook on science to be written by an American:

The Great God has contrived a mighty *Engine*, of an extent that cannot be measured, and there is in it a contrivance of *Motions* that cannot be numbered. He is infinitely gratified with the view of this *Engine* in all its *Motions* . . .

Comets, of course, were part of the 'mighty engine'. That in itself would not prevent their serving (as they did for Whiston) as the instruments of spiritual powers and hence portending untoward events like war and pestilence. However, by the time he wrote the *Christian Philosopher*, Mather had also read 'the admirable Sir Isaac Newton, whom we now venture to call the *Perpetual Dictator* of the learned World in the *Principles of Natural Philosophy*'. Among other things, Mather picked up on Newton's speculations in the *Principia* about the vapours of comets replenishing the water supply on earth. Newton's speculations had been motivated by a concern for the stability of the system of nature (mirrored always in the stability of early modern society). The facts were these: comets periodically spewed vapours into space; and the water supply on earth was gradually being converted into solid vegetable matter and earth. Therefore, Newton reasoned, a balance would be maintained if the excess caused by one made up for the deficiency caused by the other.

'If this be so', wrote Mather, 'the Appearance of *Comets* is not so dreadful a thing, as the *Cometomantia*, generally prevailing, has represented it.' Mather's concern was apparently the pastoral one of delivering people from fear of the unknown rather than the more scientific one of balancing the processes of nature. Still, he was hedging his bets: his citation of Newton was followed by quotations from other authorities who still held that cometary vapours were potentially noxious and could be instruments of divine judgement.

There was more at stake here than just an emphasis on mechanisms and cycles in nature: a fundamental shift was taking place in the meaning of a numinous natural phenomenon. Since ancient times, comets had been ominous clues to the meaning of history, cosmic copulas that bound the heavens together with human life in mutual sympathy. Newtonian comets were life-supporting but silent; they ensured that the water supply would not run out, but they did nothing to make human life more bearable or history more meaningful.

Comets, however, were just one of many traditional links between heaven and earth. Mather could afford to trade them away partly because he still had meteors, tempests and thunder to ensure the continued activity of spirits in the everyday world: '. . . the *Heavens do Rule'*, he said (1719), 'and the *Invisible World* has an astonishing share in the Government of *Ours*.'

Clearly, Cotton Mather was an eclectic more than a Newtonian in the strict sense. His distance intellectually from the mainstream of English Newtonian thought may help to account for the fact that, while adopting the new cosmology, he did not follow the theological trend towards Arianism and Unitarianism. Like many English Latitudinarians and Dissenters of his time, Mather emphasized the reasonableness of Christian faith. He even offered a simplified formulation of doctrine (1717) that would allow all genuine believers to join together in a pan-Christian union. His aim again was the pastoral one of avoiding the excesses of theological controversy and easing the consciences of lay Christians uncertain about the finer points of doctrine. But unlike some of his colleagues, Mather included the Trinity (doctrinal formulation unspecified) as one of the non-negotiable truths common to all true believers.

Mather was aware of Arian leanings among his English colleagues as early as 1699. He became concerned about the challenge of his 'learned friend Whiston' in 1711 and was even assailed by doubts himself. But Mather prayed to God and received 'sweet satisfaction . . . in His truth, concerning three eternal persons in His infinite Godhead'. Like William Derham, Mather finally gravitated towards another sun besides Newton, and it wasn't Leibniz.

Cotton's view of human reason was more theistic than naturalistic. Like most of his colleagues, he viewed reason as a divine gift and was optimistic about the possibility of understanding God's works with its aid (cf. section 1.2). But the grounding of reason in the divine image implied for Mather that direct illumination by God was both possible and required. Reason was not autonomous, but a participant in a larger reality and responsive to the voice of God. Hence there was no 'contradiction' between following reason and receiving divine guidance.

The difference between Mather's stance and that of Isaac Watts became clear in the wake of the Salters' Hall controversy of 1719. Both were motivated by a desire to unite dissenting Christians around the essentials of the faith. But, whereas Watts saw the imposition of subscription to a trinitarian standard as exceeding the clear requirements of Scripture and potentially divisive, Mather saw the lack of doctrinal imposition as a refusal to rally round a common, biblical standard and as opening the fellowship of the Church to heretics. The underlying difference seems to be that of most English Latitudinarians and Dissenters took God the creator to be the focus of their piety. Mather's religion, on the other hand, was centred in the immediate lordship of Jesus Christ over the Church, the state, and personal life. Any attempt to allow doubts about the divine status of Christ was as much an attack on the New England way of life as witchcraft was.

The examples of Watts and Mather indicate the pervasiveness of mechanistic and Newtonian ideas in early eighteenth-century English-speaking culture. There is little evidence here of any 'conflict' between science and religion. On the other hand, serious questions were being raised about the impact of Newtonian natural theology on biblical faith and on the doctrine of the Trinity in particular. Accordingly, some of the anti-Newtonian figures we shall consider later (section 4.3) made the Trinity foundational to their own distinctive natural philosophies.

Continental Newtonians from Boerhaave to Boscovich

Newtonian ideas were first introduced into France in the late seventeenth century by Oldenburg and Malebranche, but it was not until their championing by Boerhaave, Maupertius and Voltaire in the 1730s that they began to attract many followers in continental Europe. As we shall see, the manner in which Newton was interpreted differed greatly, with Boerhaave and Maupertius tending towards the materialist side and Euler, Voltaire and Boscovich opposing that tendency in various ways. Boerhaave's younger colleague, s'Gravesande, who had already popularized Newtonian ideas in 1720, went so far in the materialist direction that we shall treat him in the following section.

Boerhaave and Maupertius

Herman Boerhaave (1668–1738), the son of a Dutch Reformed minister, began his studies at Leiden in the fields of theology and philosophy before turning to medicine. He eventually became professor of medicine, chemistry and botany, thus holding three of the five chairs on the Leiden Faculty of Medicine.

Boerhaave is often regarded as the founder of 'rational' medicine and chemistry: his system of medicine (1708) was so influential that the early eighteenth century was known among contemporary physicians as the 'Age of Boerhaave'. The new system's approach to natural science was empirical and eclectic, based on the chemical philosophy of Van Helmont (iatrochemistry) as well as the mechanical philosophy of Bacon and Boyle (iatrophysics). As early as 1715, Boerhaave incorporated Newton's idea of attraction at a distance into his chemistry. This overall synthesis was later popularized in his *Elements of Chemistry* (1732).

Boerhaave's most important contribution to the Newtonian tradition was his view of elemental fire as the basic active principle that pervades the cosmos. Fire played an instrumental role in chemical reactions by altering the forces of attraction between the atoms of various substances. Boerhaave's fire was material, but not ponderable; that is, it had no weight, offered no resistance, and could penetrate solid matter. It radiated from the sun (an old hermetic idea) and circulated through the solar system revitalizing motion and life, particularly on the earth. Though consistent with Newtonian speculations on the ether and on comet vapours, Boerhaave's ideas pointed in the direction of hylozoic materialism and had a deep influence on early vitalists like s'Gravesande, Haller and Shaw (section 4.2).

In medicine, Boerhaave is significant for his notion of a supra-mechanical 'Aura' or *Spiritus rector* which presided over the body and directed its functions. This Aura had been implanted by God in each living creature at creation. Clearly Boerhaave's Aura was related to Van Helmont's *archeus* and Mather's Nishmath-Chajim. Spiritualist ideas were thus alive and well in the early eighteenth-century Netherlands and America in spite of their association with the radical fringe in seventeenth-century England (section 3.3).

Pierre Louis Moreau de Maupertius (1698–1759) was as much a Newtonian as Boerhaave and like the latter shifted in a materialistic direction, though with a very different emphasis and far more radical consequences. Whereas Boerhaave followed the anti-speculative, empiricist side of Newtonian research, Maupertius developed the mathematical and philosophical side. And, whereas Boerhaave combined Newtonian ideas with the Helmontian chemical philosophy, Maupertius combined them with Leibniz's monadology (section 3.3). He was thus transitional from Newtonian natural theology to hylozoic monism and could just as easily be treated in the following section on post-Newtonian materialists.

In 1728, Maupertius visited England and became a convinced exponent of the Newtonian philosophy. He was instrumental in introducing Newtonian ideas into both France and Germany, where he served (after 1746) as president of the Berlin Academy at the invitation of Frederick the Great. When in his later work (1750s) Maupertius turned in a decidedly materialist direction, he was partly responsible for introducing Leibnizian ideas back into France.

The development of Maupertius's thought is therefore a confirmation of a materialist tendency we have already seen in Newtonians like William Derham and Roger Cotes. On the other hand, the steady anti-Leibnizianism (tending towards neo-mechanism) of his younger colleague at Berlin, Leonhard Euler (1707–83), is further evidence of the variety of possible directions Newtonians could develop. Whereas Maupertius combined Newtonian ideas with Leibniz's pansophism, Euler combined them with the very Cartesian mechanism Maupertius opposed.

Maupertius began as a perfectly responsible Newtonian, however. In fact, he was responsible for 'verifying' (1736–7) one of the key predictions of Newton's *Principia* – the flattening of the earth at the poles – over against the equatorial constriction predicted by the rival Cartesian philosophy then popular in France. With the awesome reputation of 'Flattener of the Earth', Maupertius then campaigned against the Cartesians arguing that Newton's concept of action at a distance was perfectly acceptable in physics and need not be replaced by a mechanistic explanation of gravitation. An adequate rationale for Newton's physics could be found instead, Maupertius contended, in a 'Principle of Least Action' which he offered (1740–46) as an antidote to Cartesian mechanism as well as to Leibniz's principle of the conservation of *vis viva*.

'Action', a foundational concept of modern physics, was first defined by Maupertius as the product of the velocity (or momentum) and the distance through which a material body travels at that velocity. From the empiricist point of view, action was clearly a second-order concept, less closely tied to immediate observation than the standard Newtonian concepts of distance and velocity, or even mass, force and momentum. It turned out to be a more fundamental concept, however, and it has played a role in several major advances in nineteenth- and twentieth-century physics.

The 'Principle of Least Action' was a reformulation of Newton's laws of motion in teleological terms using the concept of action: given the starting and ending points of its path in space, the trajectory of a body (position and velocity at each point) between those points must be such as to make its cumulative action a minimum (in general, an extremum). In other words, the slightest deviation from that trajectory would result in an increase in the cumulative action. This truly amazing result was bound to raise theological questions. How does a bit of matter know enough to move in just the right way to realize such an economy of motion?

In Maupertius's view, the Principle of Least Action was a necessary consequence of the wisdom of God and hence provided a metaphysical foundation for natural philosophy. Conversely, the experimental verification of least action in nature could be used as a proof of the existence and basic attributes of God. Moreover, the gradual decrease of the total amount of action in the universe due to inelastic collisions indicated the need for periodic divine intervention to keep things going.

At this point in his career, Maupertius followed the natural theology of Newton, though he appealed to a teleology inherent in Newton's equations rather than the supra-mechanical nature of active principles like gravitation. On the other hand, he rejected Newton's argument that initial features of the solar system like the co-planarity of the planets could not be explained by mechanical principles and hence had to be referred directly to divine manipulation. In this step towards neo-mechanism, Maupertius resembled other Newtonians like Whiston and Watts.

An earlier 'minimum principle' for light, using increments of time, had been suggested by Pierre de Fermat already in 1661. Maupertius regarded his Principle of Least Action as more general than Fermat's, applying to both solid bodies and to light (which was regarded as corpuscular by Newtonians in any case). He thus suggested a unification of mechanics and optics that remained a guiding ideal of theoretical physics until it was realized in nineteenth-century Hamiltonian, and twentieth-century quantum, mechanics.

While the Principle of Least Action was a legitimate mathematical development of Newton's mechanics, philosophically it owed much to the pansophism of Newton's antagonist Leibniz. Even brute matter in Leibniz's view displayed a degree of intelligence by virtue of its God-given ability to function in accordance with prescribed laws. In his early work (1740s), Maupertius was influenced mostly by Leibniz's ideas (in opposition to Descartes') on final causes in nature. In fact, he became embroiled in a priority dispute (1751–2) with the one of Leibniz's disciples concerning the origins of the Principle of Least Action. In an alternative form the idea may have been stated by Leibniz as early as 1707.

In the final decade of his life (1750s), Maupertius developed a hylozoic materialism similar to that of Buffon and Diderot (section 4.2). He was impressed by recent evidence for spontaneous generation gathered by John Tuberville Needham (late 1740s). He also did studies of his own, demonstrating the inheritance of traits from both matriarchal and patriarchal lines of descent. Newton's principles, Maupertius concluded, were adequate (once supplemented by the Principle of Least Action) for the purposes of physics and astronomy, but biological problems like spontaneous generation and heredity required additional principles like appetite, perception, memory, and will as properties of atomic matter itself. Mental activity, he concluded, was not a separate substance as Descartes and the mechanical philosophers held, but a fundamental property of matter like extension. Even human thought was the result of the combined activity of the elementary atoms. Various forms of life and intelligence could, therefore, have evolved naturally from mere matter through the inheritance of acquired traits and natural selection.

Maupertius was thus an important forerunner of the evolutionary ideas of Lamarck in the late eighteenth and early nineteenth centuries. Still there was no conflict between natural selection and theology in his view. Since the laws of nature and the properties of matter were God's own work to begin with and reflected divine wisdom, there was no contradiction between attributing such powers to matter and believing in God.

The ease with which Maupertius shifted from Newtonian natural philosophy to hylozoic materialism is breathtaking! As contributing factors we have noted the tendency of some Newtonians (e.g., Roger Cotes) to anchor active principles in matter, the direct influence of Leibniz, and experimental evidence for spontaneous generation and bilineal descent. Behind all of these partial explanations, however, was the multivalent idea of creation itself. As in the Middle Ages and Renaissance, the idea of creation could inspire awe for the power of the Creator, but it could also evoke faith in the power of God's creature.

Voltaire and Boscovich

In the face of the mounting threat of neo-mechanism and materialism, Newtonians in France and Italy rallied around the Newtonian standard. The prestige of Newton was exploited particularly by French social moderates like Voltaire and Boscovich to counter more radical tendencies in philosophy and politics.

François-Marie Arouet de Voltaire (1694–1778) was nearly contemporary with Maupertius both in age and in championing the ideas of Newton. After visiting England and consulting with Newtonians like Clarke and Pemberton (1726–9), he published his famous *Philosophical Letters on the English* (1734) in which he contrasted Newton with Descartes to the decided advantage of the former. Voltaire's gift of expression still conveys a sense of the enormity of the choice in worldview that he and his philosophical contemporaries faced.

A Frenchman arriving in London finds philosophy changed as well as everything else . . . At home it is the pressure of the moon which causes the tides; in England it is the sea which gravitates towards the moon. According to the Cartesians, everything happens by virtue of an incomprehensible impulse; according to Newton, it is by an attraction of which the cause may not be understood.

Realizing the importance of natural philosophy for an integrated picture of the world, Voltaire studied Newton's work for five years (1736–41). Not being trained in mathematics himself, he relied on the help of his mistress, his 'Lady Newton', the Marquise du Châtelet, who studied Newtonian physics with Maupertius and his pupil Clairaut. Voltaire's *Elements of the Philosophy of Newton* (1738), largely based on the work of Châtelet, was a vibrant declaration of independence from Descartes' necessitarianism and from the Church's authority as much as a defence of Newton himself.

Descartes' ideas had been adopted by conservative scholars like the Jesuits in the early eighteenth century as the result of their newly-alleged consistency with Catholic dogma. Now Voltaire exulted in Newton's sense of divine sovereignty as a symbol of human freedom from all worldly systems. Whereas English latitudinarians valued their Church as comprehensive and socially-beneficial, Voltaire and other French *philosophes* abhorred theirs as power-hungry and bigoted. One might well ponder the change that had taken place since the eleventh and twelfth centuries when the sovereignty of God had been cited by conservative Catholics as an antidote to the strictures of Aristotelian dialectic and the power of the state (section 1.4).

Voltaire was anti-clerical, but not really anti-religious as such. 'People must have a religion', he quipped, 'and not believe in priests, just as they must have a diet and not believe in physicians.' On the other hand, religion (like diet) was only a part of life for Voltaire and should not be allowed to interfere with secular affairs like investments in the stock market. His comments on the secularity of contemporary business practice perfectly express the way in which moral and religious considerations had been confined to social enclaves of personal preference:

Enter the London Stock Exchange, that place more respectable than many a court . . . There the Jew, the Mohammedan, and the Christian deal with each other as if they were of the same religion and give the name of infidel only to those who go bankrupt. There the Presbyterian trusts the Anabaptist, and the Anglican honours the Quaker's promise. On leaving these peaceful and free assemblies, some go to the synagogue, others to drink; . . .

others go their church to await the inspiration of God, their hats
on their heads, and all are content.'

In order to appreciate the peace and joy Voltaire experienced in the
London Stock Exchange of all places, one must recapture some
sense of the pain and disillusionment with doctrinal differences that
had been occasioned by religious disputes in Western Europe in the
two centuries since the Reformation.

Voltaire's dislike of authoritarianism perhaps accounts as much
as anything for his break with Maupertius, since 1746 the autocratic
president of the Berlin Academy of Sciences. For reasons that are
now hard to reconstruct, the two took opposite sides in the dispute
(1751–2) over the authorship of the Principle of Least Action, Voltaire being content to associate the non-Newtonian idea cherished
by Maupertius with the name of Leibniz. In a diatribe of 1752, he
created a hilarious scene in which Maupertius was himself reduced
to 'least action' by a Leibnizian bullet travelling at the square of
its speed, thus ridiculing the Principle of Least Action and the
conservation of *vis viva* with a single stroke.

But there was a serious issue at stake between the two as well.
Maupertius, as we have seen, followed a current of Newtonian
thought that led from active principles within nature, but external
to matter, to a dynamic view of matter imbued with active principles
of its own. Voltaire resisted this tendency. His study of Newton
had convinced him that matter was completely passive and that its
present order was impressed upon it and maintained by God.

The liberal, cosmopolitan culture so dear to Voltaire depended
on the assumption that human beings were basically the same everywhere, regardless of their times, nationality or religion. But the
equal accessibility of reason and faith to all peoples required universal divine providence as its ground. It also required that human
nature, and all nature, had always been what it now appeared to be
to an enlightened French philosopher! The suggestion that there
might be a progressive development in revelation, or in nature itself,
would only lead back to the authoritarian claims of a guardian of
tradition like the Church. In other words, the only binding system
could be one that antecedes all process of development, whether in
religion or in nature. In religion, such a system was that of the basic
truths common to all people and known in the West by the name
of Deism. In nature it was that of Newton's laws.

In the late 1740s, John Tuberville Needham's research on spontaneous generation was published. Father Needham had found that
jars of mutton broth and dishes of grain would putrefy and produce

micro-organisms even when heated and sealed off from the outer world (twenty years later Spallazani and Pasteur proved otherwise). Buffon, Maupertius and Diderot were impressed by Needham's work, but Voltaire satirized it (since worms could be produced from rye-flour, perhaps humans could be made from wheat-flour!) and accused Father Needham (wrongly) of materialism and atheism. Beginning around 1765, Voltaire waged a major campaign against the new materialists, attacking their notion that motion was inherent in matter and insisting that only God could be credited with the generation and maintenance of motion.

The continental Newtonians we have looked at have all had approximate counterparts in England and America. Boerhaave reminds us in some ways of Cotton Mather; Maupertius, in some ways of Whiston and in others of Cotes; and Voltaire, of Clarke. The Jesuit Abbé Roger Joseph Boscovich (1711–87), a native of Croatia and sometime professor of mathematics at the Collegium Romanum (1740–59), might be said to remind us of John Keill, Gowin Knight and Isaac Watts. Like Keill, Boscovich stressed the insignificance (in bulk) of matter. Like Knight, he saw force as the most important aspect of physical reality. Like Isaac Watts, he was concerned to ensure the priority of spirit to matter.

Descartes and the mechanical philosophers, it will be recalled, tried to reduce all phenomena in nature to the effect of collisions between solid material particles. Newton allowed for such collisions, but added that the more interesting phenomena were due to forces acting at a distance and only accounted for in part by the intervening ether. Boscovich went a step further away from the mechanical philosophy and hypothesized (1745, 1758) that atoms were merely mathematical points and that all interactions, even seeming collisions, were the result of forces acting at a distance between those points. In complete contrast to the Cartesians, there was no such thing as extension in the material sense: there were only forces acting between dimensionless point-masses. Minimizing matter even more than Keill and Pemberton did, Boscovich held that all the matter in the universe would not fill even a nutshell.

Since contact forces were repulsive and operated only near the surface of a body, while chemical-bonding forces were attractive at medium range and gravitation was attractive and long-range, Boscovich hypothesized (1758) the existence of a single field with alternating zones of force around each mass point. The force surrounding a particle alternated sign from one zone to another, being repulsive at small distances from the centre and alternatively attractive and repulsive at larger distances. The force-field also diminished in peak intensity with increasing distance from its centre. Then all the phenomena of physics and chemistry – including cohesion, fermentation, and chemical combination as well as gravitation and collisions – could be reduced to a single, unified force law as Newton himself had once suggested.

Like Voltaire, Boscovich was concerned about the current tendency of many natural philosophers to treat spirit as a property of matter. By reducing matter to extensionless points, he hoped to negate its power in the minds of his contemporaries. But by reducing everything to force, he may have encouraged some like Priestley who came to see all matter as inherently dynamic. Boscovich was deeply chagrined at the way in which Priestley later (1777–8) exploited his ideas.

Newtonian principles first successfully challanged the older ideas of Descartes on the Continent in the 1730s. But, by the 1750s, continental Newtonians were themselves on the defensive in the face of a new movement towards materialism. Theologically, the progression was from a clear-cut matter-spirit dualism (Descartes), to matter-spirit symbiosis (Newton), to matter-spirit identity (the later Maupertius and Diderot). The corresponding shift in physics was from a science restricted to geometric quantities (Descartes), to a more comprehensive one of dynamic quantities (Newton), to a science so comprehensive that it could not be quantified at all (Diderot).

Scottish Newtonians: Colin Maclaurin and James Hutton

The last two Newtonians we shall consider are the Scots, Maclaurin and Hutton. As with the Anglo-American and continental Newtonians there is as much diversity as unity among them, with Maclaurin tending towards materialism and Hutton towards neo-mechanism, though the Scots do exhibit a distinctive common interest in the implications of natural philosophy for moral life.

Colin Maclaurin

Colin Maclaurin (1698–1746) became professor of mathematics and physics at the University of Edinburgh in 1725 upon the recommendation of Newton. He disseminated Newtonian ideas through his lectures and gave the reading public a faithful rendering of the master in his *Treatise of Fluxions* (1742) and his *Account of Sir Isaac Newton's Philosophical Discoveries* (published posthumously in 1748). As it turned out, the computational methods of Newton were too tied to geometrical constructions ('fluxions') to allow further progress in mathematical physics, and the hegemony of Newton's ideas in England and Scotland led to the neglect of current advances in continental mathematics based on the calculus of Leibniz and Euler.

According to Maclaurin, Newtonian science provided a solid foundation for both natural religion and moral philosophy. It pointed to God as the source of all efficacy in nature, equally present and active everywhere. The scientist could never actually reach the First Cause as the result of scientific demonstration, but the increasing simplicity, generality and beauty of scientific laws inferred, and the gradual transcendence of mechanical explanations were, clear signs of his presence and his attributes.

The publication of Maclaurin's textbook also reflected a distinct growth of interest in the ether speculations found in some of Newton's writings. Boerhaave, as we have seen, popularized the idea of a fiery substance permeating the cosmos in the 1730s. In 1740, an anonymous *Examination of the Newtonian Argument for the Emptiness of Space* was published in which Newton's subtle ether was identified with Boerhaave's fire, and the resulting universal medium was credited with all the phenomena of physics, including gravitation, cohesion, electricity, and magnetism. Maclaurin adapted this quasi-materialistic interpretation of Newton by stipulating that the efficacy of the ethereal medium was solely due to the underlying power and free will of the Deity. In contrast to Boscovich, who tried to account for all physics in terms of force-fields between particles with mass but no extension, these two ether-theorists suggested an explanation in terms of subtle matter-fields with extension but little or no mass.

Though active principles and ethers depended on the immediate will of God for their creation and continued general operation, their particular effects, Maclaurin was careful to point out, were not 'immediate volitions' of the Deity. For one thing, the supra-mechanical powers of nature were subject to the constraints of mechanical principles like Newton's law of action and reaction. But, more than that, as subordinate powers they had their own 'proper force and efficacy' in accordance with the common course of nature. In other words, Maclaurin's Newton was not an occasionalist, but more of a deist: once his God had established the laws of nature, things operated pretty much on their own until a general reformation was required analogous to the original formation of the world-system.

Like many other Newtonians, Maclaurin treated induction as the only proper scientific method despite his own bold theorizing on subtle ethers. The Newton he presented to his public was 'distinguished for his caution and circumspection'. Maclaurin's concern here was to oppose the hypotheses invoked by the mechanical philosophers to account for what Newtonians took to be supra-mechanical phenomena. His theological argument was that God's wisdom and ways far transcended human powers so that humans could not understand nature by speculative reason alone. Such an emphasis on the inscrutability of nature and the limitations of human reason did not, however, negate the underlying faith in the ultimate comprehensibility of nature common to the historic creationist tradition (section 1.2). The comprehension of nature remained an ideal that could and would be attained, if not in this life, then in the next.

Similar inductivist epistemologies had been advocated by Newtonians like Clarke, Boerhaave and Pemberton and were later to be championed by the 'common sense' philosopher Thomas Reid (1710–96). Newton himself had been highly ambiguous on the question of scientific method. He claimed that he 'feigned no hypotheses', while boldly proposing speculative principles like supra-mechanical forces and imponderable ethers. Reid, on the other hand, used strict inductivist principles as an argument against speculative hypotheses like Maclaurin's imperceptible ether. He could be said to have reflected the cautious side of Newton's personality. The other, bolder side was better reflected in the hypotheses of Maclaurin and Hutton.

James Hutton: Uniformitarianism versus Catastrophism

James Hutton (1726–97) attended the lectures of Maclaurin at the University of Edinburgh (early 1740s) and studied medicine at Edinburgh and Leiden (1744–9), coming under the influence of Boerhaavian ideas along the way. He took up farming in Berwickshire where he formulated his basic ideas about the importance of erosion for various soils. Moving back to Edinburgh in 1768, he then turned his attentions to the relatively new field of geology, a field of which he has long since been regarded as one of the founding fathers.

Hutton is best known for his 'principle of uniformity' (1788, 1795) – the supposition that all geological change has always involved the very same natural processes that we find at work today. Hutton proposed his Uniformitarianism as an alternative to 'Catastrophism', the view that significant change had taken place through one-time events like the passing of a huge comet or the Great Flood.

Hutton's principle of uniformity is just the traditional idea of a common course of nature (section 1.4) applied to the long-range history of nature. Like Newton, Hutton assumed that the world-system has always been fundamentally the same as it is now: since the day of creation it has been in a steady state, the perfect order of which reflects the perfect wisdom of God. The difference is that

Hutton attempted to include processes of geological change like the building of mountains into the system, whereas Newton had only been concerned with the orbits of the planets in space and with processes like chemical change on earth. Moreover, Hutton saw no need for the periodic reformations which Newton had assigned to divine intervention.

In other words, in comparison with Newton's, Hutton's was a higher order concept of the system of nature which included not only the present structure of the world, but the process (or natural history) by which the present structure had come into existence and was maintained. As with Newton, and in contrast to materialists like Buffon and neo-mechanists like Laplace, the origins of the system were beyond the scope of science for Hutton: in nature itself, he found 'no vestige of a beginning – no prospect of an end'. But Hutton came about as close to being a neo-mechanist as one possibly could without abandoning the Newtonian framework of God and nature. Only the Newtonian stipulation that God had personally designed the present system of nature stood between natural theology and the retirement of God from science altogether.

Hutton viewed nature as an entirely self-contained system. This was seemingly in contrast to Newton, but quite in line with the tendencies of some of his followers. Like Derham and Cotes, Hutton believed that God had implanted active principles in nature at creation sufficient to account for all its normal functions. From Boerhaave, Hutton took the notion of a fiery substance emanating from the sun, circulating throughout the planetary system, and revitalizing life on earth (cf. Newton's cometary vapours). From Gowin Knight, he took the idea of two totally different types of matter: one type was Newton's ordinary gravitational (attractive) matter; the other was Boerhaave's solar (expansive) matter and was responsible for heat, light and electricity (cf. Newton's and Maclaurin's subtle ethers). As with Knight, matter and force were thus interdependent aspects of the system of nature.

In Hutton's geology, for instance, the heat within the earth formed new rock and raised up new continents (expansion) and thus compensated for the continual erosion of land caused by the downhill course of water (gravitation). The perpetual circulation of solar matter and the balance of attractive and repulsive forces in nature thus provided a comprehensive cyclical mechanism that Hutton felt could account for all the operations of nature without the need for divine intervention. Actually, Hutton's system of nature was no more cyclical than Newton's; it was just that God was no longer involved as part of the cycle.

We need to examine two dimensions of Hutton's natural philosophy that are external to the discipline of geology itself: one is technological; the other, theological.

Historically, fundamental shifts in worldview have often been accompanied, and in part occasioned, by changes in technology. In fact, there is a two-way interaction between the two. Cosmologies are ideal systems based on metaphors taken from everyday life, and the metaphors used in new cosmologies are frequently taken from new or impressive technologies. Conversely, technology is often a construction in miniature of what a culture takes to be the nature of the cosmos as a whole. The partial dependence of theoretical science on technology does not imply a lessening of the ideological nature of science or a reduction of superstructure to substructure (Marx). Technologies have ideas and ideals of their own and can reflect creationist ideas as well as scientific theories can (section 1.5).

In ancient times, hierarchical cosmologies had been reflected in towers with many levels and temples with many antechambers. The development of homocentric cosmologies from Eudoxus and Aristotle to the Arabs was accompanied by the manufacture of armillary spheres and water clocks all of which required a continuous and variable input of energy in order to function. The late medieval idea of impetus and the increasing sense of the autonomy of the world-machine came together with the development of the first truly mechanical clocks in the fourteenth century. Descartes' mechanical philosophy was really the perfection of the late medieval notion of impetus. Newton's system of supra-mechanical forces, on the other hand, was based on the realization that the cosmos was more complex than any machine existing at that time.

The rapid development of technology in the eighteenth century must also be viewed as an important factor in the changing views of the cosmos. Two major innovations were experimental devices that exploited electric and magnetic forces and the steam engine. Whereas invisible gravitational forces seemed to transcend the terms of known mechanisms to Newton, they gradually appeared to be as mechanical as nuts and bolts to those like Knight who were familiar with the production and operation of artificial magnets. Similarly, whereas fire and heat had been known primarily for their cataclysmic, destructive effects, they could appear to be controlled and constructive to someone like Hutton who was familiar with Watt's new, more efficient steam engines (c 1769–90).

On the theological front Hutton was motivated by the importance of two things: divinely appointed ends to be realized in this life, and the possibility of moral perfection in the next. In effect, Hutton traded off one form of divine involvement in nature for another, less immediate, one. He completely eliminated the role of God as an efficient cause in nature – e.g., in maintaining active principles or restoring the quantity of motion in the system (Newton's ideas). On the other hand, he heightened the scientific importance of final causes, ends to which the normal processes of nature are fitted as means.

Like any good machine, the system of nature was designed (by God) to accomplish a certain task, in this case, the creation and maintenance of a habitat suitable for human beings. Hutton's early work in agriculture had impressed on him the fact that good soil is produced by erosion. Yet erosion was also a seemingly destructive process and would eventually lead to the destruction of the continents if there were no compensating mechanism. Faith in the wisdom and benevolence of God, however, required that the processes of nature be entirely suited to human good. The apparent contradiction was resolved by Hutton's ideas of the continent-raising power of subterranean heat described above.

In keeping with the thinking of his time, Hutton also saw a deep relationship between natural and moral philosophy. A major tenet of the moral philosophy of the time was the notion of a life after death. Without such a belief, it was thought, there would be no motivation even to try to be moral in this life. On the other hand, the best evidence for life after death, Hutton thought, would be evidence for the beginnings of a moral development in this world that could not be completed in one lifetime. The best evidence for such a development in human life, in turn, would be the existence of a purposeful scheme in nature itself. Conversely, if the intentions of God for human good were effectual in nature, then it was reasonable to suppose that they would be effectual in the moral realm as well.

Though not without its problems, Hutton's Uniformitarianism was as legitimate an interpretation of the idea of creation as any of its eighteenth-century alternatives. However, Hutton's ideas were interpreted as divorcing God from nature by most of his contemporaries, supporters (e.g. Toulmin and Playfair) and opponents alike. As a matter of fact, then, Hutton's principle of uniformity was a major stimulus to the development of 'flood geologies' like that of William Buckland in the early nineteenth century.

Conclusion: The Modernity of Flood Geology

It is as important to understand the underlying dynamics of developments in science and theology as it is in geology itself. In our discussion of Samuel Clarke, we noted six distinct ways in which God was normally understood to be active in the world of nature and history. The three that Newton emphasized as the theological basis of his system (formation of the solar system, active principles and periodic reformations) all appeared to have been replaced by strictly naturalistic accounts (taking the popular 'atheistic' reading of Hutton) by the close of the eighteenth century. The original creation (*ex nihilo*) had apparently left no trace other than the inscrutable existence and lawful motion of nature itself. The historic occurrence of miracles (transcending natural second causes) was being questioned by both philosophers and biblical scholars: miracles had ceased in the minds of most Protestants, so they could be neglected for most scientific purposes in any case.

That left only occasional intrusions of spiritual beings (through the medium of second causes) in dramatic natural phenomena to signal to humans that there was a God in heaven and that the cosmos was somehow tuned to their existence on earth. Even here strictly naturalistic explanations were beginning to prevail. Events like storms at sea and comets from heaven were not so awesome as they had once seemed. Due to advances in science and technology, nature had been completely domesticated by the end of the eighteenth century. For those with religious or romantic impulses, that presented a serious problem. Uniformity of natural processes in a closed system of cause and effect proved to be as difficult to live with as the violence-ridden and life-threatening world of an earlier generation. Whereas the earlier generation (lasting through Hutton) needed to be convinced that this earth was a stable environment for humanity, the new one needed to be convinced that it was a meaningful one.

The Great Flood, however, was an event so stupendous, so clearly described in Scripture, and, on the new geological timescale, so recent that it naturally became a *cause célèbre* among theologically interested scientists in late eighteenth and early nineteenth century France and England. If it could be shown that God had acted in such a definitive way in Noah's time, it could more readily be believed that he was still in control and that he could act again even in our own. The Flood thus became for many, as it still is for some today, the one remaining scientifically verifiable sign of God's activity and hence of the fundamentally personal character of the world of nature. What the containment of terrestrial waters had been for Luther, the immobility of the earth for Calvin, the active principles and periodic reformations of the world for Newton, and the balance of erosion and continent-building for Hutton, the Universal Deluge became for Buckland. The gradual shift over three centuries is seen in the fact that the Reformers cited the normal condition of the absence of flooding as evidence of God's supernatural intervention, whereas the early Buckland (1819, 1823) appealed to geological evidence for the Flood itself as evidence of God's creative intervention, operating strictly as a final cause within the natural framework of cause and effect. Paradoxically, flood geology was the product of the advance of science just as much as Uniformitarianism was.

We have reviewed a representative sampling of natural philosophers who worked within Newton's framework of a symbiosis between God and nature. The overwhelming variety of types of Newtonianism and the tendency of most of its exponents towards either monistic materialism (Derham, Cotes, Boerhaave, Maupertius, and Maclaurin) or neo-mechanism (Clarke, Whiston, Watts, Euler, and Hutton) indicate the basic instability of the Newtonian paradigm. We recall that Newton originally developed his notions of absolute space and active principles as alternatives to two other systems: spiritualism, which held to a deeper unity of God and nature; and the mechanical philosophy, which posited a sharper dichotomy. Monistic materialism and neo-mechanism were in a sense the eighteenth-century equivalents of the spiritualism and mechanism of the seventeenth. Newton's innovations thus devoured the older alternatives and brought forth two new ones in their place.

2. POST-NEWTONIAN MATERIALISTS

In this section we consider the work of a variety of non-Newtonians who advocated a fundamentally dynamic view of matter, in some cases leading to hylozoic materialism. In general, these figures were reacting against the Newtonian ideas of the passivity of matter and the dualism of matter and spirit. They were deeply influenced by the spiritualism of Helmont and the pansophism of Leibniz (section 3.3). Theologically, they tended towards pantheism rather than biblical theism. The British matter theorists made matter entirely autonomous thus eliminating the third tenet of the creationist tradition. The French materialists undercut the first tenet – the comprehensibility of the world based on the creation of the world according to the plan of God and the creation of the human mind in the image of God. However, the other two points of the historic creationist tradition – the unity of nature and the ministry of healing – were retained and developed in a secularized form.

We shall discuss three groupings: the early continental vitalists, British matter theorists (non-Newtonian), and French materialists.

Early Continental Vitalists: Stahl and s'Gravesande

We begin our survey with two continental matter theorists who, under the influence of spiritualist and Leibnizian notions, departed from the Newtonian framework in the direction of materialism.

Georg Ernst Stahl (1660–1734), a devout Pietist best known as the author of the phlogiston theory of combustion, clearly demonstrates the continuity of seventeenth-century spiritualism and eighteenth-century vitalism as well as their common antipathy to the mechanical philosophy.

To begin with, Stahl was the pupil of Johann Joachim Becher (1660–82), a German chemist who was himself influenced by Paracelsus and Helmont. Becher revised the Paracelsian *tria prima* (salt, sulphur and mercury) and developed a classification (1664) of three kinds of earth that played a role in chemical reactions: one vitreous (like salt, gives substance), one fatty (like sulphur, gives colour and combustibility), and one fluid (like mercury, gives odour, form and weight). Chemical combustion was an organic process made possible by the presence of the second, 'fatty' earth (*terra pinguis*), which Becher also called sulphur *phlogistos* ('combustible sulphur'). Sulphur *phlogistos* was released from a compound through heating (calcination) or combustion ('oxidation' in modern chemistry) and could be restored by heating with charcoal ('reduction'). In spiritualist terms, it was the equivalent of the vital principle or soul which animated the body of a living creature.

Stahl took over Becher's idea of different types of earth, combined it (1723) with Newton's notion of attractive forces between the atoms of a chemical compound, and used the result to develop a viable alternative to the Newtonian chemistry. To Becher's fatty earth or sulphur *phlogistos* he gave the name 'phlogiston'. Substances like sulphur and phosphorus were richly endowed with phlogiston by their natural (organic) formation in the earth. The process of combustion released the phlogiston to the air and left behind an acid (vitriol). Air was not an agent in the chemical process itself; it only served to carry away phlogiston so that it could be re-absorbed by plant life and the cycle of nature could continue.

The identification of three fundamentally different kinds of matter implied that atoms had intrinsic properties that qualified them as belonging to one type rather than another. As in the spiritualist tradition, however, such properties were regarded as granted by God at creation.

Though the idea of phlogiston had to be discarded once the existence and chemical action of oxygen were properly understood (Lavoisier), Stahl's theory was an excellent unified theory of the various facts of chemistry known in the early eighteenth century. It remains an important historical witness to the ideal of the unity and activity of nature which has motivated so much of modern science even though it has gradually been divorced from its creationist roots.

Willem Jacob s'Gravesande (1688–1742) was a professor of mathematics and astronomy and colleague of Boerhaave at Leiden. His *Mathematical Elements of Physics* (1720) was one of the first publications in continental Europe to advocate the natural philosophy and God-nature symbiosis of Newton. Accordingly, he could have been included in our treatment of continental Newtonians (section 4.1). However, s'Gravesande was also one of the first Newtonians to convert wholeheartedly to the Leibnizian camp. Already in the Newtonian treatise mentioned, he followed Boerhaave and others in treating fire as a subtle substance different from ordinary matter and responsible for the phenomena of heat, light and electricity.

Such notions were still compatible with a generally Newtonian stance as we have seen in the cases of Boerhaave, Maclaurin and Hutton. But when s'Gravesande tried to refute Leibniz's claims for *vis viva*, he concluded (1722) that the Leibnizians were actually correct – force (or what we could call energy) was really inherent in a moving body and not just impressed from without. Consequently, according to s'Gravesande, effects proceeded automatically and necessarily from their natural causes.

In developing his new view of matter (1736–7), s'Gravesande had to answer the argument of Samuel Clarke that positing a necessary order in nature would lead to atheism. This he did by appealing to the wisdom of God as manifested in the order of nature, as Leibniz had done, and by arguing against Clarke that tying providence to the maintenance of the properties of matter was an unnecessary constraint on the exercise of divine power. While certainly missing the intent of Newton and Clarke, s'Gravesande had a valid point here. As we have seen, Newton's God was free only in the sense of being ceaselessly occupied with the maintenance of every single particle in the universe in accordance with a freely chosen set of exact mathematical laws. In comparison, the Leibnizian-Gravesandian view suggested a more economical operation of nature and a more relaxed (if not idle) God.

British Matter Theorists from Hales to Priestley

The English and Scottish scientists who tended towards materialism were pioneers of the relatively new discipline of chemistry. In contrast to their Newtonian contemporaries (section 4.1), they stressed quantitative experimental techniques rather than mathematical models and were less concerned with natural theology.

Prior to the philosophical and theological materialism of David Hartley and Joseph Priestley, the materialist tradition in Great Britain was decidedly non-theological. Even though continental vitalist ideas made an impact, their spiritualist associations were entirely eliminated in keeping with the anti-spiritualist tenor of moderate British thought since the mid-seventeenth century. Consequently, we mention here only a few of the more important early British matter theorists prior to Hartley and Priestley to give an idea of the progressive secularization of historically creationist ideas.

Secular British Matter Theorists from Hales to Black

Stephen Hales (1677–1761) treated air (1727) as a universal agent in chemical reactions somewhat similar to Stahl's phlogiston. Like phlogiston, Hales' air (in modern chemistry, just the carbon dioxide component) could be bound or 'fixed' in compounds and then released by heating or fermentation.

Hales established the discipline of pneumatic chemistry by collecting the 'airs' released by various reactions and analysing their properties. Thus, like Stahl, he abandoned (1733) the Newtonian programme of reducing all chemical phenomena to the interaction of atoms by means of forces acting at a distance. But, in as much as Hales was an Anglican clergyman, his ideas lacked the spiritualist associations of Stahl's.

Peter Shaw (1694–1764) was responsible more than anyone for introducing materialist concepts into England through his translations of Boerhaave (1727, 1741) and Stahl (1730). Shaw started out as a Newtonian and in a sense continued the alchemical side of Newton's own work. But, like Stahl and Hales, he eventually came to the point of rejecting the reduction of chemistry to atoms and forces as the Newtonians required. The concepts and methods of mathematical physics only 'scratched the shell and surface of things and left the kernel untouched'. Shaw's chemistry was instead based on the role of active principles, like Boerhaave's fire, that were inherently material and observable. But, as in the case of Hales, the spiritualist ideas associated with the work of Boerhaave and Stahl were conspicuous by their absence.

Cadwallader Colden (1688–1776), a colonial American physician

trained at Edinburgh, was more explicit in his secularizing of Newtonian and spiritualist notions (1746, 1751). Like Gowin Knight
and others, Colden allowed for inherent differences in the qualities
of matter. In fact, he postulated three species of matter distantly
resembling Paracelsus' *tria prima*: one was self-moving (light); one
transmitted motion from one body to another (an elastic ether); and
one actively resisted motion (ordinary inertial matter). Not only did
Colden's scheme attribute distinctive properties to each species of
matter over and above the primary mechanical qualities common to
all three; it also attributed a peculiar kind of activity to each species,
even interpreting inertial resistance to motion as a form of activity.

The theological significance of Colden's ideas is seen from the
title of his first work: *An Explication of the First Causes of Action in
Matter; and of the Causes of Gravitation* (1646). Whereas earlier
scientists had attributed primary causation to God and allowed only
secondary causation (if any) to creatures, Colden located the seat of
causation, even that of Newton's gravitation, in matter itself. In a
second work (1751), Colden explicitly rejected Newton's contention
that all motion was directly sustained by God as 'very unphilosophi-
cal'. In other words, it was more economical to suppose that the
principles of motion Newton had discovered were inherent in matter
even though they were radically different from the properties originally attributed to matter in the mechanical philosophy. Matter,
even inert matter, was no longer strictly passive. From the Newtonian standpoint, God was out of a job – or rather, his job had
been taken over by matter.

Another example of the secularization of Newtonian ideas is William Cullen (1710–90). Cullen taught chemistry at Glasgow and
Edinburgh – his lectureship at Glasgow (1747) was the first position
in chemistry to be established independently of the discipline of
medicine. In Glasgow and Edinburgh, he was associated with such
giants of Enlightenment thought as David Hume and Adam Smith.

Like Peter Shaw, Cullen was influenced by the vitalism of Stahl
to adopt a more materialist interpretation of Newtonian ideas. For
example, Cullen explained gravitational attraction in terms of a
gradient in the ether density between gross material bodies. Chemical reactions and functions of the nervous system could also be
described in terms of the ether. Newton himself had speculated
along such lines but never regarded such ether mechanisms as complete explanations that might exclude the active role of God. Cullen,
however, cast Newton's ether the role of primary causal agent in
nature thus eliminating God altogether.

Joseph Black (1728–99) was a pupil of Cullen at Glasgow, completed his M. D. at Edinburgh (1754), and succeeded his mentor in his chairs successively at Glasgow and Edinburgh. Like Cullen, he was associated with major figures of the Scottish Enlightenment – Adam Smith, David Hume and James Hutton. Like Stahl, Hales and Shaw, he rejected the Newtonian matter theorists' programme of reducing chemical phenomena to forces acting between minute atoms. Black laid the basis for quantitative analysis by improving Stephen Hales' experimental methods for differentiating the various kinds of air given off by chemical reactions.

Like Boerhaave, s'Gravesande and Cullen, Black regarded heat as an active material substance involved in both physical and chemical change. Noticing that ice remains on the ground long after the temperature rises above freezing, he did a few measurements, and discovered that the temperature of the water dripping off the melting ice was still at the freezing point. Black concluded that there must be a 'latent heat' in water that is given up in the process of freezing and that must be restored in melting before further heat input will raise its temperature above thirty-two degrees Fahrenheit. Black also discovered (following the work of Fahrenheit) that different materials had different capacities for absorbing heat, or different 'specific heats'. For the first time a clear distinction had been made between the temperature of a body and the amount of heat it absorbed.

The ideas of latent and specific heat are foundational to modern thermodynamics and physical chemistry. In fact, Black's notion of latent heat was instrumental to James Watt's understanding the equivalence of mechanical energy to heat and the consequent redesign of a more efficient steam engine in the 1760s. Though the use of Black's concepts does not require a materialist understanding of heat in modern physical science, that understanding was clearly helpful to Black in his new insights into matter theory.

David Hartley and Joseph Priestley

In order to fill out the background of Joseph Priestley's religious version of materialism, we need to glance briefly at the work of Priestley's mentor in the area of philosophy and psychology, David Hartley (1705–1757). Hartley did not contribute to the physical sciences as such, but his psychological and social ideas indicate one way in which traditional notions of the creationist tradition could be carried on in a radically materialist manner.

The son of a poor Anglican clergyman in Yorkshire, Hartley at first prepared for the ministry. Though devoutly religious, he was unwilling to subscribe to the Thirty-Nine Articles after completing his degrees and was thus unable to pursue a career in the Church. Consequently, he devoted himself to the practice of medicine without formal training, yet with the Christian ideal of serving rich and poor alike.

Hartley deeply admired the work of Newton and pictured himself in his major work, *Observations on Man* (1749), as extending Newton's methods to the phenomena of mental and moral life. For example, as a parallel to the law of cohesion for matter, Hartley developed a 'principle of association' for ideas: one idea, stimulated by sense perception, could evoke a related idea in the mind as naturally as one vibration could excite another in the brain. The moral sense in an individual then emerged as an aggregate of simple ideas relating to action and united by association. Hartley here argued against moral philosophers like Shaftesbury, Hutcheson and Reid and moderate Newtonians like Derham who held that the moral sense and other such instincts were implanted directly by God.

Even though Hartley did not attribute thought to matter itself, his emphasis on the material basis of the mind may strike the reader as being atheistic in intent. However, Hartley saw himself, like Newton before him (and Priestley after), as a champion of revealed biblical religion. A comparison of his ideas with the historic creationist tradition shows that there was some merit to his claim. For one thing, Hartley argued that the world in which the human mind is formed by sensation and association is itself a system of comprehensible order and benevolence in as much as it reflects the wisdom and benevolence of God. Hartley's materialistic associationism, then, was merely the means by which the traditional notions of the image of God in humanity – art, science and morality – were made effective. It was the French materialists who first challenged the creationist basis for belief in the comprehensibility of the world.

A second way in which the radical implications of the creationist tradition were continued by Hartley was in his political philosophy. Whereas moderate British Newtonians and moral philosophers tended to treat humans as unequally gifted and to legitimate a hierarchically structured society on the basis of the biblical notions of sin and the fall of Adam, Hartley's associationistic psychology implied that all humans could strive to perfect the image within by rooting out perverse associations and replacing them with pious ones. Thus through proper education and self-examination the effects of the Fall could be reversed and the original condition of God's creation restored. However naive such views may seem to us today, they were clearly not secular or irreligious in intent. It would be instructive to investigate the possible origins of Hartley's egalitarian political views in the Christian ideals he imbibed from his medical practice. However, Hartley was far from an idealist himself. He clearly recognized the pervasiveness of selfishness among humans, particularly among professors of science who, he charged, topped all others for their 'vain-glory, self-conceit, arrogance, emulation, and envy'. In many ways Hartley reminds us of the early Christian critics of Greek science (section 1.5)

Joseph Priestley (1733–1804) was both a devout Christian and a deterministic materialist, a combination that might be thought impossible today. In fact, the combination already appeared to be an outright contradiction to Leslie Stephen (1832–1904) who lived almost exactly a century after Priestley. In his classic *History of English Thought in the Eighteenth Century* (1876), Stephen spoke approvingly of Priestley as a pioneer of free thought and political liberalism, but could not refrain from chiding him for retaining 'puerile superstitions' such as his belief in miracles and the imminent return of Christ. Seeing Priestley through the late-nineteenth century eyes of Stephen gives us some idea of the change in English thought over the intervening century. It also serves as a warning to historians who would find absolute contradictions where their subjects were blissfully unaware of them. As we shall see, Priestley's system of thought was highly coherent.

Having received his early education 'in all the gloom and darkness of Calvinism', Priestley spent his formative (university) years at the Dissenting Academy of Daventry. There he first read Hartley's *Observations on Man* and was encouraged by the differing views of his teachers to develop unconventional views of his own. By the time he graduated from Daventry (1755), Priestley had adopted Hartley's psychological determinism and had moved from orthodox trinitarianism to Arianism (the position of Newton, though Priestley probably did not know it).

In the late 1760s, Priestley was ordained and began serving a Presbyterian church in Leeds. There he performed his first systematic experiments in chemistry, studied the work of Stephen Hales, continued his theological studies and became convinced of the truth of the Socinian (Unitarian) position. He came to the conclusion that the notion of a pre-existent Logos, like that of a pre-existent soul, was a pagan intrusion into the pure teaching of Jesus.

At this point, Priestley was reacting most immediately to Arian teaching according to which Christ was the first angel or a disembodied soul created by God. However, as we saw in our study of Isaac Watts, the notion of a pre-existent human soul was closely related to trinitarian thought in Dissenting academies during the eighteenth century. It appears that Priestley had this field of associations in mind when he rejected the distinctive doctrines of orthodox Christianity, in as much as the notion of the Logos he singled out for attack as pagan was that of an emanation from the mind of God rather than the Arian notion of a primordial creature.

The three basic components of Priestley's thought – materialism, determinism and Unitarianism – were all well in place in the early 1770s. In 1772 Priestley gave his first paper on gases to the Royal Society of London, and in 1774 he published his first major philosophical work, a critique of the Scottish 'common sense' philosophy of Thomas Reid, in which he first articulated his distinctive view of Christian materialism. The following year he brought out a new edition of Hartley's *Observations on Man*.

Priestley was more clearly committed to materialism than Hartley was. In place of Hartley's avowed parallelism of mind and brain, he substituted (1775, 1777) a complete identity. Conscious thought was a function of bodily matter and was therefore entirely deterministic. Two conclusions followed. For one thing, there was no such thing as free-will since thoughts followed one another according to a strict law of association. Even the thoughts of the writers of Scripture were determined; they were not 'inspired' in the sense of having thoughts outside the ordinary course of their mental lives. There was thus no place in Priestley for the dualism between inner freedom and outer determinism that became so popular in nineteenth-century thought.

Secondly, there was no mind or soul separate from matter; the mind or soul was just the form of the body. The soul slept when the brain ceased to function at death, and the believer had only the future restoration of the soul together with the body to look forward to. Political radicalism was thus associated with mortalist ideas in Priestley much as it had been in many left-wing Puritans and sectaries of the mid-seventeenth century. The converse was also true: conservative, particularly anti-French, political views tended to occur together with support for the traditional standards of the Church. The most dramatic instance of popular opposition to all Priestley stood for occurred in Birmingham in 1791 when a 'Church and King' mob destroyed Priestley's home as well as the Unitarian meeting house where he ministered to celebrate the second anniversary of the fall of the Bastille.

Among Priestley's most important contributions to science were the formulation of an inverse-square law (1767), analogous to that for gravitation, for the force surrounding an electric charge; and

the 'discovery' of oxygen (1772–5). The inverse-square law for electric force was later confirmed by Charles Cavendish and Henry
Augustin Coulomb (1785) and became known to generations of
physics students as 'Coulomb's law', one of the four fundamental
laws governing electro-magnetic fields. Priestley's discovery of
oxygen (also discovered independently by Carl Wilhelm Scheele)
was important in that it helped show that common air was actually
a mixture of different kinds of air and provided an experimental
basis for Lavoisier's later notion of a plurality of chemical elements.

Although Priestley himself worked within the framework of
Stahl's phlogiston theory of combustion (he referred to oxygen as
'dephlogisticated air'), his data made it possible for Lavoisier to
substantiate an alternative (oxidation) theory of combustion based
on the combination of a substance with oxygen, rather than the
release of phlogiston. Priestley never accepted Lavoisier's reading
of the evidence, however. For him the idea of phlogiston made
sense since it was an active principle in chemistry similar to the
forces of electricity and gravitation that dominated physics. Priestley's sense of the unity of nature prevented him from allowing a
multiplicity and combinatory mechanics of elements entirely divorced from the universal principles of physics.

Priestley's most important work for our purposes was his speculation (1777) concerning the relationships between the three heterodox views he held in science and theology: materialism, determinism
(or philosophical necessitarianism), and Socinianism (or Unitarianism). He firmly believed that there was a mutual dependence of the
three though the source of his data was science for the first two and
Scripture for the third. Here we shall approach the inter-relationship
first from the starting point of science (to theology) and then from
the angle of theology.

On the basis of Newton's concept of forces acting at a distance
and the idea of some Newtonians that such forces were a property
of matter itself, Priestley concluded that all matter possessed the
power of sensation and thought. The attribution of mental life to
humans was therefore not subjective or unscientific; it was only a
statement of what was true for organized matter in general. Thus,
Priestley hoped to eliminate the difficulties with Christian faith
occasioned in the minds of 'philosophical unbelievers' by the traditionally held dualism of body and soul.

Priestley saw no inconsistency between materialism and true
Christian faith, however, since all the powers of matter were derived
from and continued to depend on the power of God. In fact, for
Priestley, all activity in nature was really a continuous direct mani-

festation of the activity of God. This was consistent with the biblical picture of God 'filling all in all' (1 Cor. 15:28). Priestley's God was not identical with matter; he was the inner power, life and soul of matter – a view very close to classical Stoicism.

The close association between God and matter worked two ways for Priestley. On one hand, it prevented matter from being autonomous as it seemed (to Priestley) to be in the mechanical philosophy and even in Newton. On the other hand it made the material world eternal: without God's power there would be no matter. Conversely (for Priestley), given God's eternal (viz. everlasting) power, there must be eternal matter. Of course, the possibility of an eternal creation had been considered speculatively by earlier divines like Origen and Aquinas. But Priestley's position was a form of determinism or philosophical necessitarianism quite unlike that of earlier speculative theologians. God acted always by necessity as the deterministic structure of the laws of physics seemed (to Priestley) to imply.

Priestley did not equate God's eternity with everlastingness as Newton did, but he did agree with Newton in placing all the acts of God somewhere along an infinite time line. However, whereas Newton could then place the 'begetting' of the Son (as an angelic creature) before creation on the line, Priestley had learned to associate the pre-existence of Christ with that of the soul and rejected both ideas as pagan notions which were inconsistent with his monistic materialism.

One can also approach Priestley's thought from the theological angle of Unitarian doctrine. Historically, it has proven difficult for Jews and Christians to attribute any personality or activity to God without positing some person or thing in relation to which he could relate and act. Since a commitment to the Hebrew-Christian Scriptures entails an active personal God, the further constraint that there be no multiplicity (e.g. of persons) in the Godhead then implies the necessity of a creation in relation to which God can be eternally personal and active. The reality of Priestley's God was thus actualized only through the (eternal) process of creating.

In other words, for Priestley as for Newton, the created world took the place of the eternal Son of God in traditional Christian theology. Priestley made this substitution explicit in his *Institutes of Natural and Revealed Religion* (1782) by mimicking the Athanasian affirmation of the eternity of the Son:

    . . . there never was a time when this great uncaused Being did not exert his perfection, in giving life and happiness to his offspring. . . . the creation, as it had no beginning, so neither has it any bounds. . . .

So the material world was necessary to the full being of God, and this necessity in turn ruled out the possibility of any dualism between the two or between spirit and matter in general.

In a sense, Priestley was simply a consistent Newtonian. Newton had originally posited the existence of active principles over and above the primordial properties of matter in order to avoid the matter-spirit dualism and apparent autonomy of nature suggested by the mechanical philosophy of Descartes. On the other hand, he postulated the regulation of God's activity in accordance with invariable mathematical laws like that of universal gravitation. Finally, consistent with the need for a universal divine presence in nature, he posited an absolute space taking the traditional place of the divine Logos as the emanent effect of God (section 3.3). Priestley merely eliminated the residual dualism in Newton: he made inert matter a function of active principles and hence of divine power and arrived at a monistic system that was at once materialist, determinist and Unitarian.

French Materialists from La Mettrie to Holbach

The philosophy of materialism is most dramatically represented by the radical *philosophes* La Mettrie, Buffon, Diderot, Robinet, Holbach, and Cabanis who were active in the second half of the eighteenth century. These French materialists are the source of the familiar image of materialism as atheistic. Yet, while they emphatically rejected biblical theism, they retained many biblical insights in secularized form. Their main departure from traditional Christian doctrine was their tendency to assign divine attributes like eternity and self-determination to matter itself.

Because of their high view of the potentialities of matter, the French materialists were able to maintain their faith in the power of the human intellect (the product of organic matter), and to press that faith to unprecedented extremes, while at the same time abandoning the notion of creation in the image of God upon which that faith had traditionally rested. For example, Julien Offray de la Mettrie (1709–1751) argued that matter contained within it the potential for producing living creatures, even humans with souls, by a process of pure trial and error. As La Mettrie put it in his *System of Epicurus* (1750): 'Nature, without seeing, has made seeing eyes and, without thinking, has made a thinking machine'. In other words, the Deity was not eliminated by the materialists; it (or aspects of it) were merely absorbed completely into nature.

It should be pointed out that there was nothing inherently inconsistent between believing in the transcendence of God and affirming the unlimited potentialities of matter. The two had been integrally related in the historic creationist tradition, for example, in Basil, Aquinas and Leibniz. Since the twelfth century, however, the more prevalent view in science and theology had been that the sufficiency of matter and the direct involvement of a transcendent God were mutually exclusive alternatives by definition. At the outset of the eighteenth century, this view had been made normative by the Newtonians.

Here we shall focus on the work of Buffon, Diderot and Holbach whose ideas had the most direct bearing on theology and the physical sciences. All three reacted against Newton's stress on mathematical, active principles and attempted to develop more empirical theories based on the character of matter rather than on (what appeared to them to be) abstract formalisms.

Buffon

The work of Georges Louis Le Clerc, Comte de Buffon (1707–1788), represents a major watershed in Western ideas about nature. Buffon's massive *Natural History* (36 vols., 1749–88) was the first comprehensive naturalistic account of the origins and evolution of the terrestrial environment. Still partly under the influence of Newton, Buffon was a transitional figure. Thus he did not try to account for the formation of the cosmos as a whole (as Kant was to do) or the origin of species (as Lamarck was to do). He held that most species emerged directly by spontaneous generation from organic molecules as the earth gradually cooled and the prerequisite environmental conditions arose. But he took a critical step beyond the modest suggestions of Whiston towards a complete natural history of the planetary system. Following the example of left-wing creationists before him (e.g., Adelard of Bath, Albert the Great, Buridan, Bacon, and Leibniz), Buffon also argued that scientists should refrain from appealing to supernatural causes whenever possible (which meant, practically always).

Unlike more radical materialists, however Buffon did not deny the existence of God or the initial creation of matter out of nothing. Creation was for him still the only possible explanation for the origin, laws and initial condition of the world. Buffon stated this traditional motif rather eloquently in his own personal hymn of creation (1764):

Minister of God's irrevocable orders, depository of his immutable decrees, Nature never separates herself from the laws which have been prescribed for her; she alters not at all the plans which have been made for her, and in all her works she presents the seal of the Eternal.

This statement is clearly a paraphrase of the idea of the relative autonomy of nature (section 1.4) found in classic creationist texts like Ecclesiasticus 16:26-8.

But even in its original condition, all matter, for Buffon, was imbued with motion and the potential for life. As the result of its creation, it is a manifestation of the living, immense and all-embracing power of God. Hence, nature too is 'a living power, immense, which embraces everything and animates everything'. Here Buffon clearly shows the influence of the pansophist ideas of Leibniz and his disciple Christian Wolff, which had been brought to public attention in France by Madame du Châtelet in 1740.

As a result of the self-sufficiency of nature, everything since the first moment of creation, even the emergence of life itself, had happened in accordance with immutable laws of nature. Or, turning the problem around, human reason could now reconstruct the history of nature, going all the way back to the first moment of creation, simply on the basis of the laws and present state of the world.

In order to account for fossil remains and other geological data on strictly naturalistic assumptions, Buffon concluded that there had been a succession of seven stages, analogous to the seven 'days' of Genesis 1–2, but lasting far longer than twenty-four hours each. First, the earth was formed as a hot fragment of the sun broken off by the grazing impact of a comet (after Whiston); then, as the earth cooled, rock consolidated, the mountains rose, and the organic molecules needed for life were formed in the warm seas; then huge seas temporarily covered the earth (not to be equated with the biblical flood of Noah), depositing marine fossils on otherwise dry land; when the waters receded, volcanoes became active; then land animals emerged – tropical ones at first which inhabited the entire globe, even the northern regions; later the continents separated from each other to give their present configuration; and last came the age of humanity in which the character of the earth was transformed by technology.

Thus, in contrast to later uniformitarians like Hutton, Buffon allowed for a succession of radically different eras in the history of nature. But he regarded the products of those eras (e.g., mountains and volcanoes) to have remained relatively unchanged since their initial formation. In other words, Buffon dissociated the idea of unchanging laws of nature from that of a steady state of nature: immutable laws could give rise to a succession of different states; conversely, a succession of states could be understood in terms of a single set of fundamental laws.

Buffon's estimates of how much time was required to allow all this to happen ranged from 75,000 to three million years. Though these figures seem modest by our present-day standards for the age of the earth (in the thousands of millions of years), they represented a profound challenge to the traditional thought of Buffon's time. In fact, the first volume of the *Natural History* was vehemently criticized by the theologians of the Sorbonne (1751), and Buffon was obliged to affirm his complete faith in the Genesis account of creation.

Buffon's work marked a critical step in the development of modern Western thought. In retrospect, its effect can best be understood in terms of two resulting paradoxes concerning the relationship of natural science to history and the relationship of modern social optimism to cosmic pessimism, respectively. Thus, although Buffon was ostensibly less Christian than earlier representatives of the creationist tradition, his work was profoundly theological in its character and implications for modern thought.

For the first time in human history the age of the cosmos could be estimated using scientific methods that were not based on ancient texts. This led to the first paradox: a discipline that was the outgrowth of the special history of a peculiar culture had now become so comprehensive and so well established that its view of the world appeared to be entirely independent of the discipline of history itself. Science, like history, can be understood either as a human construct or in terms of what it tells us about the world in which we live. Its credibility has become so great that we tend to identify it with the world of facts and lose sight of its dependence (for better or worse) on particular historical and cultural circumstances. With Buffon, we see this shift taking place before our very eyes as the entire vista of human history becomes a mere fraction of the natural history constructed by science.

The other significant change was the separation of objective science from human ideals. Buffon could estimate not only the time since the creation, but also the amount of time left before the earth would become too cold to support life any more. The figure he arrived at was about 93,000 years: in another 93,000 years all life would cease on earth. In one sense this was a direct challenge to biblical faith which traditionally held that the present age would be terminated by divine intervention. But, paradoxically, Buffon's projection was an even deeper challenge to the widespread eighteenth-century faith in limitless human progress, a belief which Buffon himself shared. By the time the earth became too cold, the more massive planet Jupiter would have cooled down to the point where it could support human life (Mars was already too cold). But, even though humans were extremely adaptable and could continue for thousands or even millions of years somewhere in the solar system, they would eventually become extinct like the tropical species that once inhabited the northern regions of earth.

So the elimination of the biblical projection of the future from science made it appear that the present age would last much longer than earlier generations had thought. However, it provided no hope for an age to come. In fact, Buffon's naturalistic projection ruled out any objective basis for the hopes and ideals that he and his generation had imbibed from the creationist tradition concerning the possibility for the realization of human potential in a future world. Buffon had effectively separated objective scientific inquiry from his personal vision for the future of Western civilization.

The fact that the bleakness of scientifically established prospects for the future are no hindrance to continued optimism concerning the future of human life is one of the most difficult features of modern thought to account for. It may reflect the fact that Western humans have come to see themselves more in relation to their technology than to the world of nature. Buffon was acutely aware of this shift in perspective himself. Partly due to his work as keeper of the Royal French Botanical Gardens, he well appreciated the impact of human ordering on the environment:

> The state in which we see nature today is as much our work as its; we have known how to temper and modify it, bend it to our needs and desires; we have founded, cultivated, fructified the earth: the aspect under which it presents itself is, then, very different from that of times anterior to the invention of the arts.

Buffon had understood the essential malleability of nature as taught by creationist – particularly the apocalyptic and hermetic – traditions. The biblical and patristic sanction for technology as a ministry of healing and restoration had been eliminated, however, and with it any sense of reliance on the name of Christ and the Spirit of God (section 1.5). For Buffon, the rationalization and transformation of nature were willed and planned by humans alone – they were the result of technology; the subject of pure science, on the other hand, was the natural state of the earth untouched by human hands and unrationalized by human intellect.

The independence of modern science from history thus had as its converse the independence of social imperatives from the worldview of modern science. In other words, a dualism of objective worldview and subjective belief was emerging as the result of the fragmentation and secularization of creationist ideals.

Diderot

Dualism certainly did not characterize the thinking of Denis Diderot (1713–84), the figure most often cited as marking the transition from static to dynamic, organismic thinking in the mid-eighteenth century. The ideal of the unity of all reality was affirmed by him as it rarely has been before or since. For the mature Diderot (after 1749), nothing was fixed or exact in nature. Everything was ephemeral and in continual flux into everything else: matter, organisms, species, even the human soul. The price of such unity: the comprehensibility of the world, at least, in terms of analytic reason and mathematical physics.

Diderot thus rejected the traditional creationist notion of the comprehensibility of the world. For one thing, he argued that nature functioned on the level of wholes, rather than just parts, and that scientific analysis was not suited to dealing with such wholes. But he also abandoned the traditional underpinning of the belief in comprehensibility – the ideas of creation of the world in accordance with divine reason and creation of humanity in the image of God. In contrast to contemporaries like Buffon, Diderot saw the primordial condition of the universe as one of total chaos with only momentary appearances of order like the one we presently observe. From the historical-theological point of view, he was entirely consistent here. In times when the tools of science have seemed inadequate to the task of understanding the real world as a whole, it has only been faith in a Creator that has sustained serious scientific endeavour.

Diderot's reaction against the abstract classification and mathematization of nature was enshrined in the multi-volume *Encyclopedia of the Sciences, Arts and Trades* (1751–72; initially co-edited with d'Alembert), a monument to the techniques and ideas of the burgeoning small industries of Western Europe. The practical ideals embodied in the *Encyclopedia* were derived from the medieval and Renaissance tradition of lay craftsmanship: Diderot was himself the son of an artisan in Langres. Such ideals had historically been formulated in opposition to the mathematical emphasis of Neoplatonism. They stressed practice rather than theory, an intuitive grasp of nature rather than rational analysis, and service to other humans rather than personal prestige. Some earlier exponents of these ideals that we have studied are Cusa, Agricola, Paracelsus, Bacon, and Helmont.

Diderot clearly belongs in this stream of the creationist tradition even though he completely secularized its ideals. Like his forebears, Diderot berated mathematical science for imposing human categories on nature and exercising the intellectual hubris of the scientist. In contrast, Diderot's ideal craftsman was dedicated to harnessing nature by intuitive understanding and respect for the nature of this material. But, while Diderot believed fervently in the limitless progress of human technology and applied the traditional criterion of human benefit (immortalized by Bacon), there is little indication of his preserving the biblical motive for healing or service to others.

From the perspective of the historic creationist tradition the difference between Diderot and Buffon is this: Buffon secularized the idea of the comprehensibility of the world; Diderot secularized the ideal of the ministry of healing and restoration; and both secularized the notion of the relative autonomy of nature.

Holbach

Paul Henri Thiry, Baron d'Holbach (1723–89) is best known for his *System of Nature*, first published anonymously in 1770. Holbach's *System* was a manifesto for reductionism, materialism, determinism, and practical atheism.

For Holbach, motion was neither added to matter at creation (mechanical philosophy), nor sustained by active principles in accordance with divinely imposed laws (Newton). In fact, there was neither a Creator (in the biblical sense) nor a creation *ex nihilo*. All such religious beliefs were merely the result of the superstitious awe in which primitive peoples held the unknown powers of nature. Now that modern science was capable of giving a rational explanation of these powers in terms of an unbroken chain of cause and effect, there was no excuse for recourse to the supernatural. Holbach allowed that there might be an unknown 'Cause of causes', but only in so far as it was a necessary postulate of reason; there was no longer any room for Christian, or any other, faith.

Instead, both motion and the forces that generated it were eternal, primary qualities of matter, as essential to its being as extension itself. The power of Holbach's argumentation rivalled that which he attributed to matter:

The idea of Nature necessarily includes that of motion. But it will be asked [by Newtonians like Voltaire], and not a little triumphantly, from whence did she derive her motion? Our reply is . . . that it is fair to infer, unless they can logically prove to the contrary, that it is in herself, since she is the great whole out of which nothing can exist. We say this motion is a manner of existence that flows, necessarily, out of the nature of matter; that matter moves by its own peculiar energies; that its motion is to be attributed to the force which is inherent in itself . . .

In other words, once Descartes' a priori identification of matter with extension was eliminated, the source of motion could be found in matter as easily as in God.

Moreover, all reality – even human phenomena like feelings, ideas, religion, and art – was, for Holbach, just the by-product of matter in motion:

The universe, that vast assemblage of everything that exists, presents only matter and motion: the whole offers to our contemplation nothing but an immense, an uninterrupted succession of causes and effects.

This was one of the most thorough statements of reductionism and determinism since the ancient Epicureans. The traditional creationist ideal of the unity of nature was effectively replaced by a thoroughgoing materialist view of homogeneous matter in motion.

There was a profound contradiction between Holbach's deterministic, reductionistic view of the world and his personal passion for moral issues, a contradition that has plagued modern secular thought ever since. Lacking Priestley's identification of natural self-determination with the work and will of God, Holbach had no real grounds for believing that human judgments concerning moral issues were anything other than the blind product of interacting atoms that knew nothing of human feelings or morals. However, this did not prevent him from making sweeping moral judgements of his own about contemporary institutions like the Church. Whereas Diderot had merely secularized the traditional Christian ideal of human benefit, Holbach turned it around and used it as a weapon against the Church itself. Christianity, he charged, was responsible for most of the ills of modern society: among other things, it encouraged prejudice, depreciated nature, and discouraged self-fulfillment.

Holbach was not unaware of the difficulty. His solution was to propose a new morality based on self-interest and the natural desire for pleasure, yet independent of any religious faith. The inconsistency lay in the fact that Holbach's materialism made no room for the potentiality for valid moral judgements in the brute matter from which humans evolved. There was, therefore, no more scope for judgement in a human than in a tree. But it took a wily pragmatist like Frederick the Great to see the dilemma:

> What foolishness and what nonsense! If everything is moved by necessary [material] causes, then all counsel, all instruction, all rewards and punishments are as superfluous as inexplicable; for one might just as well preach to an oak and try to persuade it to turn into an orange tree.

A predestinarian like Calvin or a Christian materialist like Priestley could argue the compatibility of moral judgements with belief in predetermination based on the all-determining power of a moral God. Holbach tried to base morality on the study of human nature but then had only brute matter to appeal to as the basis of human nature.

Conclusion: From the Creationist Tradition to Materialism

We have noted the partial continuity, fragmentation and secularization of creationist themes in the French materialists. There was a particularly close link between eighteenth-century materialism and seventeenth-century spiritualism and pansophism (Leibniz) with early eighteenth-century vitalism acting as the intermediary. Continuity was evident primarily in the common view of matter as imbued with relatively autonomous powers and in the lay-oriented critique of established elites on the basis of egalitarian principles. In the spiritualist tradition, however, powers were present in matter by virtue of creation and were only relatively autonomous; in materialism they became eternal and entirely autonomous. In spiritualism, moreover, the critique of established interests was based on the biblical concepts of the Spirit and the Church; in materialism it was based on the natural equality of humans by itself and was directed against the established Church. The causes of this dramatic shift in theology are complex, but our survey suggests at least the following five factors.

(1) The increasingly specialized nature of natural science allowed the adoption of selected ideas from early eighteenth-century figures like Boerhaave and Stahl without reference to their Christian faith.

(2) The involvement of the French Church in national politics was such as to make implacable enemies of the more radical *philosophes*, particularly Diderot and Holbach.

(3) Newtonianism set the standard for understanding the relationship between God and nature. Newton found plenty of scope for divine activity in nature, but, in order to make room for an active God, he had to make matter itself entirely inert. In other words, Newton reinforced the underlying assumption of the mechanical philosophy that more power for matter implied less power for God.

(4) Guardians of orthodoxy in France had exploited dualistic, Cartesian ideas for the defence of religion. Some *philosophes* like Voltaire had adopted the Newtonian symbiosis of God and nature. But the alternative, spiritualist, tradition had not been a vigorous movement in France as it had in England, Holland and Germany.

(5) Underlying all these contemporary factors were several longer range tendencies we have observed in Western thought since the twelfth century: the tendency to press the comprehensibility, unity and relative autonomy of creation to the point of making nature entirely self-sufficient; the tendency to define the self-sufficiency of nature and the direct operation of God as mutually exclusive alternatives; and the tendency to treat the gifts of healing and reform on secular terms in contrast to the 'spiritual' ministry of the clergy.

On the basis of all these points, eighteenth-century materialism can be seen as a legitimate expression of the creationist tradition as much as the medieval Catholic emphasis on God's *potentia absoluta* or the Reformation emphasis on perpetual miracles within God's *potentia ordinata*.

3. BRITISH AND AMERICAN ANTI-NEWTONIANS

There was a variety of reactions to Newton's symbiosis of science and theology in the eighteenth century. Among them were several groups that rejected Newton's ideas as encouraging monistic materialism (like that discussed in the previous section) or otherwise compromising religious principles. It is important to give these figures due consideration. Their critiques preserved some traditional features of the creationist tradition and the alternative systems they inspired, though now mostly forgotten, were positive stimuli in their time.

There were at least three different groups of people who developed an anti-Newtonian stance:

(1) High-Church Anglican Tories like Jonathan Swift and Samuel Johnson;

(2) Anti-materialists like George Berkeley, Jonathan Edwards and William Blake;

(3) The followers of John Hutchinson.

These names include some of the most prominent figures of the time. Although we cannot possibly do justice to them individually, we can gain a sense of the breadth of the interaction of humanities, science and theology in the eighteenth century.

High-Church Anglican Tories

On the whole, the High-Church party viewed itself as being on the defensive against the emerging power of the Latitudinarians and Whigs in the late seventeenth and early eighteenth centuries. The more conscientious of them (the Nonjurors) refused to declare their allegiance to William and Mary after the 'Glorious Revolution' of 1688 and were naturally bypassed in the appointments of the new regime. They briefly reasserted themselves, however, during the Tory ascendency in the latter part of the reign of Queen Anne (1710–14). During that time High Churchmen were responsible for two significant movements that raised up widespread concerns about the impact of the new science: one ecclesiastical (the temporary prosecution of Samuel Clarke) and the other literary (the campaign of the 'Scriblerians' against the scientific projects of the Royal Society).

High-Church Criticisms of Clarke

Samuel Clarke's doubts about the orthodox version of the Trinity (section 4.1) were due to his subordination of revelation to reason according to Nonjurors like George Hickes (1642–1715), the nonjuring Bishop of Thetford, and Roger North (1653–1734), a solicitor to Queen Anne. North noted what appeared to conservatives to be a certain arrogance on the part of Newtonians like Clarke: their promotion of one particular natural philosophy against all others (Cartesian, Leibnizian, etc.) was paralleled by their attempt to pass judgement on the divine essence using the tools of human reason. North accepted that space was infinite but rejected Newton's notion of absolute uncreated space as encroaching on the power of God (whereas for Newtonians it was a manifestation of divine omnipotence).

It appears that the Nonjurors' sense of the transcendence of God and the majesty of his revelation was related to their high conception of the Church and insistence on its autonomy in relation to the state. The dynamics of the period is strikingly similar to that of the late eleventh and early twelfth centuries when a dispute over the relation of revelation to Aristotelian dialectic was similarly related to the struggle between papal and secular powers for control of the Church (secton 1.4).

The Scriblerians and Samuel Johnson

The Scriblerians (or Scriblerus Club) included John Arbuthnot (1667–1735), Jonathan Swift (1667–1745), and Alexander Pope (1688–1744). Some of their ideas were later developed by Samuel Johnson (1709–84).

The Scriblerians were not opposed to Newtonian science as such or to the use of science for the improvement of human life – Arbuthnot wrote an important paper for the Royal Society (1710–12) that provided the basis of modern mathematical statistics, particularly the work of Laplace. But they viewed the propaganda of the Royal Society with enough detachment to see its humorous and farcical aspects. Arbuthnot and Swift were particularly concerned with the latitudinarian policies (tolerating Dissenters) of many members of the Royal Society and rejected any relaxation of conformity to the standards of the Church of England as a matter of principle. They clearly associated current science with a pragmatism that neglected the spiritual side of human nature and a self-interest that conflicted with true Christian charity. The rivalry between opposing schools of scientific thought was also held to be needlessly divisive for the Church. To some extent their concerns paralleled the early Christian critique of Greek science (section 1.5): according to the Scriblerians, many scientists were motivated by arrogance and pride rather than by a genuine love for God and their fellow humans.

Swift had earlier criticized the modern 'philosophers' for erecting edifices in the air in *A Tale of a Tub* (1704). The Latitudinarians' use of the phenomena of nature to infer the existence of God as its designer was parodied by his description of a religious sect that worshipped an idol in the form of a tailor because their world had the appearance of a suit of clothes.

In *Gulliver's Travels* (1726), Swift ridiculed the Royal Society by depicting a Grand Academy of Projectors in the city of Lagado. The preposterous schemes of the members of the Academy included experiments to extract sunbeams from cucumbers and develop a breed of naked sheep. These 'projects' were pursued with such single mindedness that the people's homes and lands went to ruin.

Gulliver also visited the more theoretically inclined Laputians whose obsession with the effects of a recent – and soon to return – comet clearly reflected on the theories of Newton and Whiston. The Laputians thus exhibited the plight of a science-based society for which knowledge of the future was of no avail in controlling it.

Swift also criticized his own culture by having Gulliver belittle the mores of the lands he visited in ways that clearly reflected back those of his home country. For instance, when the king of Brobdingnag refused to consider Gulliver's proposal to exploit the destructive potential of gunpowder, Gulliver attributed this to his 'Narrowness of thinking' and 'unnecessary scruple, whereof in Europe we can have no conception'. Swift's sensitivity to the abuses that could result from new technologies in the service of political interests was partly the result of his own witnessing of the English exploitation of Ireland. Here again parallels could be drawn to earlier models, e.g., the Jewish experience of the superior technologies of colonial powers in the ancient world (section 1.5).

Though initially more sympathetic to the efforts of the 'projectors' than Swift, Samuel Johnson became increasingly critical of the apparent smugness with which Latitudinarians explained the decrees of God and the structures of nature in terms of each other. For Johnson, the will of God could not be accounted for through human deliberation, and the natural world was not there just to be exploited for experimental or apologetic purposes. He argued against defenders of vivisection that the insensitivity to animal pain required by many experiments was the direct cause of many physicians' callousness towards their human patients. Johnson could also adopt the animal's point of view as a literary device critiquing anthropocentrism in his attack on the argument from design popularized by Latitudinarian scientists and theologians: a mother vulture explains to her children that humans are endowed with a natural propensity to war so that they may have a regular supply of food.

No stranger to the struggle for economic survival himself, Johnson exhibited a unique sense of moral absolutes in an age characterized by overt self-interest. In his earlier writings, he upheld the Baconian valuation of science as a means towards the amelioration of the human condition and as a vehicle for the expression of Christian charity; only when pursued as an end in itself would science become vain and destructive. With the writing of *Rasselas* (1759), however, he came to the grim conclusion that the desire to control nature would lead to the madness of imagining oneself in the place of God even when exercised in the interests of Christian service. At the time, Johnson was grieving over the loss of his mother – he wrote the work in order to pay for her funeral expenses. His undoubted depression only partly accounts for his onesided view of the current science, however: literary criticism shows the basic continuity with his earlier writings.

The critique of these literary figures was haphazard, and they offered no coherent alternatives. Moreover their social and religious conservatism made them unappreciative of the legitimate needs for radical change in their society. However, their concerns about the public uses of science and technology were to find ample support in subsequent history. Their writings thus provided an important precedent for future generations of writers who sought to express their concerns about science and technology through the medium of fantasy and science fiction.

Ani-Materialists: Berkeley, Edwards and Blake

George Berkeley and Jonathan Edwards were two of the most sophisticated thinkers of the eighteenth century. Far from attempting to characterize their thought as a whole, we are concerned here only with their reactions to contemporary science – the ideas of Newton in particular – and the role their theology played in those reactions.

George Berkeley

George Berkeley (1685–1753) was one of the earliest critics of Newton's natural philosophy. He aimed his attacks directly at those entities in Newton's system that acted as intermediaries between God and passive matter – absolute space and supra-mechanical force. Newton himself had intended by these notions to ensure an active role for God in nature, but they seemed to others to make God more remote and lead to deism and even materialism.

Absolute space, Berkeley argued (1710) must either be God himself (which Newton denied) or else 'something beside God which is eternal, uncreated, infinite, indivisible, immutable' – either of which notion is 'pernicious and absurd'. Newton's ideas of force and gravitation, on the other hand, were convenient tools for the purposes of calculation, but they had no more reality than the epicycles of medieval astronomers. For Berkeley (as for Aristotle and Descartes), the real causes of motion could only be spirits: thus they could not be investigated by science but were reserved for metaphysics and theology.

In effect, Berkeley challenged the Newtonian synthesis of physics and theology at its very core. Like the materialists (section 4.2), he took over Newton's notion of a subtle ether and Boerhaave's idea of a cosmic fire, but he concluded that such an active substratum for empirical phenomena must be a form of mind rather than matter.

Rather than distancing God from the phenomena of nature as Newton's universal active principles appeared to do, Berkeley's idealism ran the opposite danger of eliminating any intrinsic lawfulness from nature. His stated intention, however, was not to reduce the laws of nature to epiphenomena of the divine mind so much as to insist on their plurality and specificity in opposition to the universal principles of Newton. His reaction to Newton was thus not unlike that of earlier Christians to Aristotle's subordination of terrestrial events to cosmic cycles. Like the Church fathers and Reformers, Berkeley saw the world as a plurality of principles which found their unity in God rather than a hierarchy of principles subordinate to each other.

Jonathan Edwards

Like Berkeley, though independently of him, the American theologian Jonathan Edwards (1703–58) opposed current tendencies to materialism and rejected Newton's hierarchical view of God and nature. But like Newton and unlike Berkeley, he followed Henry More in holding that space is a necessary manifestation (for human minds, at least) of the divine being. Instead, he took aim at Newton's dualism between active principles or ethers and solid atomic matter.

For Newton, gravitation was a supra-mechanical principle imposed on matter while solidity (hardness, impenetrability) was a primary quality of the primordial particles themselves. Whereas many Newtonians and materialists attempted to overcome the dualism by making gravitation an intrinsic property of matter, Edwards solved it by making solidity a direct manifestation of divine power like gravitation. The substratum of all qualities was God himself: space was God acting, and Newton's laws could be understood as simply describing the manner in which God acted in space and time. Thus the mutual attraction of atoms was as much the result of divine energy as the mutual love between two minds: both were reflections of the mutuality of the eternal self-expression and love of God in the Trinity.

Edwards was probably not aware of the fact that Newton was an Arian, but he did know of the cultivation of Unitarian ideas among his followers and, like Cotton Mather, he defended the traditional doctrine of the Trinity. There is no need to suppose a cause-effect relationship between the different aspects of his thought, but clearly his ability to see the activity of God equally in all the phenomena of nature was facilitated by his dynamic sense of the inner life of the Godhead.

Like Berkeley, Edwards ran the risk of emptying nature of any structure or principles of its own. The truth of divine providence was established at the expense of the doctrine of creation. Creation, for Edwards, was simply the first exercise of the power God has wielded ever since.

Belief in the utter dependence of all things in God did not prevent Edwards from supposing that the principles of mechanics could account for the operations of nature. As in the mechanical philosophy of Descartes and Boyle, the activity of God in sustaining nature was supposed to be regular and predictable. In fact, God established the primary qualities and mechanical laws of nature at creation in such a way that all the inanimate forms of this world would be produced from a primordial chaos in accordance with those qualities and laws. Only the production of plants and animals required the imposition of new structures and laws (as with Boyle and Derham). Edwards clearly followed Descartes rather than Newton at this point. Evidently, his sense of the utter dependence of all nature on God – primary qualities and active principles equally – made it unnecessary for him to reserve a special role for God in the formation of the solar system as Newton and Clarke did.

Neither Berkeley nor Edwards made any significant contribution to the development of science. Nor do their critiques of Newton seem to have inspired any attempts to develop alternative systems of natural philosophy. Still their ideas have frequently been cited in retrospect, particularly in the twentieth century when a relational view of space has been developed not unlike Berkeley's, and matter and fields of force have been united in a single physics reminiscent of the views of Edwards.

William Blake

The visionary poet and artist William Blake (1757–1827) lived and died a full century after Newton (1642–1727). His work reflects the late eighteenth-century quest for radical reform more than the seventeenth-century quest for stability. Blake's political sympathies were with the Jacobinism and Republicanism associated with the French Revolution. He viewed Newton (together with Bacon and Locke) as a symbol of the established order rather than an original thinker in his own right. Still Blake's fantastic symbolism captured some of the essential features of Newton's system as well as any physicist or historian could have done.

Like Berkeley, Blake took issue with two key Newtonian ideas: absolute space (and time) and supra-mechanical force. Both notions presupposed the complete passivity or inertness of matter. From this perspective, Newton's worldview had the same meaning as the mechanical philosophy of Descartes and Boyle. The only difference was that it substituted a Neoplatonic hierarchy of force over matter for the mechanical dualism of spirit and matter. Blake himself was more in tune with a third tradition of natural philosophy (section 3.3), the spiritualist tradition of Paracelsus, Helmont, and Boehme which imbued matter with living force and energy.

The problem with Newton's hierarchy for Blake was that it robbed matter of its intrinsic energy and subjected it to extraneous forces and laws. This subordination was not simply a matter of physics for Blake. It carried over into the social and political arena where it was associated with the pragmatic (Malthusian) policies of William Pitt and the conventional Augustan norms of morality and art.

Blake's image of Newton is best known from the large colour print dated 1795. Immersed in a sea of space and time, Newton bends over a scroll spread out on the seafloor and uses a compass to plot the sparse geometry of nature. His body is rooted in rock and sand and his bright reddish hair stands out against the dark expanse beyond. The scroll on the ground is the extension of a cloth; the cloth, in turn, is the projection of Newton's own thought. While heroic in his own way, Newton thus symbolizes the ascendency of calculation over imagination and of external force over the intrinsic energy of life. As Blake put it in *Jerusalem* (15:11–20, written 1804–20):

For Bacon & Newton sheathd in dismal steel, their terrors hang
Like iron scourges over Albion, Reasonings like vast Serpents
Infold around my limbs, bruising my minute articulations.
I turn my eyes to the Schools & Universities of Europe
And there behold the Loom of Locke whose Woof rages dire
Washd by the Water-wheels of Newton: black the cloth
In heavy wreathes folds over every Nation; cruel Works
Of many Wheels I view, wheel without wheel, with cogs tyrannic
Moving by compulsion each other; not as those in Eden: which
Wheel within Wheel in freedom revolve in harmony & peace.

The contrast of the constructions of the wheels of Newton and of those of Eden indicates the difference between a gravitational system and one based on divine energy and prophetic inspiration (cf. Ezek. 1:15–21).

Blake's abhorrence of Newton's mathematical system of forces operating on inert matter carried over into a rejection of the very idea of creation as Newton and others of his time understood it. Blake regarded the God who subjected all nature to measure, number, and weight (Wisd. 11:20) as a mere demiurge who acted out of ignorance and compulsion. The most common name for this god in Blake's mythology was Urizen (pronounced like 'your reason'), best known from the colour print, 'The Ancient of Days', which served as the frontpiece of Blake's *Europe* (1794). Like Newton, Urizen stoops and reaches downwards toward earth, a giant compass in his left hand, to create geometric structure in an otherwise dark void. The idea of the compass originally came from the text of Proverbs 8:27: 'When he drew a circle on the face of the deep'. It had also been used by Milton in his positive portrayal of creation by the Son of God in *Paradise Lost* (VII.224–31). In Blake's mythology, however, the imposition of mathematical form on nature signified the enslavement of the human spirit, 'Petrifying all the Human Imagination into rock & sand' (*Four Zoas* 24:6).

What made Blake's critique of Newtonianism so devastating was the fact that he attacked it, not as an agnostic, but as a believer who was thoroughly imbued with biblical imagery and sensitive to biblical standards of justice. The three creationist ideas of the comprehensibility, unity, and relative autonomy of nature were no longer creative ones for this poet and prophet. They now signified abstractness, uniformity and compulsion, and all three seemed to deny the possibility of healing and restoration that the creationist tradition had traditionally affirmed. What Blake saw in his vision was the demise of the creationist tradition in Western culture.

But Blake also saw beyond the current distortion of creationist ideas to a reconciliation of reason and imagination, external force and internal energy. According to the Introduction to Blake's *Songs of Experience* (1794), the Word of God would finally take control of the celestial mechanics of Newton ('the starry pole') and rouse the earth from its sleepy subjection to external force ('the slumberous mass'). Indeed, in his youthful apprenticeship, Jesus had already taken up the compass as one of the tools of his trade and effected a reconciliation of reason and imagination.

In the words of the well-known poem in the Preface to *Milton* (1804), Jerusalem could be rebuilt in the midst of the 'dark Satanic Mills' of Newtonian physics and the nascent industrial revolution it heralded. Indeed, according to Blake's *Europe* (13:1–5), only the mighty spirit of Newton himself could sound the trumpet that would signal the end of the present world order and the beginning of a new age of imagination, peace and love.

In the restored world, the representatives of abstract reason (Bacon, Newton and Locke) would join together with Blake's heroes of the imagination (Milton, Shakespeare and Chaucer) in an antiphonal chorus of modern mathematics and Renaissance art. The problem with the present age was not Newton's mechanics so much as the Druid Spectre of exploitation and warfare that Blake so closely associated with it. In keeping with the fourth point of the creationist tradition (section 1.5), Blake saw that human science and technology could not fulfil their god-given purpose unless they were directed towards the healing and restoration of the human condition.

The Hutchinsonians

The Hutchinsonians were a small group of thinkers inspired by (though not always agreeing with) the work of John Hutchinson (1674–1737). The most influential of them were William Jones (curate) of Wayland (1726–1800) and George Horne (1730–92), Bishop of Norwich, both of whom had High-Church affiliations and were opposed to the Latitudinarianism and Deism often associated with Newton's philosophy. Hutchinson's works also provided an alternative natural philosophy – more acceptable than Newton's – to conservative Christian educators like John Wesley.

The basic concerns of the Hutchinsonians were:

(1) that the physico-theologians' interpretation of Scripture in terms of the latest scientific theories led to rationalism and naturalism,

(2) that Newton's inclusion of active principles like gravitation in physical science substituted matter (the subtle ether, perhaps) for God and led to atheism.

The Hutchinsonians proposed a view of nature that was more mechanistic, but one based on a 'literal' reading of Scripture that ensured God's transcendence over nature. In contrast to those Newtonians and materialists who disliked Newton's retention of the Cartesian notion of passive matter, they insisted that matter was entirely inert and rejected Newton's notion of active principles.

Hutchinson's response to Newton was published under revealing titles like *Moses's Principia* (1724–27) and *Glory or Gravity* (1733–34). Scientists and theologians had been labouring, he argued, under the false impression that Moses was not interested in natural philosophy. In the original (unpointed) Hebrew language, each letter stood for a sense object and that object in turn was the type for a spiritual reality. In Genesis chapter 1, Hutchinson was thus able to find clear references to the elements of fire, light, and air (or spirit). They were referred to as the 'heavens' in the English version Genesis 1:1 (Hebrew: *shmym*), but the correct translation was 'Names' (root *shm*), meaning the fundamental constituents of the universe. These elements therefore stood for three beings with names, in this case the three members of the Trinity: fire for the

Father, light for the Son, and air for the Holy Spirit. Like the members of the Trinity they were three manifestations of a single substance – a subtle fluid – but in contrast to God, and unlike Newton's subtle ether – they were completely passive and had to be set in motion by God.

Once set in motion the fluid continued in perpetual circulation and became the source of all other motion in the cosmos. It was emitted from the sun in the form of fire, travelled out through the solar system in the form of light, and condensed and returned to the sun in the form of air. In the process of circulation, the subtle fluid initiated and sustained all of the motions we observe in nature. The pressure of outward-bound light, for example, was responsible for the cohesion and hardness of bodies; the pressure of returning air was the cause of their apparent gravitation towards the sun. Thus nature was in perpetual motion and did not require periodic interventions by God, as Newton thought, in order to keep it from collapsing.

It is worthwhile comparing Hutchinson's anti-Newtonian system to Jonathan Edwards'. Both wished to reaffirm the traditional doctrine of the Trinity in an age of theological doubt. Both were enabled by their more dynamic view of the Godhead to view the normal operations of nature as perfect manifestations of divine power and avoid any appeal to a 'God of the gaps'. The difference was that Edwards countered Newton's dualism by making the hardness of matter an immediate expression of divine power like gravitation and viewed all such inter-atomic forces as analogous to the unity of the Trinity. Hutchinson, on the other hand, made gravitation and cohesion equally the result of contact forces of a mechanical fluid that more distantly reflected the dynamic of the life of the Trinity. Edwards made matter continually dependent on God, while Hutchinson emphasized God's transcendence and granted the power of perpetual motion to matter. Edwards stressed providence at the expense of creation; Hutchinson limited the action of God to the first moment of creation and occasional subsequent interventions and left no room for regular divine providence.

For the most part, Hutchinson's physics was hopelessly inadequate to deal with the increasingly technical issues of physical science. There is one way in which his ideas may have indirectly contributed to the development of science, not in physics itself, however, but in chemistry. Newtonians held that all the phenomena of chemistry could be reduced to the varying interparticulate forces between the atoms of a homogeneous substratum of matter subject to different concentrations. A corollary was the possible transmutation of any element into any other, a phenomenon that played an essential role in Newton's world system. For example, the transmutation of cometary vapours into terrestrial water was responsible for replenishing the earth's diminishing water supply.

Hutchinson, on the other hand, took the different kinds of atoms as immutably distinct. (It is not clear how these atomic elements are related to the three 'Names' discussed above.) Apparently, the incessant circulation of the subtle fluid made the transmutation of one form of matter into another appear to be superfluous. At any rate, Hutchinson encouraged chemical speculation along lines radically different from those of orthodox Newtonianism.

Several of Hutchinson's followers popularized this aspect of his thought. For example, William Jones denied the homogeneity of matter and postulated the existence of solid, immutable atoms and went so far (1781) as to infer the shapes of the atoms from the properties of the substances they constituted (earth, water, etc.).

Towards the end of the century, an associate of John Dalton named George Adams (1750–95) propounded similar notions in an effort to counter the atheistic tendencies of a prominent 'modern philosopher of France' (presumably Laplace) and the materialism of Joseph Priestley, both of which he and others associated with the disruptive forces of the French Revolution. It is known that Adams was influenced by Hutchinson and Jones though it is not clear to what extent Dalton himself was also so influenced. The fact that the two shared a common concern about the new wave of materialism may be sufficient to account for the similarity of their ideas. But the least that can be said is that the *preparatio* for Dalton's atomic theory of chemistry was provided through the anti-Newtonianism of John Hutchinson and his followers.

The eighteenth-century controversy between Newtonians and anti-Newtonians brings out the variety of roles that theology could play in the history of science. In the propaganda of the Royal Society, theology provided social legitimation to the efforts of struggling proponents of a hitherto unrecognized profession. In the writings of the Scriblerians and Samuel Johnson, it ensured that all such projects would continue to be scrutinized in terms of longer range social and spiritual goals. In the case of the Newtonians, theological notions contributed to the development of alternatives to the mechanical philosophy and granted a degree of respectability to the new science. In the case of the anti-materialists (Berkeley and Edwards) and Hutchinsonians, theology ensured the consideration of alternative paradigms once Newtonianism had become established. If there has been a positive contribution of the creationist tradition to the development of Western science, it has stemmed from its balance and flexibility in charting direction rather than from any ability to determine the contents of a correct science.

4. POST-NEWTONIAN COSMOGONISTS AND NEO-MECHANISTS

The final grouping of the eighteenth century we shall consider is the one that established the scope of cosmological speculation and the rigour of mathematical analysis that has characterized physical science ever since. It was thus the first group of scientists to develop a natural philosophy whose comprehensiveness could be demonstrated rather than just assumed. The nineteenth-century image of Newtonian science as an all-embracing, deterministic system is due to our present subjects, not to Newton himself. Whereas Newton understood his principles to account only for the general operation of the world once it had been set up by God, the cosmogonists and neo-mechanists demonstrated their ability to ensure the permanent stability of the solar system and applied them also to the problem of the origins of all systems, both planetary and galactic.

The development of analytical mechanics was largely the work of the French mathematicians, d'Alembert, Lagrange and Laplace. There were several others, however, English, Scots and Germans, who first developed the ideas about cosmogony – the so-called 'nebular hypothesis' – later taken up and developed more rigorously by the French. The shift from Newtonian thought to neo-mechanism is most clearly seen in their work.

Early Cosmogonists: Wright, Ferguson and the Early Kant
Three major innovations of the mid-eighteenth century prepared the way for the 'nebular hypothesis' of Laplace:

(1) the notion that the sun and stars were not 'fixed', but in motion under mutual gravitation (Wright);

(2) the hypothesis of a primordial condition out of which the solar system was formed by the force of gravity (Ferguson);

(3) the hypothesis of a primordial chaos out of which the entire universe was formed by the force of gravity (Kant).

Kant's contribution was partly inspired by Wright's, but independent of Ferguson's.

A Dynamic Theocentric Universe: Thomas Wright
The first person known to have suggested the dynamic nature of the universe within a Newtonian framework was Thomas Wright

of Durham (1711–86). Impelled by a desire to synthesize his faith with contemporary astronomy, Wright imagined (1734, 1750) the universe as an infinite expanse with the throne of God as the source of light and power at its centre and eternal darkness in the outer regions. Like Thomas Digges and Giordano Bruno (whom Wright quoted) in the sixteenth century (section 3.2), he argued that the unbounded power of God required an infinite universe as its proper object. At the outer fringe of the visible universe was the Milky Way, the most distant part of our own galaxy, which Wright surmised to have the form of either a ring (like one of the rings of Saturn) or a spherical shell (with the solar system located in the body of the shell). Beyond the Milky Way were an infinite number of other galaxies extending into the realm of outer darkness. Between light and darkness, heaven and hell, all the stars were in motion under the power of mutual gravitation. The thought barrier between a static cosmos and dynamic one had been penetrated.

The details of Wright's theory were not well worked out, but the general idea was later picked up by Kant. Eventually it led to a consistently mechanistic account of the origins of the present structure of the cosmos and became a source of concern for believers: there no longer seemed to be a role for God as Newton and others had imagined. Nor did the origin of the cosmos have any apparent relationship to the aspirations and fates of humans.

But in its inception Wright's departure from Newtonian thought was motivated by the desire to ensure a correlation between the moral and physical orders. The sun was displaced from its central role and all the stars put in motion in order to reserve the place of unique fixed centre for the visible manifestation of the Deity. The regions of the universe closest to the throne of God were designed to be the eternal home of the righteous with different types of planetary system suited to different degrees of reward. Beyond the Milky Way were more distant galaxies with their own stars and planetary systems: these were the future abodes of the unjust with different types of planetary system suited to different forms of punishment. Fantastic as Wright's scheme may sound to us today, it at least prevents us from supposing any general divorce between science and theology in the mid-eighteenth century. The same is true in the case of the second figure we are to examine, James Ferguson.

A Mechanically Formed Solar System: James Ferguson

At about the same time as Kant, a Scots astronomer and instrument maker, James Ferguson (1710–76), suggested that gravitation could account for the formation of the solar system as well as its current dynamics. Isaac Watts and Jonathan Edwards had argued in a general way that the formation of all things occurred in accordance with the laws of God established at the moment of creation. But neither of these men was a scientist and neither was concerned specifically with the potential and limits of gravitation as a formative principle.

Though not proficient in current mathematics, Ferguson had a good grasp of observational astronomy and began lecturing on the new science in 1748. His *Astronomy Explained upon Sir Isacc Newton's Principles* (1756) went through thirteen editions and was translated into Swedish and German. Ferguson also specialized in the production of mechanical models of the solar system which surpassed in detail and accuracy any other of the time.

Ferguson assumed that the atoms that later constituted the sun and planets were originally separate and distributed (inhomogeneously) through space. They were endowed by God with the power of gravitation – each attracting all the others in accordance with Newton's law. Given time, therefore, the atoms naturally clustered into various massive bodies with the most massive, the stars, surrounded by a number of smaller planets. The resulting co-planarity and co-rotation of the planetary bodies was striking evidence of the skill of the Creator in giving the atoms the proper initial distribution and framing the laws imposed on them. But, given that initial distribution, co-planarity and co-rotation followed naturally without any further intervention on God's part.

Ferguson's cosmogony differed from the 'nebular hypotheses' later developed by Kant and Laplace in that it did not impose the constraint of randomness in the original distribution of the atoms. Ferguson thus preserved the role for God of giving some form to the atomic matter he created. On the other hand, he did go beyond Newton in supposing that the present order of the solar system could be entirely accounted for in terms of a prior, more basic, structure.

A Cyclical Universe: Immanuel Kant

Immanuel Kant (1724–1804) is best known for his tomes of philosophy which moved in an entirely different world of faith and thought from the relatively simple piety of Thomas Wright and James Ferguson. Kant's mature work (beginning with the *Critique of Pure Reason*, 1781) marked the clear separation in Western thought between the moral and physical orders. Kant affirmed the existence of both but grounded them in entirely different modes of human experience: the moral in the universal inner sense of ought, and the physical in sense experience and the empirical judgements based thereon.

Here we are concerned only with early ('precritical') work of Kant which contributed directly to natural philosophy and still worked within a theistic framework. The point we wish to make is that the separation of moral and physical realms that characterized Kant's later thought was already implicit in this earlier work.

The aim of Kant's early natural philosophy was to reconcile the contrary views of Newton and Leibniz. From the one he took the law of gravitation, the explanatory power of which had been suggested to him by Thomas Wright. From the other he adopted a sense of the sufficiency of the laws of matter to account for all the phenomena of nature. But Kant went beyond both Newton and Leibniz (or behind them both to Descartes) in supposing that these principles could be applied to the previously intractable problem of the formation of the present order of the universe. The result was his *Universal Natural History and Theory of the Heavens* (1755), subtitled 'An Essay on the Constitution and Mechanical Origin of the Whole Universe Treated According to Newtonian Principles'.

The new view of the formation of the universe Kant proposed was startlingly austere (by contemporary standards). Like Ferguson, he claimed that the entire process could be understood in terms of strictly mechanical causes. (Gravitation was now included in the scope of the mechanical, contrary to Newton.) As to the original state of the universe, however, Kant hypothesized an infinite *random* distribution of matter (not a pre-arranged one like Ferguson's). Then, on the basis of Newton's theory, the region that happened to have the highest density in this random distribution would condense most rapidly under the power of gravitation and give rise to the first galaxy of stars each with its own planetary system. The stars would orbit around their common galactic centre just as the planets orbitted around their respective suns. Gradually further regions of space would also condense so that the formation of stars and planets would continue indefinitely, extending further and further from the first galaxy (the latter being the centre of galactic formation).

Kant still had to suppose a first moment of creation *ex nihilo* (something he considered to be a paradox in later writings). But that moment was now completely separated from the process of formation and stripped even of any design of the original distribution of matter with a view to the subsequent location of the sun and planets (as for Ferguson). The formation of the universe as it appears at present was a process governed entirely by the laws of physics acting on a random distribution of matter.

Kant not only emptied the idea of creation of most of its content; he also pushed the moment of creation back further than had ever been previously imagined. 'A series of millions of years and centuries' might have elapsed, he suggested, to allow the emergence of the ordered universe we see around us today.

Given enough time, stars and planetary systems would not only be formed; according to Kant, they would also eventually collapse. Like Newton, Kant supposed that the orbital motion of the planets would gradually slow down so that the planets would all eventually fall into their respective suns. As a result the suns would heat up, one after the other, and explode. The incinerated remains would then provide the material for the formation of new galaxies in accordance with the same mechanical laws. These cycles of formation and dissolution would continue without end. Like Hutton's theory of the earth, Kant's view of the universe was ultimately a steady-state theory, not a truly evolutionary one.

There was no conflict for Kant, however, between this austere view of the origin and destiny of the galaxies and religious faith. The immensity of an infinite universe was, as for Digges, Bruno and Wright, a fitting expression of the infinity of God. And its unlimited productivity was an indication of divine omnipotence, which for Kant, as for Leibniz (against Newton), was expressed through the means of material causation, not over and above it.

The prospect of the eventual destruction of our own and every galaxy, naturally occasioned 'profound astonishment' in Kant's mind. He took consolation in the thought that the destiny of the human soul was eternal life independent of the fate of heaven and earth. The soul would survive the death of its planet as well as the death of its body. In the future life it might even visit other worlds and find a home there – temporarily. But the machinery of the universe would grind on, making and unmaking worlds, and would never constitute a 'new heavens and a new earth in which righteousness dwells' (2 Peter 3:13).

Here, the contrast between Kant's vision and that of Thomas Wright is striking. For Wright the structure and destiny of the cosmos was the vehicle of human fulfilment; for Kant it was merely a foil. So the separation of the physical and moral realms that characterized Kant's later thought was not an arbitrary imposition: it was already implicit in his earlier work. The new concept of the universe which Kant developed in 1755 was that of an amoral phenomenon indifferent to the aspirations and struggles of humans.

The consonance between the productivity of the universe and the power of God which Kant so highly valued had no apparent relation to the parallel correlation between moral obligation and the Supreme Good. The moral dimension of human life could not be denied, but it could no longer be tied in with the origin and destiny of the external world either. Consequently, it would have to be grounded in a distinctive experience and granted a realm of discourse of its own.

French Neo-Mechanist: D'Alembert, Lagrange and Laplace

The notion of classical physics as an abstract deterministic mathematical system is due to three major figures of eighteenth-century French science: d'Alembert, Lagrange and Laplace. They were rigorously mathematical in their work and consistently agnostic on questions of ultimate causation or meaning. The label 'neo-mechanist' is appropriate in that they reinterpreted Newton's dynamics by eliminating the metaphysical and theological dimension and reaffirmed the earlier (Cartesian) notion of nature as a machine. In effect, the notion of what constituted a machine was broadened to include principles which Newton's generation had understood to transcend mechanics. Such a generalization was made plausible by the fact that new types of apparatus were being developed in the eighteenth century that exploited forces like electricity and magnetism previously thought to be supra-mechanical.

Jean d'Alembert

Jean le Rond d'Alembert (1717–83) made a clean break with those scientists who fostered a synthesis of science and theology and laid the basis for the later positivism of Condorcet and Comte. He roundly criticized Maupertius, for example, for incorporating teleological and theological notions into his science, and he treated the *vis viva* controversy between Newtonians and Leibnizians as a mere battle over words with no real bearing on science. Scientists should get on with their work and not become embroiled in metaphysical controversies that might never be resolved. On the basis of those laws, particularly those governing organic creatures, one could indeed infer the existence and intelligence of a Being who was their author. But the existence and attributes of God were of no consequence for positive science since God could not be counted on to intervene in worldly affairs in any predictable manner.

The different types of knowledge must not be confused, d'Alembert argued. The truths of revealed religion (like the Trinity or creation *ex nihilo* or transubstantiation) transcended reason: they had to be supernaturally impressed on the soul by God and received through the internal sense of faith – what Pascal had referred to as the 'heart'. The truths or laws of natural science, on the other hand, could be demonstrated objectively by comparing the deductions of human reason with the observation of nature (1759). D'Alembert's emphasis on the priority of reason, as distinct from sense experience, reflected the influence of the French rationalists, Descartes and Malebranche. Like them he held that the laws of motion were logically necessary and could be demonstrated without recourse to experiment. But d'Alembert went beyond Descartes and Malebranche in holding that the laws of the world system were just those that matter *left to itself* would follow and need not have been imposed by an external agent. As d'Alembert's followers, Condorcet and Laplace, were to put it, the present state of the world could have been predicted by a rational being who knew only its initial condition and its laws of operation. Like their materialistic contemporaries, Diderot and Holbach, they held that more power for matter (or mechanism in this case) meant less power for God. The tendency to define the powers of God and matter as mutually exclusive alternatives, as we have seen, dated from at least the twelfth century and had been reinforced by the mechanical philosophers and the Newtonians.

Did d'Alembert then turn his back on the creationist tradition? The underlying motifs of the creation of matter out of nothing and laws of nature as the decrees of God subject to his ratification and amendment were no longer a vital idea for d'Alembert and the neo-mechanists. But one must also consider the meaning of their departure from the historic tradition in context.

D'Alembert's programmatic elimination of theology from the work of the scientist did not occur in a vacuum. The context was one in which the principal proponents of French theology were incessantly in conflict with social and scientific progressives. Of course, d'Alembert particularly despised the Jesuits who worked to suppress the *Encyclopedia*, of which he was the scientific editor (1751–58). But, to d'Alembert, all varieties of priests and theologians – Jesuits, Jansenists, Doctors of the Sorbonne, and ministers of Calvinist Geneva alike – were characterized by bigotry and intolerance. They were more concerned with the maintenance of their own authority and privileges, he felt, than with the welfare of the people. For centuries they had made open war on natural philosophy. All spiritual authority, it appeared, was corrupted when exercized in a secular context. If the Church would not reform itself (as it did in the eleventh and the sixteenth centuries), then it was up to less religious people to take the initiative in ridding secular affairs (e.g., the administration of the universities) of ecclesiastical control and scientific research of theological presuppositions.

In retrospect, it appears that a son of the Church imbued with the Christian ideal of public service could only be faithful to that aspect of his calling by attempting to eliminate the influence of the Church and its theology in matters of public concern. One might say that the creationist tradition was rejected by d'Alembert. D'Alembert, on the other hand, might have argued that it was merely rescued (in a secularized form) from the power of its previous guardians.

If the principle enunciated by Jesus has any meaning for the history of science, we must take the latter possibility seriously: '. . . the kingdom of God will be taken away from you and given to a nation producing the fruits of it' (Matt. 21:43). If that principle applied to the priests of Jesus' time, it could have applied to those of the eighteenth century as well. And it could also apply to the present-day guardians of the skills and tasks God has bequeathed to humans, the 'high-priests' of current science and technology.

Lagrange and Laplace on the Stability of the Solar System

The science of analytical mechanics was brought to a new level of formal completion through the efforts of two of d'Alembert's pro-tégés: Joseph Louis de Lagrange (1763–1813) and Pierre Simon de Laplace (1749–1827). The two competed with each other, assisted each other, and incited each other to some of the most spectacular accomplishments of eighteenth-century physics. Among their many contributions we shall discuss only two that occasioned attention from a theological viewpoint: Lagrange and Laplace's work on the stability of the solar system; and Laplace's cosmogonic speculations – the so-called 'nebular hypothesis'. We shall conclude with some reflections on Laplace's secular theology.

Newton, it will be recalled, had been concerned about the fact that the orbits of the planets about the sun would be perturbed when planets came close to passing comets and to each other. He concluded that the solar system was not stable and consequently that periodic interventions by God were required to prevent a total collapse. Leibniz ridiculed Newton's notion that God would create such an imperfect planetary system but could not show that he was wrong. Kant had followed Newton in supposing that the solar system would eventually collapse, but assumed with Leibniz that the system was still perfect and that God would do nothing to prevent such a collapse. The mathematical difficulty of the problems was immense, given the methods of the time, but Lagrange and Laplace approached the issues with complete confidence that they could be solved. Their faith in the comprehensibility of the world can only be compared to that of earlier believers like Kepler and Newton.

There were two possible types of perturbation: secular and periodic. Secular perturbations were cumulative and would lead to long-range disruption. But periodic perturbations were cyclical: a variation in one direction would be compensated for by an equal variation in the other. Lagrange and Laplace set out to demonstrate that all the perturbations among the planets were of the periodic type – even the apparently secular ones were really periodic with very long periods – and hence that the solar system was secularly stable. In other words, the periodic interventions by God were made superfluous by the periodic nature of the perturbations themselves. Lagrange and Laplace were clearly motivated by a belief in the perfection of the system (like Leibniz) and a desire to eliminate Newton's recourse to the supernatural.

Working independently, Lagrange and Laplace showed mathematically that certain overall rules governed variations in the motions of the planets. The importance of these for our modern concept of the cosmos is so great that a few details are in order.

One of the principal items of concern was the interaction of the two largest planets, Jupiter and Saturn. The orbital motion of Jupiter appeared to be gradually accelerating, while that of Saturn was slowing down. Between them, Lagrange and Laplace were able to show (1774–76) that the variations of the inclinations and eccentricities of the orbits of Jupiter and Saturn were bound by fixed limits: in other words, the values of the inclinations and eccentricities of the two planets had to oscillate about mean values within those limits. Thus the single worst threat to the stability of the solar system had been diffused by the late 1770s.

In 1785–88, Laplace was able to calculate the periodicity of variations in the orbits of Jupiter and Saturn: it came out to 929 years. He also showed that the total eccentricity, as well as the total inclination, of all the planetary orbits was a constant: an increase in the eccentricity or inclination of one had to be compensated for by an equivalent decrease for the others. Since the eccentricities and inclinations were all low to begin with, no planet could change its eccentricity or inclination anywhere near enough to change the overall dynamics of the system. And again the alterations were periodic.

The foundational results of Lagrange and Laplace were synthesized at the turn of the century in Laplace's *Treatise on Celestial Mechanics* (1799–1825). Some finishing touches were that the masses of the comets were far too small to affect the stability of the planets and that the accelerating effect of solar radiation pressure was counterbalanced by the decreased gravitation of the sun due to mass loss (1805). The important result was that the solar system was secularly stable as a whole, regardless of the masses of its constituents, provided that all its members orbit the sun in the same direction (which they do for the most part).

The picture was somewhat complicated by the behaviour of an eighth planet, Uranus, which had been discovered by William Herschel in 1781. Not only was the motion of Uranus itself found (in the 1840s) to be erratic, but two of its moons had orbits so highly inclined to the ecliptic that Herschel classified their motion as retrograde (1799). Two of the asteroids discovered in the early nineteenth century also had high inclinations and so did not completely fit the assumptions of Lagrange and Laplace.

No one, however, any longer resorted to Newton's God-of-the-gaps to account for the unresolved problems. For the first time in history, the level of confidence in the scientific method was high enough that the existence of gaps in the world picture could actually be used to predict new discoveries. In other words, the gaps pointed not to God, but to previously unknown constituents of the universe itself.

In the case at hand, the erratic behaviour of Uranus led to the search for new planets. Neptune was discovered in 1846, and Pluto in 1930, and the belief in the long-range stability of the solar system was largely vindicated. There are still residual perturbations in the orbits of Uranus and Neptune that have not been accounted for to this day. But the exclusion of God from scientific discourse is a *fait accompli*. It was a philosophical commitment on the part of the neo-mechanists, not the result of scientific data themselves any more than the earlier arguments in favour of the existence of God were.

The Nebular Hypothesis of Laplace

In 1796, Laplace published a semi-popular *Exposition of the World System* as an introduction to his more technical work on celestial mechanics. At the very end of this work, he allowed himself to depart from his usual rigour to speculate on the problem of the origins of the solar system and the nature of the universe as a whole. There is no evidence that Laplace was basing his thought on the work of Ferguson or Kant at this point. It is more likely that he was motivated by his overall ambition to reduce the areas Newton had left to divine providence. As he put the question in a later (1813) edition of the *Exposition*: 'Could not this arrangement of the planets be itself a result of the laws of motion? And could not the supreme intelligence that Newton made to intervene have made it depend on a more general phenomenon [instead of intervening]?'

The hypothesis Laplace developed in successive editions of the *Exposition* (1796–1824) was this: the planets were formed from the primordial solar atmosphere – a large, nearly static cloud (nebula) of gas surrounding the sun. Gravitational attraction caused the material to fall in towards the sun and hence to rotate in order to conserve angular momentum (presumably it had an initial, very small net rotation to begin with). As the cloud condensed the outer regions of material in the equatorial plane would begin to rotate fast enough to counteract the gravitational pull of the sun and would thus form stable rings around the sun. The condensing gas cloud would form a succession of rings at varying distances from the sun in this way. As these rings cooled they would break up and form smaller, planetary nebulae and eventually coalesce into the present planets with their respective moons. As a result, the planets and their moons would all rotate in the same direction and in the same plane (low inclinations) with nearly circular orbits (low eccentricities) as generally observed. The comets had highly eccentric orbits because they were captured from material outside the solar system. The peculiar structure of the solar system was the result neither of chance, not of divine formation (as Newton held), but resulted from the behaviour of matter under the force of universal gravitation.

Laplace had developed the nebular hypothesis out of strictly theoretical considerations – only his appeal to the universal force of gravitation was based on the empirically based research of Newton. When he became aware of William Herschel's work on stellar nebulae (early 1790s), however, he felt that it confirmed his ideas. Herschel, an observational astronomer, had determined that certain nebulae in space were stellar atmospheres rather than groups of unresolved stars. He concluded that the stars were in various stages of formation as the result of the gravitational collapse of the nebulae. Here, then, was the same process that Laplace had postulated in the case of the sun, being witnessed for other stars.

Both the theoretical and observational aspects of stellar evolution were still rudimentary in the late eighteenth century, at least by today's standards. But even at this early stage, the power of cosmological speculation was appreciated. Hypotheses were not just inferred from data: they could also be conjectured on a purely speculative basis (as earlier by Descartes and Kant) and then verified (or falsified) by observations. And a new appreciation was developing for the fact that unaided human reason, while far from infallible, was also able in a remarkable way to anticipate the results of observation. Laplace referred to the agreement between his hypothesis and Herschel's results as 'a marked coincidence' and apparently did not reflect on the matter further. He was, after all, still conditioned by Christian faith in the comprehensibility of the world. The problem of this kind of coincidence would become more acute as the range of human science exceeded normal human experience while the creation faith that sustained belief in the comprehensibility of the world became increasingly marginal.

The best known aspects of Laplace's career are some of his encounters with Napoleon Bonaparte. In October of 1799, three weeks before the *coup d'état* that made him First Consul, Napoleon was formally presented by Laplace with copies of the first two volumes of the *Treatise on Celestial Mechanics* and promised to read them if he had the time (he estimated six months to be sufficient!). Appearing again before Bonaparte in 1802, Laplace is reported to have defended his case – stated earlier in the *Exposition of the World System* – that natural causes could account for the formation and stability of the solar system.

The best known encounter, and unfortunately the least documented, was one in which Napoleon allegedly told Laplace that he had looked through his *Exposition* to see what role God played in the formation of the solar system. According to a later source, he then remarked: 'Newton spoke of God in his book [second and third editions of the *Principia*]. I have perused yours but failed to find his name even once. How come?' And Laplace's oft-quoted reply: 'Sire, I did not need that hypothesis.'

The earliest known record of this exchange dates from 1864, thirty-seven years after Laplace's death and at least six decades after the purported encounter. However, the incident corresponds so well with what we do know of the encounters between Laplace and Bonaparte, that no distortion of the facts is incurred by its frequent citation. It captures the haughtiness and determination of the great mathematician in a single phrase: Newton's God had been retired as far as physical science was concerned.

The Secularized Theology of Laplace

As we have seen, Laplace's accomplishments were far from being theologically neutral. His efforts to demonstrate the natural origins and stability of the solar system and thus the completeness of the laws of nature had a clearly theological agenda. Like Leibniz,

Laplace criticized Newton for his appeal to supernatural intervention where the laws of physics seemed to fail as the expression
of ignorance. Unlike Leibniz, however, Laplace assumed (as did
other *philosophes*) that the elimination of the supernatural meant
that there was no longer any role for God in the natural world.

Like d'Alembert, Laplace referred to the 'Author' of nature, but
worked to eliminate the remaining grounds for any reference to God
in discussions of nature. Whereas Newton and others were motivated to heroic lengths by their desire to demonstrate the activity
of God in nature, Laplace was motivated by the desire to eliminate
whatever grounds remained for such reference to the divine. In
effect, his science was his religion.

The secular theology of Laplace is most clearly seen in his statements of the ideal of physical determinism. As he first put it in
1773:

> The present state of the system of nature is evidently a result of
> what it was in the preceding instant, and if we conceive of an
> Intelligence who, for a given moment, embraces all the relations
> of being in this Universe, it will also be able to determine for any
> instant of the past or future their respective positions, motions,
> and generally all their affections . . .

On the more practical level of celestial mechanics, for instance:

> . . . in order to determine the state of the system of these large
> bodies in past or future centuries, it is enough for the mathema-
> tician that observation provide him with their positions and speeds
> at any given instant.

Earlier statements of this ideal had been made by d'Alembert (1758)
and Condorcet (1768), but it was Laplace that gave it its first precise
formulation and whose words have been quoted ever since as typify-
ing the determinism of classical physics. Given the positions and
velocities (and masses) of all of the bodies in the universe, both past
and future were entirely determined (in principle) by Newton's
laws.

The 'Intelligence' Laplace hypothesized (following Condorcet)
stood for the set of laws governing the universe. It was a device for
affirming the existence of such a set of laws as an ideal towards
which human science aspired. The fact that the universe had such
laws and the fact that human minds were able to grasp them,
however imperfectly, were taken on faith. The comprehensibility,

unity and autonomy of the universe could thus be affirmed without reference to God.

The secular ideals of d'Alembert and Laplace are important because they have become the motivating ideal of many physical scientists of the nineteenth and twentieth centuries. We are suggesting that they are the product of a particular history and theology, not a necessary concomitant of progressive science. Those who single-mindedly pursue scientific research will generally be motivated by ideals of some sort. The ideals in question must be ones that appear to vindicate faith in the comprehensibility, unity and relative autonomy of the world. As long as Christian theology was clearly associated with these beliefs, it was conducive to good scientific work and constructive criticism of science as we have seen. But, in the seventeenth and eighteenth centuries, a long-range tendency to view the active role of God and the innate properties of matter as alternative modes of explanation gained credence to the extent that the ideals needed for the furtherance of science could no longer so readily be sustained by positive Christian commitment.

From an historical viewpoint, this development resulted from the tendency of theological parties to define themselves by the exclusion of others at the expense of the integrity of the creationist tradition as a whole. This is perhaps most clearly seen in the naturalist-conservative split of the twelfth century (section 1.4) and the latitudinarian-spiritualist controversy in seventeenth-century England (section 3.3). There is no reason to believe that the development was inevitable or that it could not have pursued a different course. Therefore, there is no reason to suppose that the future development of science might not find its motivation once again in the creationist tradition, particularly if its present secular orientation is found to fail.

ADDITIONAL READING

Alexander, H. G., ed., *The Leibniz-Clarke Correspondence* (Manchester, 1956).

Anderson, W. E., ed., *Works of Jonathan Edwards, Vol. 6: Scientific and Philosophical Writings* (New Haven, 1980).

Baumer, F. L., *Modern European Thought* (New York, 1977), chap. 3.

Beall, O., and Shyrock, R., *Cotton Mather: First Significant Figure in American Medicine* (Baltimore, 1954).

Cantor, G. N., and Hodge, M. J. S., eds., *Conceptions of Ether: Studies in the History of Ether Theories, 1740–1900* (Cambridge, 1981).

Ferguson, J. P., *An Eighteenth-Century Heretic: Dr. Samuel Clarke* (Kineton, 1976).

Force, J. E., *William Whiston, Honest Newtonian* (Cambridge, 1985).

Gay, Peter, *The Enlightenment, Vol. 2: The Science of Freedom* (London, 1973).

Goodman, D. C., ed., *Science and Religious Belief, 1600–1900: A Selection of Primary Sources* (Dorchester, 1973) chaps. 13–22.

Grimsley, R., *Jean D'Alembert* (Oxford, 1963) chap. 7.

Hankins, T. L., *Science and Enlightenment* (Cambridge, 1985).

Harman (Heimann), P. M., ' "Nature is a Perpetual Worker": Newton's Aether and Eighteenth-Century Natural Philosophy', *Ambix* 20 (1973) pp. 1–25.

idem, 'Voluntarism and Immanence: Conceptions of Nature in Eighteenth-Century Thought', *Journal of the History of Ideas* 39 (1978) pp. 271–83.

idem, and McGuire, J. E., 'Newtonian Forces and Lockean Powers: Concepts of Matter in Eighteenth-Century Thought', *Historical Studies in the Physical Sciences* 3, ed. R. McCormmach (Philadelphia, 1971) pp. 233–306.

Jacob, M. C., *The Newtonians and the English Revolution, 1689–1720* (Ithaca, N.Y., 1976).

Jaki, S. L., trans., *Immanuel Kant: Universal Natural History and Theory of the Heavens* (Edinburgh, 1981).

Kieft, L., and Willeford, B. R., eds., *Joseph Priestley: Scientist, Theologian and Metaphysician* (Lewisburg, Penn., 1980) chaps. 1, 3.

Lindberg, D. C., and Numbers, R. L., eds., *God and Nature: Historical Essays on the Encounter between Christianity and Science* (Berkeley, 1986) chaps. 9–12.

McEvoy, J. G., and McGuire, J. E., 'God and Nature: Priestley's Way of Rational Dissent', *Historical Studies in the Physical Sciences* 6, ed., R. McCormmach (Princeton, 1975) pp. 325–404.

Olson, R. G., 'Tory-High Church Opposition to Science and Scientism in the Eighteenth Century', *The Uses of Science in the Age of Newton*, ed. J. G. Burke (Berkeley, 1983), chap. 7.

Roger, J., 'Buffon', *Dictionary of Scientific Biography* 2, pp. 576–82.

Russell, C. A., *Cross Currents: Interactions between Science and Faith* (Grand Rapids, 1985) chaps. 5–7.

Schofield, R. E., *Mechanism and Materialism: British Natural Philosophy in the Age of Reason* (Princeton, 1970).

Silverman, K., *The Life and Times of Cotton Mather* (New York, 1985).

Thackray, A., 'Matter in a Nut-Shell: Newton's *Opticks* and Eighteenth-Century Chemistry', *Ambix* 15 (1968) pp. 29–53.

idem, *Atoms and Powers: An Essay on the Newtonian Matter-Theory and the Development of Chemistry* (Cambridge, Mass., 1970).

Toulmin, S., and Goodfield, J., *The Discovery of Time* (Harmondsworth, 1967).

Vartanian, A., *Diderot and Descartes: A Study of Scientific Naturalism in the Enlightenment* (Princeton, 1953).

Wilde, C. B., 'Matter and Spirit as Natural Symbols in Eighteenth-Century British Natural Philosophy', *British Journal for the History of Science* 15 (1982) pp. 99–131.

5

THE CREATIONIST TRADITION AND THE EMERGENCE OF POST-NEWTONIAN MECHANICS
(nineteenth and early twentieth centuries)

1. THE NINETEENTH-CENTURY CONTEXT

An operational faith in God as creator was a vital factor in the development of all branches of science until the late eighteenth century. It constituted a tradition – the creationist tradition – which provided the matrix of faith for the professional endeavours of Western European scientists both Catholic, Protestant, and Nonconformist, from Bede and Adelard of Bath to Boscovich, Hutton and Dalton.

The situation in the nineteenth century was radically different for both theology and science. On the theological side, the problem was that few parish ministers or theologians were adequately informed or even concerned with current developments in the physical sciences. The dramatic developments of nineteenth-century geology and evolutionary theory attracted attention, but the equally revolutionary changes in basic physics and chemistry passed largely unnoticed or misunderstood. As most people perceived them, developments in physical science were far removed from the practical exigencies of parish life and religious experience. This, paradoxically enough, at a time when basic discoveries were being made that would transform the technological structures of everyday life more than any of the scientific advances of previous centuries – for example, the laws of electricity and magnetism.

The paradox of apparent irrelevance in the face of revolutionary change had at least three causes. One was the fact that nineteenth-century physics had become highly mathematical and often dealt with entities that were not directly observable: this made it less accessible to the average lay person. This departure from common-sense reality and greater abstraction became progressively more pronounced with the development of field theory and statistical mechanics in the late nineteenth century and again with the development of relativity theory and quantum mechanics in the early twentieth.

A second cause was the fact that, with the progress of the industrial revolution, the public gradually developed a truncated image of physical science. In the popular mind, science was generally equated with a fictitious method of objectivity and induction, on the one hand, and with impressive new technologies and the latest consumer goods, on the other. There was very little public awareness of the basic science that lay behind the new technologies, much less the history of their development or the complex creative processes and theological motifs that were involved in that history. Personal ideals and objective methods and artefacts were generally relegated to two different spheres of existence.

This leads us to a third factor. The more creative theologians of the nineteenth century had to defend the place of religion in a world for which this truncated view of science had become a major norm for evaluating truth claims. As a consequence, they tended to redefine the sphere of theology and religion in terms of the personal, experiential and moral side of life (e.g., Friedrich Schleiermacher, Matthew Arnold, Albrecht Ritschl). The validity of rational, natural theology was increasingly questioned, and the idea of creation was reduced to a useful fiction (Kant) or a statement of the human experience of absolute dependence (Schleiermacher).

On the scientists' side of the issue, there was a corresponding tendency toward a professional segregation of personal religious convictions from the discipline of research and publication. In France, a positivist style of science had come into vogue already in the late eighteenth century with the work of d'Alembert and Laplace (section 4.4). In Germany, England and America, a similar progression occurred in the second half of the nineteenth century – it was seen as an effective way of guarding the autonomy of the various scientific communities in the face of political and ecclesiastical interests. Towards the end of the century, some apologists for science even argued that organized religion had always been hostile to the development of their discipline. Whatever the merits of this particular view of past history (the evidence has been assessed in earlier chapters), it was itself an indication of an increasingly intentional separation of the sciences from religious faith rather than an ongoing conflict in the nineteenth century itself.

This broad historical shift in European thought calls for a corresponding shift in our approach to the creationist tradition. We are not able to review here the development of the entire breadth of the physical sciences as we have attempted to do in past chapters. Nor are we concerned here with the ideas of 'science' in the inductivist tradition of John Stuart Mill or in the idealist tradition of post-Kantian philosophy and theology – neither idea being closely related to the actual practice of science in the nineteenth century, as we shall argue.

Instead, we shall focus on one continuing tradition of scientific research, the Anglo-Scottish tradition, which persisted in appealing to the idea of creation through most of the nineteenth century – long enough to bring us within view of the revolutionary developments of twentieth-century physics (even though, paradoxically, those developments were primarily due to German and Danish scientists, rather than English or Scottish ones). The main disadvantage of this procedure is that it bypasses scientific and philosophical developments in continental Europe that influenced the British scientists we shall discuss. We will only be able to mention some of the relevant French and German contributors to nineteenth-century physical science in passing. But, since our main theme is the creationist tradition, we must restrict our present coverage to that of a group of physicists and chemists for whom the idea of creation was still a consciously held idea and an instrumental factor in the development of science. In the Middle Ages, the Renaissance, and the seventeenth century, the creationist tradition had been much broader than the scope of natural philosophy itself, and we had to cover a variety of peripheral movements of thought in order to give a coherent historical account. Even in the eighteenth century, we considered divergent movements in relation to the creationist tradition since they either re-interpreted it (materialists) or reacted against it (some neo-mechanists). But, in the nineteenth century, for the first time in Western history, the creationist tradition had become narrower than the physical sciences and survived only in a few local traditions. The history of science and the history of theology had become two separate tracks, with only a modest degree of overlap.

The idea of creation was no longer viable as a vigorous international tradition, nor even as a public reality in Great Britain itself, but one remnant of it survived long enough to guide the chief architects of post-Newtonian mechanics into areas far removed from the experiences of everyday physical reality, areas for which guidelines were not available from the existing stock of scientific knowledge.

And here we shall stop. Tracing the more subtle ways in which creationist ideas have persisted in twentieth-century physics itself would require another book and an entirely different methodology – one orientated more to individual perspectives than an ongoing tradition of shared ideas.

But, why the persistence of an Anglo-Scottish tradition of the creationist tradition through the nineteenth century? The roots of this phenomenon go back to the eighteenth century. The heritage of Isaac Newton and his English and Scottish followers was still a potent force in Britain. Conservative nationalistic sentiments were partly responsible as evidenced by the English reaction to the radical philosophy and politics of revolutionary France and the efforts of English scientists to defend the priority of their countrymen's contributions to scientific discoveries ranging from the calculus in the eighteenth century to the conservation of energy in the nineteenth.

We recall also that the stance of the established Church towards science was perceived to be more moderate in the England of the Latitudinarians than it was in the France of the Jesuits and *philosophes*. But there had also been a major revival of evangelical Christianity in the British Isles that provided its own stimulus in the relations of science and theology, particularly in the case of Michael Faraday as we shall see below.

The major issue in nineteenth-century physics and chemistry was still the meaning and validity of the mechanical philosophy inherited from the seventeenth and eighteenth centuries. Unfortunately for the simple inquirer, present-day historians are seriously divided on the handling of this issue: some see the beginnings of a reaction against the mechanical model with Faraday and Maxwell around the mid-nineteenth century; others treat the entire development through Maxwell (and his immediate successors) as a series of variations *within* the mechanical tradition. The problem is complicated by the fact that the very meaning of terms involved in the science of mechanics changed with time. Phenomena like energy, forces and fields, which were at first thought of as supra-mechanical, gradually became assimilated to the mechanical worldview as they were harnessed by increasingly sophisticated types of machinery. If energy and force fields were not mechanical in the original Cartesian sense, at least they were believed to have their 'mechanical equivalents'. The increasing interdependence between science and technology with the progress of the industrial revolution meant that the idea of mechanism could easily be generalized to include new phenomena almost as fast as they could be discovered. In fact, the revolutionary developments of twentieth-century physics have followed much the same pattern.

It seems best to allow for both continuity and variation within the mechanical tradition throughout the nineteenth century. It will be convenient, therefore, to divide our period into three successive stages: a movement away from the existing mechanical model in the early nineteenth century (Oersted, Davy and Faraday); a strong reaffirmation and formalization of the mechanical philosophy in the middle of the century (Whewell, Joule and Kelvin); and an extensive generalization of the mechanical worldview by James Clerk Maxwell in the latter half of the century which pointed the way towards the theory of relativity and quantum mechanics in the early twentieth century. To a degree there is an analogy here to our treatment of the seventeenth century (section 3.3), with James Clerk Maxwell cast in the role of a second Isaac Newton.

2. THE MECHANICAL PHILOSOPHY CHALLENGED (OERSTED, DAVY AND FARADAY)

Our principal interest in this section is the case of Michael Faraday (1791–1867) whose work on magnetism established the basis of modern field theory. First, however, we must look briefly at the two major antecedents of Faraday's ideas, the Dane, Hans Christian Oersted (1777–1851) and Sir Humphrey Davy (1778–1829 – the figures in this chapter are all English unless otherwise stated). It has often been argued that both Oersted and Davy were influenced by the *Naturphilosophie* ('philosophy of nature') of the German idealists Immanuel Kant and Friedrich Schelling. We have discussed the mechanical philosophy of the early (precritical) Kant, but the complex metaphysics of the mature Kant and that of Schelling lie outside the scope of a work focusing on the relations of natural science and (specifically) Christian theology. The principal element of relevance in their philosophies of nature is an emphasis on the unity of all forces in nature and the conversion of one force into another, particularly under conditions of severe constraint or confinement.

Hans Christian Oersted

Oersted's experimental discovery of electromagnetism (the connection of electricity and magnetism) certainly reflected some of Kant's and Schelling's ideas – he had defended Kant's philosophy in his doctoral thesis at the University of Copenhagen (1799) and studied the work of Schelling and other philosophers of nature while travelling in Germany in the early 1800s. But Oersted also departed from the German idealist tradition in significant ways that reflect on his Danish family background (his father was an apothecary) and practical training in pharmacy. In 1812, Oersted publicly stated that there must be some inner connection between electricity and magnetism since both were fundamental forces of nature. If an electric current were passed through a resistant wire it would give off heat, light, and even magnetism, depending on the narrowness of the gauge of the wire.

Eight years later, in the course of one of his classroom demonstrations, Oersted found what he had predicted. When he held a magnetic compass under (or over) a wire carrying an electric current, he found that the compass needle pointed across the wire rather than in a northerly direction. Certainly, this meant that electric currents had magnetic effects. But it also showed that, contrary to Newtonian thought, all forces in nature were not central forces – that is, all forces were not necessarily directed towards or away from the centre of their source. In the case of Oersted's demonstration, the magnetic force was directed at right angles to both the direction of the electric current and an imaginary line drawn from the nearest point on the wire to the compass needle. So the magnetic force was not directed along the wire or toward it, but circled around the wire with the direction of the circling depending of the direction of the electric current.

Before considering the philosophical ideas that lay behind Oersted's discovery, we should say a word about the technical advances that made it possible. In 1795, the Italian Alessandro Volta had produced the first electric battery consisting of a series of rods of two different metals (silver and zinc) connected by a conducting medium. Announced in London in 1800, the invention of the 'voltaic pile' meant that, for the first time in history, electric currents could be produced and controlled at will. Oersted had developed his own version of the voltaic pile in 1801 and used it in his experiments thereafter. The demonstration of the relationship between electricity and magnetism would have been prohibitively difficult without the steady supply of electric current that the voltaic battery made possible.

The previously mentioned influence of Schelling's *Naturphilosophie* on Oersted has become a commonplace of historical literature. But it has also been questioned. The idea of the unity and mutual interchange of the forces of nature had also had a long history. The immediate source of the idea for Oersted may well have been the natural philosophies of Kant and Schelling. But the broader background was the eighteenth-century Newtonian tradition of Boerhaave and Hutton that envisaged an active fiery substance (originally coming from the sun) which circulated through the cosmos appearing variously as heat, light and electricity (section 4.1).

In Schelling's thought, the laws of nature were identical to the laws of reason as understood by the human mind. In other words, it was theoretically possible to infer the laws of nature through pure reason without scientific experiments at all. In his early years, Oersted had accepted some of the speculative notions of German *Naturphilosophie* rather uncritically. A strong dose of criticism from the French tradition of Laplace and Lavoisier soon cured him of that. Oersted did not give up his philosophic ideals, but he had his training in the experimental tradition of pharmacy to fall back on, and this made it possible for him to develop the necessary apparatus and experience that made his discovery of electromagnetism possible.

The importance of Kant's influence on Oersted has also to be questioned. The ideas of the intelligibility and unity of nature so prominent in Oersted's thought had been a major theme of natural philosophy, and particularly of the alchemical tradition, since the Middle Ages. Quite unlike Kant, Oersted attributed the correspondence of human reason with the divine to the fact that humans were actually created in the image of God. Hence the competence of human reason for comprehending nature was guaranteed by the Christian doctrine of creation; it was not just a useful fiction of regulative ('as if') truth, as it was for Kant.

Sir Humphrey Davy

If Oersted's main contribution was relating electricity to magnetism, Davy's was relating electricity to chemistry and the realization that electricity was a fundamental property of all matter.

Again the discovery was overtly experimental. Like Oersted, Davy experimented with voltaic piles, working in the early 1800s at the Royal Institution of Great Britain (London). In 1806 he announced his conclusion that electrical force was responsible for the molecular structure of matter: the force that held different elements together in a compound (e.g., hydrogen and oxygen in water) had to be electric, he reasoned, since these elements could be isolated from their compounds in voltaic piles (again the importance of techniques making electric currents readily available).

Davy's roots, not unlike Oersted's, went back to the alchemical tradition of experimentation as a means of realizing unity with nature. His experiments with electric discharges, for instance, were viewed as microcosmic (we would say 'laboratory') reproductions of lightning in the atmosphere. Davy even compared one of the elements he discovered (potassium) to one of the fundamental substances imagined by the alchemists (Paracelsus's principle of salt, section 3.1). Like Oersted, too, he was influenced by the Boerhaavian concept of the fundamental unity and inter-convertibility of active principles or forces of nature. In fact, Boerhaave had already attempted to analyse chemical affinities and reactions in terms of the active substance of fire, and Gowin Knight and James Hutton had related the latter to electricity (although all three thought in terms of imponderable fluids rather than forces in the early Newtonian sense).

Davy also believed in the existence of a single material substance underlying all the chemical elements – hence his negative reaction to Dalton's hypothesis of irreducible atoms corresponding to each chemical element (section 4.3). Again the roots of Davy's thought go back to the eighteenth century: alongside the expansive fiery substance of Boerhaave, Knight and Hutton had postulated ordinary gravitational matter as a second primary substance. The most important influence on Davy was apparently British Newtonianism rather than German *Naturphilosophie*.

Davy's insistence on the fundamental unity of matter was all the more remarkable in view of the fact that he discovered more than his share of new elements himself (e.g. sodium, potassium, calcium, and magnesium). His willingness to tolerate increasing diversity in the theory of nature was apparently facilitated by the conviction that, underlying all the so-called elements there was a fundamental unity of substance and that this unity would eventually manifest itself in experiments.

Even more clearly than in the case of Oersted, we know that Davy's belief in the simplicity of nature was sustained by his faith in its Creator. According to one recent historian, Davy was more of a Romantic than an orthodox Anglican. Perhaps the inconsistency is more of a problem for the present-day historian than it was for the early nineteenth-century scientist. With respect to the doctrine of creation, Davy was right in line with the teachings of the historic tradition we have traced in this study. His memoirs record the conviction that the unified law governing matter was due to 'an energy of mutation impressed by the will of the Deity'. On this basis, he expected to 'discover simplicity and unity of design' and 'an extensive field for sublime investigation'.

The same sort of faith in the ultimate oneness of matter was responsible for the famous hypothesis of Davy's younger contemporary, William Prout (1785–1850), which, though ahead of its time, pointed in the direction of future discoveries. Prout argued in 1815–16 that hydrogen, the lightest element, was the universal matter out of which all other elements were composed. Therefore, the weights of all other atoms and molecules should be exact multiples of the weight of hydrogen. Though Prout's hypothesis failed to account for non-integral atomic weights of elements like chlorine and magnesium (which normally consist of a mixture of isotopes), it was not forgotten. J. J. Thomson resurrected the idea in 1897 when he postulated a second universal type of matter, later known as the electron, and it was further developed in Ernest Rutherford's 1911 model of the atom, which consisted of hydrogen nuclei (protons) and electrons, which, in turn, was the basis of Niels Bohr's early quantum theory of the atom.

Michael Faraday

Michael Faraday's principal contributions were his discovery of electromagnetic induction (1831) – a means of generating an electric current using magnets (the converse of Oersted's effect) – and his subsequent conception of the idea of a magnetic field and its possible connection with the propagation of light.

Faraday served as Davy's lab assistant from 1813 until 1827 when he became Davy's successor at the Royal Institution. Davy's ideas about the identity of chemical affinity with electrical force provided the basis of Faraday's early experiments. Significantly, Davy had also developed some tentative analogies between chemical reactions and the nature of light: the two ends of the light spectrum, he suggested, were analogous to the positive and negative poles of the voltaic battery. Together with the eighteenth-century theology of nature they mediated, these ideas provided what Peter Harman has termed the 'conceptual framework' for Faraday's ongoing research programme.

Faraday supplemented Davy's idea of the unity of forces with the idea that force was a divinely created entity and hence could be neither augmented nor diminished by natural causes. Like Newton, Faraday saw force as transcending the properties of ordinary (ponderable) matter. But whereas force for Newton was an ephemeral principle, likely to decay without divine sustenance and replenishment, for Faraday it was as stable and permanent as matter itself. The philosophic difference here partly reflects the improvements in technology – by Faraday's time it was possible to generate efficiently forces like electricity and to store them for later use. Consequently, divine activity was even more closely confined to the established laws of nature for Faraday than for Newton. The only exception to the laws of nature of relevance to science was the event of creation itself. No other supernatural event or act of God was called for, at least, in matters of natural philosophy.

Since force could neither be augmented nor diminished, Faraday reasoned, no force could act at a distance – that is, no force emanating from one body could act on another without being transmitted through the intervening space in some manner. Otherwise, if it was observed that the force grew stronger as the bodies approached each other, such an intensification would require the creation of force out of nothing (or the disappearance of potential energy in the terminology of later physics).

If force was really transmitted from one body to the other, there must be some way of representing this process visually. Observing the pattern of magnetic filings suspended over a magnet, Faraday developed the concept of magnetic 'lines of force', and in 1845 he introduced the term 'magnetic field' to describe the overall structure of the pattern. At first, lines of force were perhaps just a convenient model of representation for Faraday, but in the early 1850s he clearly stated that they were not just symbols but fundamental entities in nature. In Faraday's view, space appeared to be full of forces and powers and the balance of reality was not so much in isolated bodies of matter as in the space between (and within) them. This was a significant departure from the more dualistic, Newtonian stance of Davy (active forces and inert matter) and was more akin to the idea of the primacy of force in Boscovich and Priestley (sections 4.1, 4.2). Like Boscovich and Priestley (and Newton), Faraday was encouraged to think in terms of the primacy of force by his association of active powers in the universe with the activity of God.

In 1846, Faraday articulated a further implication of the idea of lines of force – that vibrations of the lines could account for the propagation of visible light. The notion that light and magnetism were manifestations of the same underlying type of matter had been stated by Gowin Knight among others. Oersted had proven a deep connection between electricity and magnetism and Faraday had provided further evidence in his work on electromagnetic induction. But Faraday's explanation in terms of lines of force gave physicists a way of defining these connections more exactly.

We have already noted some of the ways in which theology played a role in Faraday's investigations. Much of this could be accounted for in terms of the general theological framework shared by other scientists discussed in this chapter. However, Faraday belonged not to the Church of England, but to a dissenting group known as the Sandemanians. A good deal of attention has been devoted to the religious beliefs of this group since the definitive biography of Faraday written by L. Pearce Williams appeared in 1964.

The Sandemanians had their origins in two evangelical movements that began in England and Scotland in the 1730s. In spite of their disestablishmentarian and revivalist roots, the sect's theology developed along decidedly cognitive lines in the following decades under the leadership of Robert Sandeman. Sandeman emphasized the ideas of nature as God's creation and the Bible as God's revealed word. Humans could only come to know God through his self-revelation in Scripture, but on the basis of that faith they could view nature as a book of signs manifesting the Creator's eternal power and Godhead (Rom. 1:20).

According to Williams and others, the startling boldness of Faraday's theorizing about the spatial ordering of magnetic fields was facilitated by his deep belief that nature's laws were themselves the product of a rational mind. The biblical idea of creation implied that there was an underlying order and unity to the phenomena of nature – by virtue of the forces impressed on matter by the Creator – and that the human mind, fallible as it was, could, when guided by experiments, formulate ideas that reflected those laws.

In other words, a revival of biblical thought had occasioned a reaffirmation of some of the basic tenets of the historic creationist tradition: the comprehensibility, unity and relative autonomy of nature (sections 1.2–1.4). Whereas much of the popular natural theology of the seventeenth, eighteenth, and nineteenth centuries exploited the apparent congruities of nature as evidences of the existence of God, Faraday, reflecting his more biblicist roots, relied on his faith in God as the motivation for seeking analogies in nature. As he wrote during the years he was developing his idea of magnetic lines of force and their relation to the propagation of light:

> I am struggling to exert my poetical ideas just now for the discovery of analogies and remote figures . . . for I think that is the true way (corrected by judgement) to work out a discovery.

It should be pointed out, however, that Faraday's theological perspective may have restricted his vision of science even if it had a positive effect on the progress of physics as a whole. Around the middle of the century, a new generation of physicists (considered in the next section) developed a more precise formulation of the law of the conservation of energy. Faraday had already postulated the constancy of force, but resisted making his idea quantitative and did not accept the more precise definitions which distinguished force from energy – the latter being the equivalent of force applied over an interval of distance (work). It is possible that Faraday's view of force as the medium of God's activity in the world led him to resist precise definition and mathematical formalism that might suggest a reduction to mechanistic principles like energy and work.

3. THE MECHANICAL PHILOSOPHY RESTATED AND FORMALIZED (WHEWELL, JOULE AND KELVIN)

Diverse as they were in other respects, the three figures we consider in this section – Whewell, Joule and Kelvin – had two things in common. First, in comparison with the relatively qualitative contributions of Oersted, Davy and Faraday, they all placed greater emphasis on the precise, quantitative aspects of physics. In fact, Whewell and Kelvin made significant contributions to the progress of mathematical physics.

Secondly, whereas Faraday viewed the operations of forces as the manifestation of God's activity in nature, the figures considered here all viewed nature in strictly mechanical terms. Whewell and Kelvin sought the activity of God at the limits of mechanical explanation. But Joule viewed the perfection of the mechanical system of the world as itself a manifestation of divine wisdom and power.

A comparison with Newton's thought gives another way of differentiating Whewell, Joule and Kelvin from Faraday. We recall that Newton's worldview was one of active principles (forces) operating on inert matter. In these terms, both Faraday and the figures considered here were 'Newtonian', but in different senses: Faraday emphasized the one side of Newton's thought, the idea of active principles, and the figures considered here stressed the other side, the inertness of matter. So, if Faraday was Newtonian in his distinctive emphasis on the supra-mechanical character of the forces of nature, Whewell, Joule and Kelvin were even more Newtonian in their appeal to divine activity in the origin of the mechanical systems of nature and (except for Joule) in their periodic restoration.

William Whewell
William Whewell (1794–1866, an almost exact contemporary of Michael Faraday) was a first-generation member of what has been

called the 'Cambridge school' or 'Cambridge network', a group of scholars who either studied or taught at Cambridge and who were responsible for introducing the new techniques of calculus developed in the late eighteenth century by the French and using them to formalize mathematical physics. Whewell himself wrote influential textbooks on mechanics and geology and was influential in promoting 'mixed mathematics', which included mechanics, hydrodynamics and astronomy, as well as pure mathematics, into the curriculum. More than anyone, he was responsible for re-establishing the mechanical philosophy as the framework for investigating the phenomena of nature.

Whewell is the only figure considered in this chapter who was an ordained clergyman as well as a scientist. There were others among his contemporaries like George Peacock who combined the two callings, but theirs was the last generation for which it was still common for members of the Royal Society of London to be members of the clergy. In fact, Whewell's coining of the terms 'scientist' and 'physicist' was a harbinger of the emerging professionalism that would fundamentally alter the common perception of the relation between science and theology.

Whewell's advocacy of the mechanical philosophy did not prevent him from viewing God as deeply involved in the history of nature. The two ideas were rendered compatible by his stress on the limits of the strictly mechanical account of things. One historian has described his position as a rational version of Catastrophism. In fact, it grew out of Whewell's criticism of the views of the geologist Charles Lyell, for which he himself had coined the label 'Uniformitarian'.

Whewell made a clear distinction between mechanical and historical accounts of nature, the latter being particularly important in historical sciences like cosmogony and geology. There were three basic steps in the development of any science. The first step in any science was the accumulation of data about what was observed to have happened in the history of nature and the formation of inductive generalizations to describe the data. The second step was the determination of historical sequences of cause and effect in which all the phenomena in a series could be traced back to the first cause in that sequence. Only in the third step were theoretical ideas like those of mechanics applied to the data thus gathered and organized. Here, Whewell distinguished empirical data from the a priori ideas or laws of thought. The fact that God had created the world, together with the divine attributes of goodness and wisdom, guaranteed that the laws governing nature must be rational and simple enough for the human mind to comprehend. Most important of these laws was the Law of Continuity, which stated that every event must have a sufficient cause (whether natural or supernatural) in order that there be no gaps in the overall account of things. The laws of mechanics could account for all the phenomena after the first cause in each sequence. But, in accordance with the Law of Continuity, the first cause of each sequence of phenomena, which was inexplicable in strictly mechanical terms, had to be referred back to a transcendent, supernatural cause.

According to Whewell, there were several cases of such causal sequences for which the Principle of Continuity required the direct action of God as the initial event in the series. The most obvious case was that of the formation of the cosmos: even if the formation of the solar system could be accounted for in terms of Laplace's nebular hypothesis (section 4.4), it ultimately had to be traced back to a moment of creation and a transcendent First Cause which could not itself be mechanical. So natural science itself could teach us nothing positive about the beginnings of things: the most it could (and should) do was to indicate that there must be such a beginning.

Of course, in order to support his contention that divine creation was historically continuous with natural history, Whewell had to rule out the possibility of an eternal, self-existent world. In this connection, he appealed to the recent work of Johann Encke who had computed the periodic return of a short-period comet (now known as Encke's comet) and then found that its period was shorter than predicted and was continually decreasing, presumably due to the resistance of the interplanetary medium. According to Whewell, this deterioration of motion proved that the solar system – (and, by inference, the cosmos) – could not have been eternal. Like a watch that was still ticking, it must have been wound up a finite time ago.

Other examples of causal sequences which pointed to divine initiative were the formation of new strata in the geological record, the emergence of new biological species (as evidenced in the fossil record), and the origin of human intelligence. None of these beginnings could be accounted for in terms of the nebular hypothesis or in terms of any other mechanical account of nature.

Thus, in contrast to the Unformitarianism of Charles Lyell, Whewell described the history of the cosmos as a series of cycles, each beginning with the emergence of qualitatively new forms of matter and life and initiated by a fresh exertion of divine power. The fossil record showed that the material world was inert and dead in itself. Millions of years had passed, for instance, before intelligence had emerged on earth. Without divine intervention, there would have been no intelligence, and probably not even any life at all.

Whewell's version of mechanical philosophy incorporated traditional creationist ideas like the comprehensibility of the world and the relative autonomy of nature. But it was severely limited by the traditional mechanical idea of matter in motion and did not do justice to the concepts of energy, forces and fields that were beginning to dominate mathematical physics. Still, Whewell's views established the consistency of the mechanical model with Christian faith and made it acceptable to a new generation of physicists for whom it could be broadened to include the new concepts.

James Prescott Joule

Joule is best known for his experimental proof of the exact equivalence of the heat produced and the force expended over distance (the work done) in the process of producing it, whether mechanical, electrical or chemical (combustion). As developed in the writings of William Thomson (Lord Kelvin) and Hermann von Helmholtz, this provided the basis of the law of the conservation of energy, one of the most powerful principles in modern physics.

In support of his notion of the mechanical equivalence of heat, Joule appealed to the once and for all character of divine creation. Once God had established the world and all the forces of nature, no additional act of sustenance or repair was ever needed. 'The grand agents of nature are, by the Creators' fiat, indestructible', so the forces God had created remained constant in their operation for all time. Therefore, none of the force expended in a physical process like the generation of heat could be lost to nature: the force expended and the heat produced were simply two different forms of the same thing, and so there must be a precise quantitative equivalence between them. The idea of creation thus provided what Peter Harman has called a framework for the interpretation of his experimental discoveries.

Similar ideas about the ceaseless energy of nature had been a recurring theme in the creationist tradition since the second century BC (secton 1.4) and had already been articulated in modern scientific terms by Leibniz and Faraday. But Joule translated this general idea into an exact mathematical formula: every single foot-pound (or erg or joule) of force expended must be transformed into its exact equivalent of heat. Another difference was the fact that Joule viewed electromagnetic phenomena strictly in terms of the mechanical force expended over distance rather than in terms of independent fields of force as Faraday did. In fact, using Faraday's principle of electro-magnetic induction, Joule could show how mechanical force was converted into electricity and the electricity was converted, in turn, into heat. Heat, chemistry and electromagnetism were all just manifestations of mechanical power.

The establishment of exact equivalency between mechanical force and heat raised the question of the relationship between the macroscopic and atomic levels of matter. At the macroscopic level, energy could appear in two basic forms: the energy of motion (Leibniz's *vis viva*) and the attraction between bodies due to forces like gravitation (the terms 'kinetic energy' and 'potential energy' were introduced by Kelvin and Tait in 1867). Some physicists (at this time, chiefly French) held that there was a third macroscopic form: subtle fluids corresponding to the phenomena of heat ('caloric') and electricity. But Davy and Faraday had rejected the idea of subtle fluids and treated heat, like chemical affinity, in terms of inter-particulate forces at the atomic level. Joule also rejected subtle fluids adding the theological argument that the conservation of the heat fluid by itself required the creation of mechanical force out of nothing in heat engines and was therefore impossible.

What, then, happened to mechanical force when it disappeared at the macroscopic level and was converted into heat? What did it look like at the atomic level? Joule at first suggested an electro-mechanical model of the atom in order to define its temperature. Each atom had a tiny atmosphere of electricity, and the heat was stored in the rotation of these atmospheres, with the rate of rotation being determined by the temperature. In a later, more narrowly mechanical, model, he even imagined tiny weights being attached to the rotating atoms by ropes: mechanical force could then be transferred to the weights by lifting them small distances.

The attempt to model the dynamics of atoms, which began with Joule in the 1840s, was to be a major problem in physics in the latter half of the nineteenth and the early twentieth century. The question of the nature of atoms was an ancient one, but it took on a new sense of urgency partly as the result of the rejection of subtle fluids (Davy and Faraday) and partly due to the precise definition of the equivalence between mechanical work and heat (Joule). Hitherto, macroscopic phenomena had been treated in their own terms – in terms of Newton's laws of motion, gravitation, and the newly discovered laws of electricity and magnetism – without too much concern about their relationship to the microscopic properties of matter. Most scientists, Joule among them, followed Isaac Newton in postulating what was known as the 'analogy of nature' – the supposition that the same fundamental properties and laws that applied to macroscopic objects also were applicable at the atomic level. Joule was one of those who acknowledged that the real properties of atoms might forever be beyond the reach of human science. None the less, he insisted on the importance of visualizable models of atomic phenomena in accordance with the Newtonian analogy of nature.

But now that macroscopic mechanical work was believed to have an atomic-level equivalent in heat, some account had to be given of how that equivalent was to be represented at the atomic level. Any complete account of physics, therefore, had to specify a model of the atom in terms that could be related to the properties and laws of macroscopic phenomena. Ultimately, these efforts would lead to the revolutionary new ideas of quantum mechanics and the field theory of particles. In the nineteenth century, however, natural philosophers could only speculate about the nature of the atoms by constructing hypothetical models like those of Joule and, later on, Kelvin and Maxwell.

Joule's vision of the universe was that of a well-oiled machine that would never run down. The winds still blew as strongly, and the currents of water flowed with the same force as they ever did, at least since the time of the Deluge, in spite of the continual conversion of mechanical force into molecular heat by friction. In one of his more poetic moments, Joule even compared the mechanics of the universe to Ezekiel's vision of the chariot of God:

> Thus it is that order is maintained in the universe – nothing is deranged, nothing ever lost, but the entire machinery, complicated as it is, works smoothly and harmoniously. And though, as in the awful vision of Ezekiel, 'wheel may be in the middle of wheel,' and everything may appear complicated and involved in the apparent confusion and intricacy of an almost endless variety of causes, effects, conversions, and arrangements, yet is the most perfect regularity preserved – the whole being governed by the sovereign will of God.

Joule thus gave the mechanical philosophy its strongest possible statement, and, contrary to Laplace (section 4.4), God was still very much a part of the overall picture! Whewell, like Newton, had seen the motion of the univese as an ephemeral thing – always tending to decrease. But Joule followed a path more like that of Leibniz in seeing the apparent diminishment of motion merely as its becoming temporarily invisible – being converted into other forms at an atomic level and capable of being restored to the macroscopic level at some future time. Both were versions of the mechanical philosophy, but whereas the Catastrophist, Whewell, saw the activity of God at the boundaries of mechanical causation, Joule saw it in the design of the machine itself – a view more like that of Uniformitarians like Hutton and Lyell, whom Whewell had opposed.

Sir William Thomson (Lord Kelvin)

Born in Belfast and educated at the universities of Glasgow and Cambridge, William Thomson (1824–1907) was knighted by Queen Victoria in 1866 for the contribution of his calculations to the success of the trans-Atlantic telegraph cable completed that year. In spite of the anachronism, we shall refer to him by his title of Kelvin in order to avoid confusion with several other nineteenth-century scientists with the name Thomson. We shall review Kelvin's scientific and theological ideas in two areas: First, the theory of the relationship of heat and mechanical work, based on the work of Joule – the science to which Kelvin himself gave the name of 'thermodynamics'; and second the theory of electricity and magnetism, based on the work of Faraday. As we shall see, the mechanical philosophy of Joule and the field theory of Faraday represent the two poles between which much of Kelvin's thought moved.

Kelvin on Thermodynamics

Kelvin first came into contact with Joule in 1847 when the latter presented his results on the mechanical equivalency of heat at a meeting of the British Association for the Advancement of Science. In fact, Kelvin was the first to recognize the immense significance of Joule's work and to synthesize it with the findings of other physicists. In particular, he was perplexed by the apparent contradiction between Joule's experiments, in which mechanical work and heat were shown to be mutually convertible, and Joseph Fourier's work on the conduction of heat through solids, where heat was dissipated and work was irreversibly lost to the system. In the pivotal years of 1848–52, Kelvin resolved the paradox by giving precise definition to the concept of 'energy' as the basic quantity that was conserved, whether in the mechanical form of matter in motion or work done against a force or in the molecular form of chemical bonding or heat. Based on this definition, the first law of thermodynamics (independently formulated by Rudolf Clausius in 1850) could be stated quite simply in terms of the conservation of energy: the net heat input had to balance the mechanical energy extracted from any system going through a complete thermodynamic cycle (i.e. returning to its initial thermodynamic state). Thus far,

Kelvin was in complete agreement with Joule. He even gave a theological justification for the principle of conservation similar to that offered by Joule and undoubtedly influenced by him: since only God could create or destroy anything, a fundamental quantity like energy must be conserved in all natural processes.

However, a second principle was also at work in thermodynamic systems, as pointed out by Clausius in 1850: according to this second law of thermodynamics, heat always flowed from hotter bodies to colder ones, never the other way around. Unless it was efficiently converted into mechanical work by a suitable apparatus, heat continually spread itself out, tending towards a state of uniformity or dissipation. Thus a new paradox arose: whereas the first law of thermodynamics ensured absolute permanence for energy, the second law required universal dissipation. Kelvin resolved the problem by clearly distinguishing between dissipation and destruction. The energy dissipated in accordance with the second law of thermodynamics was not destroyed – that would have contradicted the first law; it simply became unavailable for useful work. Conservation and dissipation were thus twin principles at the basis of thermodynamics.

The dissipation of energy implied that there was a definite direction to thermodynamic processes. Nature changes in ways that tend to dissipate heat rather than concentrate it. Like Whewell's (and Newton's) arguments about the degradation of motion in the solar system, then, Kelvin's version of the second law of thermodynamics implied that the universe could not be infinitely old. It must have been created in a such a way that energy was stored in concentrated sources, because after the moment of creation, it would automatically tend towards states of ever increasing dissipation. This was entirely different from the notion of the permanence of force in the cosmos as taught by Joule and Uniformitarians like Lyell. None the less, according to Kelvin, it had its own theological correlate in the biblical idea that history had a direction and moved towards an end.

The end towards which the universe moved on its own, however, was one of complete dissipation, or, to use a term coined by Clausius in 1865, a state of maximum 'entropy'. Kelvin realized this ominous cosmic implication of the second law of thermodynamics already in 1851: in an unpublished draft of a paper written that year, he even cited Psalm 102:26 (Authorized Version: 'all of them shall wax old like a garment') for biblical support. The following year, he published a paper, *On a Universal Tendency in Nature to the Dissipation of Mechanical Energy*, in which he concluded that, barring some supernatural intervention, the earth would eventually become unfit for human habitation. But, ten years later, he wrote more optimistically that civilization could progress indefinitely if the universe was infinite, since there would then be an inexhaustible supply of free energy that could be tapped. Clearly there was an ongoing struggle in Kelvin's mind between Leibniz and Joule's notion of the perfection and permanence of the cosmic machinery, on the one hand, and Newton and Whewell's sense of its instability and transience, on the other.

Kelvin's major contribution to thermodynamics was thus his formalization and synthesis of the findings of other scientists. He had a remarkable ability to identify the apparent contradictions among these results and then to rethink the concepts involved and make precise definitions in such a way as to resolve those contradictions. Since the willingness and ability to contemplate paradoxes was to become one of the major themes of late nineteenth and early twentieth century physics, it is worthwhile noting the theological framework in which this penchant occurred in the work of Kelvin.

As we have noted, Kelvin found a theological parallel to the conservation of energy in the biblical teaching of the stability of God's creation. He also found a parallel to the gradual dissipation of free energy in the theological notion of the directionality and finality of the biblical concept of history. Even if these parallels are questionable in themselves, the very ability to recognize apparent paradox in science as well as in theology is significant. In both cases, Kelvin took over ideas that were available from others and provided a creative synthesis.

Other than the bare tolerance of paradox, the most important theological aspect of Kelvin's synthesis was his understanding of the attributes of God. According to the traditional theology Kelvin imbibed at Glasgow, God was eternal and his counsels stood for all time. It followed that, with the exception of miracles, the physical world must operate at all times and in all places in accordance with the same basic laws (the moral realm was another matter). Both the conservation of energy and the universal dissipation of heat (free energy) were, therefore, evidences of divine design. Kelvin's world was far more mechanical than Faraday's. Hence, his God, like that of naturalists and mechanists since the twelfth century, was somewhat more remote than Faraday's, but the tokens of his existence were equally in evidence for both.

Kelvin on Electricity and Magnetism

A similar struggle with paradox characterized Kelvin's work in the area of electricity and magnetism. Here Kelvin adopted Faraday's idea of fields of force, but he interpreted it within a mechanical framework much closer to Joule's ideas than to Faraday's own outlook. Kelvin was willing to adopt Faraday's notion of the magnetic field's independence of matter in terms of the mathematical formalism he helped to develop. But, whereas Faraday had seen the lines of force as an alternative to the idea of an ethereal medium, Kelvin repeatedly tried to explain the transmission of electromagnetic force through space in terms of a mechanical ether and even proposed models of rotating molecular atmospheres or vortices, ideas similar to those proposed by Joule and which had since been refined by Rankine and Helmholtz.

Partly out of deference to Faraday (as indicated by their correspondence), Kelvin carefully qualified his ethereal mechanisms as mere models, analogies, or illustrations: they were not to be taken literally as physical realities. But he persisted in speculating all the same. Kelvin's long-range commitment to the importance of mechanical models was particularly remarkable in view of the difficulties he encountered in constructing one that was stable – by the late 1880s, he had virtually abandoned hopes of success.

Still, all through his long life, Kelvin insisted, as Joule had done before him, that the demonstration of the intelligibility of electromagnetic phenomena depended on the eventual development of a viable mechanical model of the ether, however hypothetical it might be. The result was a sharp differentiation in Kelvin's thought between mathematical formalism and the physical understanding of reality. This was one paradox he never quite resolved. At the end of his career, Kelvin saw his efforts to understand the relationship between fields and matter at the atomic level as a complete failure.

The reason for Kelvin's recurring attempts to construct mechanical models for electromagnetic phenomena was partly theological. Kelvin's training in natural philosophy at the universities of Glasgow and Cambridge had been in the natural theology tradition of Samuel Clarke, William Derham, Thomas Reid, and William Paley (section 4.1). According to this tradition, one should expect to find evidences of design in creation particularly in the unforseen analogies between entirely different natural phenomena. From the very beginning of his career, Kelvin had been able to identify and develop some of these analogies, particularly that between the equations of electrostatics and those for the flow of heat through a conducting body. Amazingly, the exact same equations applied in the two cases.

The formal, mathematical analogy was enough by itself to provide the fondly sought evidence of design in nature, but it also suggested that some deeper connection was probably involved between the two phenomena. If Joule's dynamical theory of heat was correct in positing an atomic basis for the phenomenon of heat, mustn't there also be an atomic basic for electricity and magnetism? The same could be said on the basis on the analogy between the propagation of light and waves of a fluid like water, which had been firmly established by A. J. Fresnel in 1821. Could the analogy be purely formal, or did it indicate a real similarity between the two phenomena? If the latter, mustn't there be a medium through which light waves propagated, a medium with a molecular structure analogous to that of water? Thus Kelvin's belief in the divine design of nature sustained his belief in the existence of an ether with mechanical properties even though his ingenious mechanical models failed to verify the idea.

Kelvin's theological conviction of the deep inner connections of nature was one aspect of what we have called the creationist tradition. However, his insistence that any acceptable mechanical description of phenomena be given in clearly visualizable terms was another matter. Like Newton, Kelvin insisted that only qualities that were absolutely universal to physical bodies could be accepted as irreducible and primary in mechanical theory. (Qualities that were, could not be absent or present in varying degrees). According to Newton, the only attributes that could be regarded as primary were extension, incompressibility, impenetrability and inertia. Other properties of matter, such as elasticity, had to be explained in terms of these more fundamental ones. Otherwise, they were not admissible. In fact, Kelvin even hoped to account for inertia in terms of molecular vortices. In these strictly Newtonian terms, the mechanical approach to the physics of atoms was eventually found to fail. The future of atomic physics lay not with the mechanical philosophy of Kelvin, but with a more flexible approach that would allow the mechanical philosophy to be generalized. The beginnings of such an approach were due to the efforts of James Clerk Maxwell.

4. THE MECHANICAL PHILOSOPHY GENERALIZED (MAXWELL)

James Clerk Maxwell (1831–79) was a Scot who studied at the universitites of Edinburgh (1847–50) and Cambridge (1850–56). Like Kelvin, therefore, he was trained in Scottish philosophical theology and the tradition of mixed mathematics and natural theology established by Whewell and others at Cambridge. He frequently cited the basic creationist ideas of laws impressed on nature (at one point citing Wisd. 11:20: 'Thou hast arranged all things by measure and number and weight') and the divine image in humanity, resulting in the comprehensibility, unity and relative autonomy of the world. The God who had revealed himself to Abraham, Isaac and Jacob was for Maxwell the same as the God of nature (cf. Ps. 146:5f.). The act of divine creation was a presupposition of all science, and, though it was not itself open to scientific explanation, it was clearly evidenced in seemingly inexplicable features of the cosmos such as the identical properties of molecules in all parts of the universe, near and far. The fact that Maxwell limited scientific investigation to the cosmos as it exists and excluded any consideration of its origin reflects the basically Newtonian (pre-evolutionary) framework within which he and other British physicists of his time worked.

Maxwell had affinities with both of the categories of nineteenth-century physical scientists we have reviewed. Like Faraday, he approached natural philosophy in an intuitive way and regarded the electromagnetic field as an independent entity, not reducible to molecular mechanics. Yet, like Kelvin, he also speculated on mechanical models for the ether and carried on the process of formalizing classical dynamics.

Maxwell belongs in a category of his own, however, due to the skill with which he synthesized and generalized the ideas of others, particularly in two areas. First, there was his pioneering work in statistical mechanics. Maxwell attempted to bridge the gap between the laws of thermodynamics and the dynamics of gaseous molecules while recognizing the relative independence of those two fields and the essential role of statistics in the overall worldview of natural philosophy. Secondly, Maxwell developed a generalized version of the mechanical philosophy that incorporated Faraday's concept of independent fields and so opened the way for developments of twentieth-century physics. As in the case of Kelvin, we shall treat these two areas in turn, beginning with statistical mechanics.

Maxwell on Statistical Mechanics

Maxwell was the first to recognize that there was no straightforward relationship between the macroscopic laws of thermodynamics and the dynamics of molecules as understood in Newtonian terms. In particular, Maxwell departed from the strictly mechanical interpretation of thermodynamic functions introduced by Rudolf Clausius (1862) and Ludwig Boltzmann (1866).

Clausius had interpreted the thermodynamic properties of heat-energy and entropy as straightforward measures of the kinetic energy and spatial configuration of the molecules. In the 1860s, however, Maxwell developed a radically new approach to the concepts of thermodynamics by utilizing the ideas and methods of the newly developed science of statistics. Concepts like temperature and entropy only applied to large aggregates, he concluded, and were meaningless when applied to individual molecules. The temperature of a system was still determined by the average of the kinetic energies of the constituent molecules, but the energy of any given molecule was largely random given the macroscopic, thermodynamic parameters.

Energy was still strictly conserved, in accordance with the first law of thermodynamics, and was time-invariant. However, the dissipation of energy required by the second law of thermodynamics was a very different matter. Not only did it imply a direction in time, as Kelvin had pointed out, but it was not mechanically determined: it was only the most probable course of the system's temporal development. In other words, we cannot be absolutely certain that energy will dissipate (i.e., that entropy will increase) in any given time interval. Thermodynamic systems are not deterministic in the same sense that mechanical systems operating in accordance with Newton's laws of motion are. But though we can not be absolutely certain, we can be morally certain that, for all practical purposes, energy will dissipate over extended periods of time.

The distinction Maxwell made here between absolute (mechanical) and moral certainty can only be understood with reference to the parallel issue of free will and determinism – an issue that he addressed in 1856 as a university student at Cambridge and again in a paper of 1873. Maxwell argued that all descriptions, including scientific theories, are at best abstractions or partial views of the complex reality of nature. For example, according to one description, we experience freedom in our ability to act as moral agents, while, according to another, we observe strict determinism in our scientific analysis of the motions of bodies.

Kant had resolved the paradox of free will and determinism by making freedom an unanalysable precondition for moral action while, at the same time, requiring a completely deterministic account of the external, objective world. Maxwell's approach was rather different. For him, the laws of mind and the laws of nature were both aspects of reality created by God, but only partial aspects. One could, therefore, arrive at a view of reality entailing either freedom or determinism depending on how one focused the instruments of observation and analysis on the events involved:

The dimmed outlines of phenomenal things all merge into one

another unless we put on the focusing glass of theory and screw it up sometimes to one pitch of definition, and sometimes to another, so as to see down into the different depths through the great millstone of the world.

The paradox of moral freedom and mechanical determinism, then, provided the paradigm for Maxwell's later analysis of thermodynamics where he found an analogous paradox of statistical laws and directionality, on the one hand, and mechanical determinism and time-invariance, on the other.

Theoretically, there could be massive random fluctuations in the dynamics of the molecules that would reverse the dissipation of energy, just as, theoretically speaking, it would be possible for millions of pieces of glass to converge and form a flawless window. Maxwell utilized the idea of an imaginary demon (dubbed Maxwell's 'sorting demon' by Kelvin) in order to show that such fluctuations could conceivably be engineered in such a way as to contradict the uniform experience of what we observe in nature, but without violating the laws of Newtonian mechanics. In other words, we may accept the validity of the second law of thermodynamics, even though it is not absolutely mechanically certain, just as we trust in the sovereignty of God in all matters and ignore the possible activity of mischievous demons. The second law of thermodynamics could not be reduced to the principles of Newtonian mechanics: it involved an additional supplementary principle which was never clearly defined, but which amounted, in Maxwell's context, to trust in the sovereignty and goodwill of God.

The student of twentieth-century physics cannot fail to see here a remarkable preview of one of Einstein's philosophical ideas. According to Einstein, the laws of nature must reflect the fact that, though God is subtle, he is not deceptive or devious. Einstein stated his own view in the context of the later debate concerning the completeness of quantum mechanics and used it to argue against the legitimacy of indeterminism in science. However, the underlying faith in the reliability of natural law, grounded in the trustworthiness of God, was characteristic of the tradition he inherited from nineteenth-century physicists like Maxwell.

One can also find a preview of Niels Bohr's principle of complementarity in the ideas of Maxwell just discussed. Like Maxwell, Bohr viewed nature as a complex reality which could not be captured in any one mode of description. Complementary descriptions of nature were required as a consequence of the differing 'possibilities of definition' in human science. In fact, Bohr, like Maxwell, cited both the paradox of moral freedom and physical determinism and the statistical nature of the laws of thermodynamics as examples of these complementary modes of definition. The nature of the historical relationship between Maxwell, Einstein and Bohr will be explored further in the concluding section of this chapter as a way of showing the influence of creationist ideas on twentieth-century physics.

Maxwell on Electricity and Magnetism

We have seen how persistent Kelvin was in the search for mechanical models of the ether sustaining electric and magnetic fields. Maxwell was more ambiguous. As in the case of Kelvin, we shall sketch some of the shifts in his thinking on the subject and then reflect on the theological aspects.

In spite of his many reservations, Maxwell still viewed the programme of the physical sciences as one of mechanical explanation as it was originally projected by Descartes, Charleton and Boyle in the seventeenth century (section 3.3). Like Kelvin, he made persistent efforts to develop a mechanical model for electromagnetic phenomena, even using Kelvin's idea of ether vortices, not as a literal physical description of reality, but as an analogy or heuristic illustration to aid in comprehension and to demonstrate that mechanical explanation of the propagation of electromagnetic force was possible, at least, in principle. Maxwell temporarily abandoned the effort to construct a model of the electromagnetic field itself in the mid 1860s but continued to the end of his life to seek molecular models of the ether that supposedly underlay the field. In his *magnum opus*, the *Treatise on Electricity and Magnetism* (1873), he made a point of formulating the equations governing the phenomena in terms of abstract parameters that made no explicit reference to the dynamics of bodies of any sort. For example, the conservation of energy was made a fundamental principle, but not expressed in terms of the dynamics of ether particles.

Thus Maxwell followed Faraday in treating the field as an independent reality in its own right: the electric and magnetic fields could even be viewed as reservoirs of their own form of energy, a form comparable to that of the kinetic energy, potential energy and heat associated with material bodies. But, unlike Faraday, Maxwell mathematized the field concept along the lines of Lagrange and Kelvin's treatment of Newtonian dynamics. He also developed a physical model in which the energy stored in the field was just the sum of the kinetic energy and potential energy of the ether particles and electromagnetic force was transmitted from particle to particle through the ether, again drawing on Kelvin's concept of molecular vortices.

As heuristic illustrations, these mechanical models did more than just illustrate the mathematical equations for the fields as they were already known. Even though an endless variety of models could be constructed that were consistent with the equations, the one that Maxwell developed in most detail turned out to have implications which suggested important changes in the equations themselves. Maxwell found that, in order to devise a model in which the ether vortices could be interlocked without cancelling each other out, he had to postulate an imaginary electric current passing between rows of the vortices. It turned out that this imaginary current (later called the 'displacement current') made a contribution of its own to the magnetic field in spaces where there was no real current but only a time-varying electric field created by the build-up of electric charge nearby. The inclusion of the term representing this contribution in the equations revealed an unforeseen symmetry between the electric and magnetic fields and led to a mathematical solution according to which the fields propagated through space as waves. Calculation then showed that the electromagnetic waves would travel through space at approximately the speed of light (300,000 kilometres per second). Light could, in fact, be understood as a special form of electricity and magnetism.

One result of Maxwell's tinkering with mechanical models was thus the unification of the science of optics with that of electricity and magnetism. A further result was the discovery of radio waves (by Heinrich Hertz in 1888) and the eventual development of the technologies on which modern communications are based.

In many ways, Maxwell's vascillations on the relation of fields to molecular mechanics are similar to Kelvin's. However, they differed in two important ways. First, in the late 1860s and 1870s, Maxwell broke with the Newtonian 'analogy of nature' – the requirement that any description of atoms or molecules be made strictly in terms of the primary qualities that apply to macroscopic bodies. First and foremost of the primary qualities of gross matter was extension. Since the time of Descartes, extension had normally been viewed as the very essence of matter. It was axiomatic, therefore, that no two bodies could occupy the same portion of space. Maxwell wondered why the properties and laws of submicroscopic, atomic objects could not be radically different from those of macroscopic bodies with which we are familiar in everyday experience. Perhaps two atomic objects could even coincide in their locations in space. The unity of nature and analogies among its various levels did not require complete uniformity!

Thus, in spite of the immense strides of physical science in his own lifetime and contrary to the views of some of his contemporaries, Maxwell did not see the work of physics as anywhere near completion. In fact, he concluded one of his last papers with the statement that it was time for physicists to adopt an attitude of 'thoroughly conscious ignorance that is the prelude to every real advance in knowledge'. The advances of nineteenth-century physics had raised unforeseen problems like those associated with the discovery of atomic spectra. In Maxwell's view, therefore, new phenomena and entire new fields of research were waiting to be discovered which would require the development of entirely new forms of thought.

This open, adventurous outlook was not just based on personal experience, or the past history of physics. For Maxwell, it was based on his belief in 'the unsearchable riches of creation' (cf. Job 5:9; Eph. 3:8) and 'the untried fertility of those fresh minds into which these riches will continue to be poured'. In other words, it was based on the twin aspects of the doctrine of creation: the cosmos as the work of an infinite and all-powerful God, and the human mind as created in the image of God and hence capable of comprehending the mysteries of nature. The courage and open-mindedness that Maxwell modelled for his twentieth-century followers was rooted in the creationist tradition.

The second difference from Kelvin was that Maxwell was able to step back from the problem of mechanical models far enough to reflect on its similarity to the paradoxes he had encountered in his work on thermodynamics. Maxwell then resolved the problem by affirming that both field and particle pictures were valid in their own way: it was good to have two ways of looking at a subject and not confine oneself to a single perspective. In his major treatise on the subject (1873), he expressed a personal preference for the more holistic, field theory of Faraday. But he backed away from Faraday's notion that fields were the primary reality and made them dependent on the presence of material bodies as their sources and sinks. Likewise, Maxwell shied away from the pure formalism of field equations and argued for the use of concrete mechanical models as a means of coordinating the mathematical formalism with physical reality. Then again, in 1870, he stated that both approaches were human abstractions which appealed to physicists accustomed to different styles of thought.

There was an important ambiguity here that has had repercussions in the twentieth-century debates about field theory. Granted Maxwell's general idea that reality is a plural unity or a unified plurality: are we to view the formal equations of the field approach as exhibiting the true wholeness of things and view the molecular models as abstractions? Or are we to identify the composite of field and particle pictures (the formal and the mechanical) as representing the whole of which both field and particle pictures are abstractions? Albert Einstein and Niels Bohr can both be viewed as disciples of Maxwell in as much as each of them adopted one of these approaches in the quest for harmony and wholeness.

5. CONCLUSION: THE CONTRIBUTION OF THE CREATIONIST TRADITION TO TWENTIETH-CENTURY PHYSICS (EINSTEIN AND BOHR)

We have traced the history of the creationist tradition in relation to the physical sciences from the second century BC through to the nineteenth century AD. Major contributors to the sciences during those twenty-one centuries were frequently inspired by the belief that God had created all things in accordance with laws of his own devising, laws which made the world comprehensible to humans and gave the world a degree of unity and relative autonomy, and that God had sent his Son and poured out his Spirit to initiate a worldwide ministry of healing and restoration.

We have also found that the creationist tradition began to unravel in the twelfth century with the polarization between theologies emphasizing the workings of nature and the truths of reason, on the one hand, and the supernatural and the suprarational mysteries of revelation, on the other. This was not a conflict between science and religion. Both sides of the issue were rooted in the creationist tradition and both made significant contributions to the development of science. At various junctures, attempts were made to synthesize nature and supernature in a recovery of biblical thought, often in conjunction with extrabiblical philosophies like those of Aristotle, Neoplatonism and Hermeticism. Nonetheless, the process of fragmentation and secularization continued to reassert itself until the decline of the creationist outlook as an international, public tradition in the late eighteenth and nineteenth centuries.

It is beyond dispute that the creationist tradition made significant contributions to the rise and development of both medieval and classical (seventeenth to nineteenth century) physics. The major breakthroughs in astronomy, medicine, mechanics, chemistry, thermodynamics, and electricity and magnetism were all associated with theological ideas related to God and creation. It would appear, however, that the triumph in the nineteenth century of individualism in religion and professionalism in the sciences had severely reduced the likelihood that scientific developments of the twentieth century would be embedded in a similar theological matrix.

Certainly physicists of the twentieth century are more diverse in their religious beliefs. Many would be reluctant to identify themselves with any theological tradition at all. And even where particular beliefs may be held privately, they are not as likely to play a dynamic role in the choice of science as a profession or in the quest for insight into nature as they were in medieval and early modern times. In any case, scientists no longer include prayers in their professional writings, as Kepler did, or draw attention to the existence of God, as Maxwell still did as late as the 1870s. The most that can be said is that a few scientists have allowed the possibility of God's existence in their more popular writings.

In this final section, however, we shall argue that remnants of the creationist tradition played a key role in the foundations of twentieth-century physics in the work of its two principal founders, Albert Einstein (1879–1955) and Niels Bohr (1885–1962). We cannot hope to do justice to the philosophies of either Einstein or Bohr in their own right – we shall not even treat them separately. But we must ask what contribution, if any, the creationist tradition has made in the case of these two figures that form a bridge from the nineteenth to the twentieth century. If ideas and beliefs have a momentum of their own, we might expect to find traces of the same beliefs in their work that inspired their predecessors, particularly those in the tradition of Michael Faraday and James Clerk Maxwell, whom Einstein and Bohr so admired and emulated.

It is a well known fact that Einstein and Bohr differed strongly on many issues, particularly ones concerning the adequacy of the quantum-mechanical formalism, the development of which they both did so much to further. Einstein's 1905 paper on the photoelectric effect first showed that light was quantized in units (later called 'photons') whose momentum and energy were directly related to the wavelength and frequency of the light waves. It is to Einstein also that we owe the mathematical formula for the probability of the radiation of light from an atom (1916). Subsequently, the ideas of discontinuity and statistical explanation became basic ingredients of quantum mechanics. Despite Einstein's pioneering work in these areas, he himself insisted on continuity and completeness of dynamical description (not to be equated with 'determinism' in the classical sense) and saw this as required by the field theory of Faraday and Maxwell.

Bohr's 1913 theory of the hydrogen atom provided the first working model of the new mechanics describing the interaction of atoms and light. Bohr also provided the most influential interpretation of the fully developed quantum mechanics of the late 1920s with his principles of 'correspondence' and 'complementarity'. Unlike Einstein, however, he judged these developments to be consistent with overall principles of natural philosophy and argued for their being foundational, if not final, in the progress of modern physics. Whereas Einstein pointed to Maxwell's field theory as the precedent for his own work, Bohr looked back to the beginnings of atomic theory under Maxwell and his successors, J. J. Thomson and Ernest Rutherford.

Culturally, Einstein and Bohr were both products of late nineteenth-century European culture. Ethnically a German Jew, Einstein was steeped in the literature of nineteenth-century German philosophy; Bohr was raised in cosmopolitan Copenhagen (his mother was also Jewish), where the primary influences mediated were those of nine-teenth century England and Germany. He further came 'under the spell of Cambridge and the inspiration of the great English physi-cists' (Thomson, Jeans, Larmor, and Rutherford) during his post-graduate studies in 1911–12.

Though religion was not taken seriously in either of their families, both Einstein and Bohr struggled with religious questions in their youths. And both expressed appreciation for the religious sense as that was understood in the liberal, romantic vein of the nineteenth century. Einstein spoke of a 'cosmic religious feeling' that was common to creative scientists and religious mystics alike. Bohr referred to a 'universal religious feeling' that exists in every age, particularly among poets, and which is in intimate harmony with insight into nature. Both Einstein and Bohr recognized the great religious and philosophical traditions of other cultures, though, it should be noted that they knew Indian and Chinese thought mostly through the German adaptations of Schopenhauer and Schiller. Einstein developed his own version of certain fundamental Jewish truths he once identified as 'Mosaic'. Bohr was well versed in the German poets, particularly Schiller and Goethe. He was also fond of Kierkegaard's *Stages on Life's Way*, though he did not agree with the thought of Kierkegaard as a whole.

The reason why neither Einstein nor Bohr were willing to adopt a positive theological stance was that they both associated religious teachings and formal doctrine with narrow-mindedness. After a brief period of religious devotion in his youth, Einstein rejected what he called the 'anthropomorphic character' of the 'God of Providence' as portrayed in the Hebrew Bible and eschewed any suggestion of personality in God or of the miraculous in his dealings with humans. Einstein's unfavourable references to the 'moral religion' and the 'social or moral conception of God' in this connection suggests that he associated the idea of a personal God with the pragmatism that characterized much German religion, both Jewish and Christian, in his early years.

Bohr was opposed, in principle, to any formal system or dogma that claimed to be the whole truth. Even with respect to his own attempt at a universal synthesis, the principle of complementarity, he disavowed any overall system or doctrine of ready-made precepts, and he never attempted to give a formal definition. Accordingly, he thought of religion primarily in terms of a 'universal feeling' and rejected any attempt to 'freeze it' in terms of the concepts of any given period of human history. Bohr referred to the anthropomorphic notion of a supernatural power with whom people could bargain for favours as a figment of primitive imaginations, and did not take the possibility of historical revelation seriously.

It is likely that both Einstein and Bohr were influenced in their views by the evolutionary theory of religion developed by Herbert Spencer, Edward Tylor, and Andrew Lang. Einstein, in particular, described an evolution of religion from a primitive stage, in which humans conceived of God in their own image, through the higher religions of social and moral value to the vision, held by a few, of a cosmic God.

The fact that for Einstein and Bohr the biblical teachings of the synagogue and church had little to do with the serious issues of science and society serves to confirm our observations concerning the decline of the creationist tradition in Western culture. Since the twelfth century, miracle had become increasingly viewed as the antithesis of natural law, and faith in a personal God had been gradually isolated from its moorings in the history of nature and culture. The positive faith of Einstein and Bohr, however, points to another important fact, seemingly at variance with the first: the survival of creationist themes in the absence of the tradition that originally mediated and sustained them.

If we were to characterize the primary object of the respective faiths of Einstein and Bohr with a single word, that word would be 'harmony'. Both Einstein and Bohr spoke of harmony in metaphysical, and even reverential, terms that would traditionally have been reserved for God.

For Einstein, the physical world was an incarnation of reason which, though manifest in various laws and principles, was inaccessible to the human mind in its profoundest depths. Thus physics itself was a quest of religious proportions. The true scientist was enraptured by 'the harmony of natural law, which reveals an intelligence of such superiority that, compared with it, all the systematic thinking and acting of human beings is an utterly insignificant reflection'.

The enterprise of physics, as Einstein understood it, was based on the conviction that the entire cosmos was governed by what Leibniz had called the 'pre-established harmony' of the parts. For instance, when Einstein described the work of Max Planck – discoverer of the quantum of action (1900) – he used words, as his most recent biographer, Abraham Pais, has pointed out, that described his own conviction and experience as well as Planck's:

> The longing to behold . . . pre-established harmony is the source of the inexhaustible persistence and patience with which we see Planck devoting himself to the most general problems of our science without letting himself be deflected by goals which are more profitable and easier to achieve. . . . The emotional state which enables such achievements is similar to that of the religious person or the person in love; the daily pursuit does not originate from a design or a programme [of one's own choice or invention] but from a direct need.

This statement may readily be compared to the teachings of Church fathers like Irenaeus and Basil or the writings of Christian natural philosophers like Paracelsus and Bacon, or Kepler and Newton. It shares with them its ideal of selfless service as well as its belief in the unity and harmony of the world. It also indicates that, however much he reacted against the current understanding of the 'personality' of God, Einstein's experience of the divine presence was not entirely an impersonal one like that generally associated with Spinoza, with which Einstein's theological views are often compared. The quest of the scientist is compared to the religious affections and the passion of a person in love. Einstein once stated that he read the Hebrew Bible often (in German translation), and he particularly admired the cosmic sense of the Psalms and some of the Prophets. At age eighteen, the young Einstein had cited strenuous labour and contemplation of God's nature as 'the angels which, reconciling, fortifying, and yet mercilessly severe, will guide me through the tumult of life'. Undoubtedly, the reference to angels here is a figure of speech for Einstein, but the sense of personal calling and guidance was very real, and it never left him. Einstein, like Newton, viewed himself and his work as an instrument in the hands of the Lord.

The pre-establishment harmony Einstein believed in manifested itself not only in the unity and harmony of the diverse phenomena of nature. It was also the basis of the physicist's intellectual self-confidence – the confidence that the human mind, finite and fallible though it might be, was capable of discerning the basic outline of the order of the cosmos. The aim of science, according to Einstein, was to comprehend human experience in as much breadth as possible while, at the same time, describing it with a simplicity and economy of assumptions. These two objectives, comprehensiveness and simplicity, are, of course, potentially in conflict with each other. Yet the belief that they could exist side by side and be accomplished together was indispensible for scientific progress. Einstein spoke of his own experience of the 'sublimity and marvellous order which reveal themselves both in nature and in the world of thought' and praised the 'deep conviction of the rationality of the universe' that enabled early scientists like Kepler and Newton to persist in their efforts in spite of social isolation and personal hardship. Here, we have the clearest possible evidence of the influence of the historic creationist tradition at the root of twentieth-century physics.

Einstein's personal self-confidence has sometimes been taken as a sign of arrogance. He felt that he could judge the adequacy of scientific ideas by their compatibility with the divine mind. He was completely certain of the truth of his general theory of relativity, for instance, and felt that any failure of experiments to verify it could only reflect unfavourably on the consistency of God. He was equally certain that notions like chance were incompatible with the divine mind and therefore could not play a fundamental role in physics.

Niels Bohr worked with the same sort of confidence. He allowed for a greater degree of plurality and apparent paradox in physical science that Einstein did. But he accepted, and even accentuated, these paradoxes in the belief that they would ultimately be resolved in a broader unity and harmony of the phenomena. For instance, in describing his semi-classical model of the hydrogen atom (1913), Bohr stated that he wanted to emphasize the conflict between the classical framework and the new quantum postulate in order 'that it may also be possible in the course of time to discover a certain coherence in the new ideas'.

The goal of science for Bohr, as for Einstein (and for Maxwell before), was to articulate principles that would exhibit the greatest possible harmony while covering the widest possible range of phenomena, however conflicting the phenomena might appear in everyday experience. As he put it in his 1954 essay on 'Unity of Knowledge':

> This attitude may be summarized by the endeavour to achieve a harmonious comprehension of ever wider aspects of our situation, recognizing that no experience is definable without a logical frame and that any apparent disharmony can be removed only by an appropriate widening of the conceptual framework.

In fact, Bohr cited (1947) Einstein's special and general theories of relativity as models in this respect: the special theory reconciled the separate ideas of space and time into a four-dimensional manifold, and the general theory further combined the space-time manifold with universal gravitation. Thus, for Bohr, through the work of Einstein, 'our whole world picture achieved a higher degree of unity and harmony than ever before'. Niels Blaedel has aptly summarized this ideal by giving his recent biography of Bohr the title, *Harmony and Unity*.

Bohr accepted the adequacy of classical physics as the foundation of the new developments in quantum theory in spite of the fact that the new developments called into question many of its basic teachings. As he put it in a lecture on the centenary of Maxwell's birth (1931):

> The developments of the atomic theory brought us . . . beyond the limit of direct and consistent application of Maxwell's theory. I wish to emphasise, however, that it was just the possibility of analysing the radiation phenomena provided by the electromagnetic theory of light which led to the recognition of an essentially new feature of the laws of Nature.

> We must, in fact, realise that the unambiguous interpretation of any measurement must be essentially framed in terms of the classical physical theories, and we may say that in this sense the language of Newton and Maxwell will remain the language of physicists for all time.

Bohr, like Einstein, viewed his work as rooted in that of his predecessors, particularly those of the British tradition of natural philosophy from Newton to Maxwell.

Bohr's insistence on the retention of classical terminology has sometimes been taken as an indication of Kantian idealism. He took the subject matter of physics to be human measurement and human language almost as much as physical reality itself. Recent studies like that of Henry Folse have shown, however, that Bohr was concerned about the problems involved in the objective description of nature and was neither an idealist nor a Kantian in the proper sense.

Both Einstein and Bohr must be viewed against the background of the ideals of nineteenth-century physics, into which they were indoctrinated. The nineteenth century was an era of great confidence: confidence in the rationality of nature and confidence in the power of the human intellect – convictions which were based on the creationist ideas of the divine law in the universe and the divine image in humanity.

This confidence had always played a role in the physical sciences, as we have seen in previous chapters of this book. Paradoxically, its importance has actually been heightened in the twentieth century due to the general acceptance of Darwin's theory of evolution. According to Darwin, the basic characteristics of the human species, including our mental capabilities, have been determined by the conditions necessary for the survival of the race over the millions of years of human evolution. The absence of any role in this theory for the divine image in humanity might well have called into question the possibility of humans comprehending areas that were completely beyond the experience of fossil hominids and unrelated to their survival. Thus, in going beyond the relatively common-sensical teachings of classical physics and delving into the mysteries of relativity and quantum theory, modern physics had exercised faith in one of the central teachings of the creationist tradition at a time when that tradition has generally been regarded as irrelevant to science.

The philosophies of Einstein and Bohr are more like the Platonic and Pythagorean ideas that the Church transmitted to the modern West than the Judeo-Christian idea of creation itself. But they could still be said to be within the creationist tradition conceived in the broad sense of its ancient Near Eastern roots and the parallel Jewish and Greek developments that the Church later synthesized. The idea of creation is no longer assumed by scientists in their work, but the values the idea embodied and transmitted live on in the lives and minds of many physical scientists independently of, or even in the absence of, personal religious faith.

Therefore, Jews and Christians who are aware of their theological tradition can afford to be appreciative of the natural philosophers of today, as much as the early Jews and Christians were of the natural philosophers of their own time. They can also afford to be as critical. Where the comprehensibility of the world is a deeply held conviction, we can recognize that as a legitimate manifestation of faith. Where sacrifices are made to alleviate the suffering of humanity through medicine and technology, we can appreciate that as part of the Spirit's work in our world. On the other hand, where the power and privileges awarded scientists in modern society are enjoyed as ends in themselves or utilized in unjust ways, we must recall the ultimate source of human science and the ultimate goals for which the gifts were poured out on us.

For the time being, science and technology are immensely successful and profitable enterprises. People with talent and ambition may be drawn to them out of self-interest as well as for humanitarian ideals. But the future is uncertain. The time may come when it takes self-sacrifice and courage to develop the ideas and invent the techniques needed for further progress. The time may even come when an operational faith, supported by a religious community and its creeds, will provide insight and inspiration for the pioneers of new scientific developments as it did in Western Europe from the Middle Ages to the nineteenth century. If that time does come, other theological traditions beside the Judeo-Christian may well play an important role. Only then will we be in a position to assess the full import of theology as a whole, and of the creationist tradition, in particular, to the history of science.

ADDITIONAL READING

Blaedel, N., *Harmony and Unity: The Life of Niels Bohr* (Madison, Wisc., 1988).

Bohr, 'Maxwell and Modern Theoretical Physics', *Nature* 128 (1931) pp. 691–2.

Brush, S. G., *Statistical Physics and the Atomic Theory of Matter* (Princeton, 1983).

Cannon, W. F., 'The Problem of Miracles in the 1830s', *Victorian Studies* 4 (1960) pp. 5–32.

idem, 'Scientists and Broad Churchmen: An Early Victorian Intellectual Network', *Journal of British Studies* 4 (1964) pp. 65–88.

Einstein, A., *The World As I See It* (London, 1935).

Everitt, C. W. F., 'Maxwell', *Dictionary of Scientific Biography* 9, pp. 198–230.

Ferré, F., 'Einstein on Religion and Science', *American Journal of Theology and Philosophy* 1 (1980) pp. 21–28.

Folse, H. J., *The Philosophy of Niels Bohr: The Framework of Complementarity* (Amsterdam, 1985).

Harman (Heimann), P. M., 'Conversion of Forces and the Conservation of Energy', *Centaurus* 18 (1974) pp. 147–61.

idem, *Energy, Force and Matter: The Conceptual Development of Nineteenth-Century Physics* (Cambridge, 1982).

idem, ed., *Wranglers and Physicists: Studies on Cambridge Mathematical Physics in the Nineteenth Century* (Manchester, 1985).

Heilbron, J. L., 'Rutherford-Bohr Atom', *American Journal of Physics* 49 (1981) pp. 223–31.

Knoepflmacher, U. C., and Tennyson, G. B., eds., *Nature and the Victorian Imagination* (Berkeley, 1977) chaps. 10, 11.

Levere, T. H., 'Faraday, Matter and Natural Theology', *British Journal for the History of Science* 4 (1968) pp. 95–107.

Olson, R. G., *Scottish Philosophy and British Physics, 1750–1880* (Princeton, 1975).

Pais, A., *'Subtle Is the Lord . . .' The Science and the Life of Albert Einstein* (Oxford, 1982).

Smith, C., 'Natural Philosophy and Thermodynamics: William Thomson and the "Dynamical Theory of Heat" ', *British Journal for the History of Science* 9 (1976) pp. 293–319.

Turner, F. M., 'The Victorian Conflict between Science and Religion', *Isis* 69 (1978) pp. 356–76.

Williams, L. P., *Michael Faraday* (London, 1964).

Wilson, D. B., 'Kelvin's Scientific Realism: The Theological Context', *The Philosophical Journal* 11 (1974) pp. 41–60.

SUBJECT INDEX

NAME INDEX

314